THERMODYNAMICS

Prentice-Hall International, Inc., *London*
Prentice-Hall of Australia, Pty., Ltd., *Sydney*
Prentice-Hall of Canada, Ltd., *Toronto*
Prentice-Hall of India (Private) Ltd., *New Delhi*
Prentice-Hall of Japan, Inc., *Tokyo*

THERMODYNAMICS

J. T. VANDERSLICE

H. W. SCHAMP, JR.

E. A. MASON

Institute for Molecular Physics
University of Maryland

Prentice-Hall, Inc., *Englewood Cliffs*, *N.J.*

© 1966 by Prentice-Hall, Inc., Englewood Cliffs, N.J.

Library of Congress Catalog Card Number

66-14515

Printed in the United States of America

91490C

Current printing (last digit):
10 9 8 7 6 5 4 3 2 1

PREFACE

This book on classical thermodynamics is intended for use in the under-graduate or graduate curriculum, or as a short reference and review book. We have used it in our own teaching from the sophomore level on. A one-semester three-hour course should be adequate to cover all the *basic* material presented; the total amount covered would depend on the level of the course. The essential elements are concentrated in the first seven chapters, while applications and additional topics are presented in the remaining seven chapters. This arrangement is designed for those who dislike skipping sections in textbooks in order to cover the more important aspects of a subject within the time limit set by the course. It also serves to outline the basic structure of thermodynamics for those interested in review without excessive dilution by illustrative applications. After the first seven chapters there are three chapters on applications, consisting of a chapter on simple systems in which such things as the Clapeyron equation, osmotic pressure, and some other properties of dilute solutions are discussed; a chapter on thermo-chemistry and on chemical equilibrium in simple systems; and a chapter on systems for which variables other than pressure and volume are important. There then follow three chapters on Gibbsian thermo-dynamics, including both open and closed systems. A final chapter on the Nernst postulate, or third law, completes the book.

A special attempt is made to delineate the boundaries of thermo-dynamics, since we feel that much difficulty arises from confusion over these boundaries. To help in this, no use is made of statistical or atom-istic concepts. Rather, emphasis is given to the fact that thermodynamics permits an extremely general and accurate description of apparently very different phenomena, that the derived relationships can be based on macroscopic observations, and that they are independent of any particular physical model. Emphasis is also given to the fact that this very generality provides absolutely no clue to the structure of matter, in contrast to such fields as kinetic theory and statistical mechanics.

We do not mean to imply that it is improper to present a statistical viewpoint of thermodynamics, nor are we unaware of the fact that thermodynamics, statistical mechanics, and kinetic theory are often taught in a single course. Our only contention is that it is important that the boundaries of these different subjects, their underlying assumptions, and their interrelationships be made clear. Unless some analysis of this kind is made for the student, he may later find himself powerless to tackle any problem but an ideal gas or a perfect crystal.

In line with the separation of thermodynamics and statistical theory is the discussion of heat. The text follows the treatment of Born in which work and energy are considered fundamental and heat is considered to be a derived quantity. Heat is also considered to appear only at the boundary of a system. This approach helps to eliminate the tendency to think of a body as having a certain amount of heat within it—a tendency which still exists today, long after the much-heralded death of the caloric theory of heat.

The second law is introduced through the statement of the impossibility of perpetual motion of the second kind. This somewhat old-fashioned historical approach emphasizes the experimental basis of thermodynamics. Students seem very willing to accept the idea that a perpetual motion machine is impossible. It is usually a surprise to them to realize the breadth of this generalization as the concept of entropy is introduced and as various applications are presented which would seem to have little connection with the impossibility of constructing a perpetual motion machine.

The first and second laws are emphasized; the so-called third law is not placed on an equal footing with these. A complete treatment of the third law requires statistical mechanics; the purely macroscopic content of the third law is rather limited. Although this fact can be used to emphasize the difference between conclusions based purely on thermodynamics and those based on statistical mechanics, it did not seem appropriate to use this text to convey this difference to the student.

The present text thus treats classical equilibrium thermodynamics; within these limits it attempts to be rigorous (but not necessarily elegant). We feel that such an approach has definite value for both pedagogical and practical reasons.

CONTENTS

THERMODYNAMICS

Chapter 1

INTRODUCTION

Thermodynamics can be characterized as the study of the equilibrium properties of large-scale systems in which temperature is an important variable. Several words in this description—equilibrium, system, temperature—will be defined rigorously later, but for the present their everyday meaning will suffice. There are two basic laws in thermodynamics and each of these can be stated in such a way as to deny the possibility of a certain kind of process. The first law denies the possibility of a process which permits an isolated machine to perform work endlessly; that is, it denies the possibility of what is called "a perpetual motion machine of the first kind." The second law cannot be stated so accurately as the first law without a good deal more preliminary discussion, but remembering that our definitions are still unformed, we can say that the second law denies the possibility of a process which permits a machine to exchange heat with only one heat reservoir and perform work endlessly. Such a (non-existent) machine would be "a perpetual motion machine of the second kind." Neither of these statements of the two laws is in a very useful form, and the laws will be treated in detail later after rigorous definitions for the necessary concepts have been presented.

A characteristic kind of problem which can be treated in thermodynamics is the calculation of a certain set of properties of a system from another set of properties, as a consequence of the impossibility of the perpetual motion processes already mentioned. Such problems are seldom treated by the direct but cumbersome process of mentally constructing hypothetical perpetual motion machines; instead more abstract mathematical procedures are first derived and then these are used to solve various problems. These indirect procedures are quite efficient, but one should not forget that their basis lies in the two laws.

1

Since thermodynamics as presented here is based on statements about processes rather than about properties of matter, it is obvious that there is no theory of matter contained in it. No statements about the structure of matter can ever come from thermodynamics. Further, since the variables with which thermodynamics deals are always macroscopic, there is no possibility of obtaining information on a microscopic scale about a system—either its structure or its internal processes. This gives thermodynamics a generality which is nowhere exceeded in physical theory. Einstein has remarked*: "A theory is the more impressive the greater the simplicity of its premises is, the more different kinds of things it relates, and the more extended is its area of applicability. Therefore, the deep impression which classical thermodynamics made upon me. It is the only physical theory of universal content concerning which I am convinced that, within the framework of the applicability of its basic concepts, it will never be overthrown."

The deliberate avoidance of any theory of the structure of matter might seem to give thermodynamics an austerity (not to say sterility) which many people at first find repugnant. The virtue of the approach is that it exhibits just those parts of a physical theory which are independent of special theories of matter. As a result thermodynamics has an immensely practical side, since it can be applied with confidence to systems which are much too complicated to be treated by any other existing theories.

* A. Einstein, Autobiographical notes, *Albert Einstein: Philosopher–Scientist* (P. A. Schlipp, Ed., Harper and Row, Publishers, New York, 1959), Vol. I., p. 33.

Chapter 2

DEFINITIONS AND BASIC CONCEPTS

Historically, thermodynamics grew out of considerations involving heat and temperature (which were often confused), and involves words and concepts which one meets in the ordinary usage of written and spoken language. These words and concepts as used in thermodynamics, however, are abstractions of the ordinary concepts, and have accordingly quite precise meanings which may now differ from the everyday usage. It is therefore necessary to begin by giving some definitions and basic concepts, of which the most fundamental is probably that of equilibrium.

SYSTEM

A system is the particular part of the observable universe in which one is interested. Typical thermodynamic systems are a quantity of gas, a liquid and its vapor, a mixture of two liquids, a solution, or a crystalline solid.

SURROUNDINGS

Everything in the observable universe except the system is called the surroundings.

BOUNDARY

A boundary separates the system from the surroundings. Ideally, boundaries are mathematical surfaces which we endow with various

3

ideal properties, such as rigidity and impermeability. Real boundaries only approximate the properties of ideal thermodynamic boundaries. A system enclosed by a boundary impermeable to matter is called a *closed system*, and one enclosed by a permeable boundary is called an *open system*.

THERMODYNAMIC VARIABLES

Thermodynamic variables are those quantities which we find necessary or convenient to specify in order to give a macroscopic description of a system. Most such quantities are drawn from other branches of physics, such as pressure from mechanics and electric and magnetic field strength from electromagnetism. Accordingly, no detailed, all-inclusive definition of a thermodynamic variable can be given, and a few examples must suffice for the present. In a thermodynamic system consisting of a gas, a liquid, or a mixture of different gases and liquids, the thermodynamic variables are the masses of the different substances present, the pressure, the volume, and the temperature. In a system in which liquid surfaces or films are considered, corresponding variables would be surface tension, surface area, and temperature. The thermodynamic treatment of a magnetic system would probably include as variables the magnetic field strength, the magnetization of the matter in the system, and the temperature. In these examples only three variables (besides mass) have been given for each system, but there may be more. Of these groups of three variables, only temperature, which is considered in detail in the next chapter, is common to all; the other variables come from branches of physics outside thermodynamics.

STATE OF A SYSTEM

When the variables necessary to describe a system are specified, the state of the system is said to be specified. The specification of the state of a system gives no information on the process by which the system was brought to this state.

EQUILIBRIUM

One of the most fundamental and important concepts in thermodynamics is that of equilibrium. The key idea is that the variables describing a system in equilibrium do not change with time. This idea does not form a sufficient basis for a definition of equilibrium, however, since it fails to exclude a number of steady-state processes (principally various kinds of flow processes) which cannot be handled by classical thermodynamic methods. To exclude these, a more restrictive definition is used: *A system is in equilibrium if and only if it is in a state from which no change is possible without net changes in the surroundings.* In steady-state processes there must continually be changes in the surroundings to maintain the variables of the system at constant values. Classical thermodynamics deals only with systems in equilibrium.

Equilibrium is an abstraction and real systems are never strictly in equilibrium, but so long as the variables do not change measurably during the time spent making a measurement on the system, then the system can be considered to be in equilibrium and thermodynamic reasoning can be applied to it. A system may be in equilibrium with respect to some variables but not with respect to others. A mixture of hydrogen and oxygen gas is not in equilibrium with respect to a chemical reaction, but may easily be in equilibrium with respect to pressure, volume, and temperature.

ADIABATIC BOUNDARY

An adiabatic boundary is one such that the state of the system can be changed only by moving the boundary or by placing the system in an external force field (such as an electric, magnetic, or gravitational field). This definition will be crucial to our later formulation of the first law of thermodynamics. The usual understanding is that an adiabatic boundary is one that is impermeable to the flow of heat. It is extremely difficult to give a precise *a priori* definition of heat, however, and much easier to make the definition of heat depend on the present definition of adiabatic boundary, rather than *vice versa*. Boundary motion in this definition includes shearing and tangential motion, and the choice of the boundary is not always trivial. For instance, if a fluid is being stirred by a paddle wheel, it may be important to choose the boundary at the surface of the paddles so that the stirring is considered to be a motion of the boundary.

DIATHERMAL BOUNDARY

A diathermal boundary permits the state of the system to be changed without motion of the boundary. The usual understanding is that a diathermal boundary permits the flow of heat across it, but again this definition is avoided because of the difficulty of defining heat.

The preceding definitions and concepts are all rather basic to the subsequent formulation of thermodynamics. The following definitions are not basic, but are convenient in many applications.

HOMOGENEOUS SYSTEM

A system whose thermodynamic variables are constant throughout the system (in the absence of external force fields) is said to be homogeneous. If force fields are present, this statement can be relaxed by requiring that the variables only change continuously rather than that they be constant. A column of gas in a gravitational or centrifugal field can be considered homogeneous even though its density varies along the field.

HETEROGENEOUS SYSTEMS

A system whose thermodynamic variables can be considered to change discontinuously is said to be heterogeneous. A system consisting of ice and water in equilibrium is heterogeneous, the discontinuities occurring at the solid-liquid interfaces. It is sometimes convenient to divide a system into subsystems (called phases) by drawing new boundaries at these discontinuities.

PHASE

A phase is a homogeneous subsystem. It is not necessary that all parts of a phase be contiguous. For instance, a system consisting of water and ice is considered a two-phase system whether the ice is in one lump or in many small pieces.

EQUATION OF STATE

A relationship among the variables pressure, volume, temperature, and quantity of substance in a system is called an equation of state.

Thus, for a given single-phase fluid it is found that of the three variables—pressure, volume, and temperature—only two can be chosen arbitrarily. The third variable is then determined by nature, as described by the equation of state. The equation of state may be approximated by an analytical expression, or it may not; but it must come from experiment or from a theory of matter. It cannot be considered to arise from thermodynamics.

Chapter 3

TEMPERATURE

Although the concepts of heat and temperature historically lie at the roots of thermodynamics, a somewhat different presentation is given here. In the present treatment, heat is given a subordinate role as a derived quantity because of the logical difficulties involved in formulating an *a priori* definition of heat, but temperature is still kept in a primary role. It should be mentioned that temperature too can be put in a subordinate role and derived from the second law (suitably stated). Some people prefer this procedure because of its elegance and logical simplicity, but the price must then be paid in the form of greater abstraction.

It is assumed that everyone has a primitive notion of temperature in the sense of "hotness" or "coldness" of bodies. The refinement and extension of this primitive notion to the point where numbers can be attached to temperatures of bodies depends on several experimental facts. On these facts are based the operation of instruments, called thermometers, for assigning numerical values to temperatures.

EXPERIMENTAL BASIS OF TEMPERATURE MEASUREMENT

The first experimental fact is that some of the physical properties of a body change with temperature. Gases, liquids, and solids expand and contract as the temperature is raised or lowered, if the pressure is kept constant. Changes in temperature also change such things as the electrical resistivity of materials or the electromotive force between dissimilar metals. These properties, which are among those that have been used for making thermometers, are called thermoscopic* or thermometric properties.

The second experimental fact is that *thermal equilibrium* exists. We can describe this by saying that when two systems are put in thermal contact with each other (i.e., separated only by a diathermal boundary) and isolated from the surroundings by an adiabatic boundary, the thermodynamic variables of both systems may change with time, but that these changes will eventually stop and each system will be in equilibrium. The two systems are then in thermal equilibrium with each other. For example, when a mercury-in-glass thermometer is put into a glass of hot water the mercury will expand, rapidly at first, then more and more slowly until the expansion has altogether stopped. The thermometer and the water have then come into thermal equilibrium with each other.

The third experimental fact is that if two systems are in thermal equilibrium with one another and the first system is also in thermal equilibrium with a third system, then the second system will also be found to be in thermal equilibrium with the third system. This "cyclic" property of temperature is necessary if meaningful numbers are to be attached to temperature. If $t_a = t_b$ and $t_a = t_c$, then t_b must equal t_c if the numbers are to be meaningful. This last fact is sometimes called the "zeroth law" of thermodynamics.

These three facts are sufficient to permit us to set up a thermometric scale—in fact, a whole series of thermometric scales. To have something specific to discuss, we shall review the manner in which a mercury-in-glass thermometer is sometimes calibrated in elementary laboratory classes. The thermometer is first put into an ice bath, and the reading is taken after thermal equilibrium is reached. Then it is put into steam and again the reading is taken. If a centigrade scale is desired, the ice-point temperature is called 0° and the steam-point temperature 100°. Linear interpolation along the thermometer stem is used for assigning numbers to temperatures between the two fixed points. This scale could be called "the elementary laboratory mercury-in-glass centigrade thermometer scale."

Notice that the conventions or choices used in setting up the scale just described are as follows:

1. The choice of the thermometric property.
2. The choice of the thermometric system and the design of the thermometer.

* Thermometers were first called thermoscopes.

3. The choice of the "fixed points."
4. The choice of the numbers assigned to the fixed-point temperatures.
5. The choice of the rule for interpolation between fixed points—linear, quadratic, logarithmic, etc.

These choices are all arbitrary, which is the point to be understood here. Suppose we should set up another thermometer scale with a coil of wire as the thermometric system and the electrical resistance of the coil as the thermometric property. If this thermometer were put through the calibration procedure just described, the temperature indicated on the resistance thermometer and on the mercury-in-glass thermometer would agree at the fixed points by definition, but the two thermometers would not necessarily agree at any temperature in between. That is, the 50° mark on the mercury thermometer stands exactly halfway between the two calibration points since we specified linear interpolation, but the resistance thermometer in thermal equilibrium with the mercury thermometer at 50° (on the mercury thermometer scale) would not necessarily indicate that the temperature was exactly 50° on its resistance scale. Its resistance change from the 0° value would not be exactly half the change of resistance from 0° to 100°. This is a way of saying that the different thermometric properties do not change equally with temperature. To say that a good thermometer should have a linear scale is meaningless here, because we cannot define an absolute standard on the basis of the definitions and facts given so far. Each thermometric scale which we could describe would be defined only in terms of the properties of the material of which the thermometer was made.

The only way in which all the possible arbitrary temperature scales must agree is in the ordering of temperatures—that is, the scales must always agree that a given body is "hotter" or "colder" than another, if they are to satisfy our primitive notion of temperature. This can only be checked by intercomparing a large number of possible arbitrary temperature scales and discarding as unsatisfactory those few which violate this ordering criterion. For example, water has a maximum density (minimum specific volume) at about 4°C and its volume thus could not be used as the basis of a thermometric scale in this region.

The second law permits the definition of temperature without reference to the properties of any material substance; that is, it permits an absolute definition of temperature. However, we need the concept of temperature in order to discuss the second law at all, and we have therefore started the chain of argument with the description of arbitrary temperature scales. Arbitrary scales also have practical uses. Using the same arbitrary scale, two experimenters could determine whether the measurements of one worker were carried out at the same temperature as that of the other, although neither of them could tell how much two different temperatures differed from one another in any absolute sense.

IDEAL GAS THERMOMETER

There is one thermometer which has a special place among thermometers and which has not yet been mentioned. This is the gas thermometer. Experimentally it is found that all gases at low pressures and out of the region of the condensation line behave in the same way so far as the effect of temperature is concerned (provided no chemical reactions occur!). If the pressure-volume product of a fixed mass of gas is used as the thermometric property, then it is found that only small differences appear in the temperatures indicated when different kinds of gas are used. (In practice the pV product is seldom used directly; either V is held constant and p is used as the thermometric property, or *vice versa*.) A nitrogen thermometer and a hydrogen thermometer at about one atmosphere pressure, when calibrated in the manner described previously, will agree with one another within about $0.02°$ over the temperature range from $0°$ to $100°$. This is important from a practical standpoint, but the real importance of the gas thermometer lies in the fact that measurements on the gas thermometer, extrapolated to the region of very low pressures, can be shown to give an experimental realization of the absolute thermodynamic temperature defined on the basis of the second law.

The ideal gas temperature scale can be defined by the relationship

$$\lim_{p \to 0} \frac{(pV)}{(pV)_{\text{ref}}} = \frac{\theta}{\theta_{\text{ref}}}, \qquad (3.1)$$

where (pV) and $(pV)_{\text{ref}}$ refer to the same mass of gas at two different temperatures, θ and θ_{ref}, one of which has been arbitrarily selected as a reference or fixed point. The lefthand side of the equation contains variables which are directly measurable and yields a definite number ratio. Therefore, assignment of a number to θ_{ref} determines the value of θ, and all temperatures on the scale are determined by the arbitrary assignment of only *one* number.

It is convenient to carry Eq. (3.1) a little further at this point and obtain the complete equation of state for any ideal gas. Experimentally it is found that pV is proportional to the mass m of the gas at constant temperature. We therefore define a constant K,

$$K \equiv \lim_{p \to 0} \frac{(pV)_{\text{ref}}}{m\theta_{\text{ref}}}, \tag{3.2}$$

and rewrite Eq. (3.1) as

$$pV = mK\theta. \tag{3.3}$$

If m is in ordinary mass units such as grams, then K has a different value for every gas. We can force K to be a universal constant for all gases by defining a new unit of mass called the *mole*, such that one mole of a gas is that mass which has the same pV value as 32.000 g of ordinary oxygen* at the same temperature and at $p \to 0$. The ideal gas equation of state can thus finally be written as

$$pV = nR\theta, \tag{3.4}$$

where n is the number of moles and R is the universal gas constant. Notice that the numerical value of R depends on the units used for p and V and on the particular number assigned to θ_{ref}. It is customary to choose $\theta_{\text{ref}} \equiv 273.16$ at the temperature at which ice, liquid water, and water vapor are all in equilibrium with one another (the triple point of water). Then it is found experimentally that $R = 8.3143$ joule/mole-degree.

INTERNATIONAL PRACTICAL TEMPERATURE SCALE

Gas thermometers are not ordinarily used in scientific work because the accurate determination of temperatures with a gas thermometer is a complicated and difficult task, and the work is carried out in only a few laboratories in the world. These gas thermometers are therefore used to measure the thermometric properties of other more convenient kinds of thermometers, and to determine the thermodynamic temperatures of various convenient fixed points, such as melting points

---

* This definition is no longer strictly correct because of the new definition of the atomic weight scale in terms of the mass of the carbon-12 isotope. It is, however, sufficiently accurate, being in error by only 37 parts in 1 million.

and boiling points. Thermometers calibrated against such fixed points are the working standards for most scientific and technical work. The interpolation formulas for these working standards are derived from measurements of their thermometric properties against the gas thermometer.

The particular type of thermometer, the design of the instrument, the temperatures to be attached to the various fixed points, and the particular interpolation formulas for the various thermometers are the subject of international agreement, the scale so defined being the International Practical Temperature Scale. This is chosen so that measurements made with properly calibrated instruments will agree with the thermodynamic temperature to within 0.01°C in most cases. Revisions of this scale so far as procedures and values are concerned are made at intervals of not less than six years. For an excellent description of this subject the following articles can be recommended:

"Heat Units and Temperature Scales for Calorimetry," H. F. Stimson, Am. J. Phys. *23*, 614 (1955).

"International Practical Temperature Scale of 1948. Text Revision of 1960," H. F. Stimson, J. Research Natl. Bur. Standards *65A*, 139 (1961).

REMARKS

Two points are worth emphasizing. First, the role of equilibrium appears in a fundamental way at the very beginning of the formulation of the concept of temperature. This emphasis on equilibrium is characteristic of the thermodynamic approach. Second, the general methods used for the assignment of numbers to temperatures are no different in principle from those used for the assignment of numbers to other fundamental physical quantities such as length, mass, and time. The establishment of standards and of methods for comparison and interpolation is something common to all such quantities, and there is nothing special about temperature in this regard.

PROBLEMS

1. Suppose that the ice point and the steam point are used to establish a centigrade scale; the interpolation formula assumed is

$$t(x) = ax^2 + b.$$

The value of x at the ice point is 2, and at the steam point is 3.

(a) Determine the numerical values of a and b.

(b) The variable x can be measured with one percent accuracy. What is the possible error in temperature at 50 degrees centigrade?

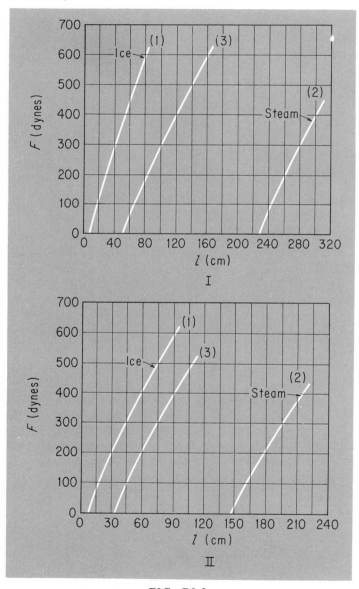

FIG. P3.2

2. (a) The graphs of Fig. P3.2 show a set of three isotherms for each of the two systems in which F, l, t (tension, length, and temperature) are thermodynamic variables. The lines marked "Isotherm 3" were obtained for each of the systems while they were separated only by a diathermal wall in an adiabatic envelope. Each of the systems is to be used as a thermometer, with length the thermoscopic property, the tension being fixed at 300 dynes. A linear relationship between the temperature associated with an isotherm and the thermoscopic property is assumed. If the ice isotherm is made to correspond to $0°$ and the steam isotherm to $100°$, then *specify the temperature of isotherm 3 on each of the thermometers*.

(b) Specify the temperature of isotherm 3 on each of the thermometers if the tension is fixed at 400 dynes.

(c) Thermometer I is put into a system which has an unknown temperature. When the tension on the thermometer is set at 300 dynes the length read is 160 cm. What is the temperature of the system according to Thermometer I? Can you specify what the corresponding temperature would be according to Thermometer II?

3. The resistance of a platinum wire is found to be 7.000 ohms at the ice point $(0.00°C)$, 9.705 ohms at the steam point $(100.00°C)$, and 18.387 ohms at the sulfur point $(444.60°C)$. The resistance at a temperature of $t°C$ is to be represented by the equation

$$R_t = R_0(1 + at + bt^2),$$

where R_0, a, and b are constants.

(a) Find the values of the constants from the measurements at the ice, steam, and sulfur points.

(b) Suppose that when this platinum wire is used as a thermometer, the value of R_t is measured with a systematic error of 0.001 ohm. Find the resulting error, Δt, in the temperature, and plot Δt as a function of temperature.

4. Suppose the thermometer described in problem 3 is calibrated only at the ice and steam points, and R_t represented by an equation which is linear in t. What temperature would this linear thermometer indicate at the sulfur point? How much in error would this value be?

5. A constant-volume gas thermometer containing 0.020000 moles of ideal gas in $1000.00 \ cm^3$ is used to measure the ideal gas temperature at the steam point $(100.00°C)$.

(a) How accurately must the pressure be measured to obtain the ideal gas temperature accurate to $0.01°C$?

(b) The thermometer bulb is made of a glass whose volume expansion is given by the expressions

$$V_t = V_0(1 + \alpha t),$$

$$10^7 \alpha = 226.52 + 0.1327t.$$

Is it necessary to make any correction for the thermal expansion of the glass in the determination of the steam-point temperature? How much in error would the measured ideal gas temperature be at the steam point if no correction were made?

6. A constant-pressure gas thermometer is constructed which utilizes a non-ideal gas whose equation of state is

$$p(V - nb) = nR\theta,$$

where b is a constant and θ is the true ideal-gas temperature. This thermometer is used by an experimenter who thinks the gas is ideal, and who obtains apparent temperatures ϕ by assuming the equation of state to be

$$pV = nR\phi.$$

(a) Show that the apparent temperature will be related to the true ideal-gas temperature by the expression

$$\phi = \theta\left(1 + \frac{bp}{R\theta}\right)\left(1 + \frac{bp}{R\theta_{\text{ref}}}\right)^{-1} \approx \theta + \frac{bp}{R\theta_{\text{ref}}}(\theta_{\text{ref}} - \theta) + \cdots.$$

Remember that ϕ_{ref} and θ_{ref} will both be chosen to be 273.16 at the triple point of water (0.0100°C).

(b) If $b = 100$ cm³/mole and the thermometer is operated at a pressure of 1 bar, by how many degrees will ϕ differ from the ideal-gas temperature at the steam point (100.00°C)?

7. A mercury-in-glass thermometer is normally calibrated at the ice and steam points and a linear interpolation along the stem used to determine intermediate temperatures. A mercury thermometer, 50 cm long with 0.10 mm² stem cross section and bulb volume of 2 cm³, is so calibrated. How accurately will this thermometer reproduce the international practical temperature scale at 50°C? Is this within the reproducibility of the mercury thermometer readings (0.1–0.2°)? The volume expansions of the glass and mercury are given by

$$V_t = V_0(1 + \alpha t),$$

$$10^7 \alpha = 226.52 + 0.1327t \text{ for glass,}$$

$$10^8 \alpha = 18144.01 + 0.7016t \text{ for mercury.}$$

Chapter 4

FIRST LAW

The first law of thermodynamics is essentially the law of conservation of energy applied to thermodynamic systems. There is a compelling analogy with certain idealized mechanical systems, called conservative mechanical systems, for which a conservation law for energy holds. In such mechanical systems two kinds of energy are distinguished, kinetic energy and potential energy, which can be defined in terms of the velocities and coordinates of the particles making up the system. The total energy is the sum of these two, and is constant unless work is done on the system by external forces, in which case the increase in the total energy is equal to the work done on the system. The analogy consists in imagining real thermodynamic systems to be conservative mechanical systems whose individual parts are too small to be perceived (atoms, molecules, etc.). The law of conservation of energy supposedly holds if the microscopic motion is taken into account, but the purely microscopic kinetic and potential energies are manifested on an experimental macroscopic scale as heat. Heat is then a form of energy, and energy is conserved.

But this is *only* an analogy, a convenient mental picture, and is useless as it stands because there is no possibility of measuring the energies involved even if the analogy were strictly correct. For a thermodynamic system no such definition of kinetic and potential energy is possible, because we do not look into the structure of the system. Instead we are forced to think of the system as a "black box" and ask what experiments will permit us to define the energy of the system, or indeed if such a definition is experimentally possible at all. The experiments which first demonstrated this possibility were performed by Joule. Before discussing his experiments, we observe that

17

the mechanical analogy does suggest that the definition of energy of a thermodynamic system might be tied to the concept of external work; that is, work performed by forces in the surroundings. Such a definition proves to be possible; it further proves convenient to restrict these external forces to conservative forces, so that dissipative forces like friction are excluded from the definition of thermodynamic work. *Thermodynamic work is therefore defined in terms of conservative forces in the surroundings.* It can always be visualized as the raising or lowering of weights in a gravitational field, even though it may actually involve other forms of work such as the charging or discharging of an ideal (lossless) capacitor.

We note that thermodynamic work is more restricted than is general mechanical work. By definition, it is measured in the surroundings, not in the system, and consists only of conservative work. Other than that, it is the same as ordinary mechanical work.

JOULE'S EXPERIMENTS

In Chapter 2 we mentioned two general methods of changing the state of a system, the first by adiabatic means, the second by diathermal means. Joule's experiments were adiabatic. Using apparatus similar to that shown schematically in Fig. 4.1, he carried out a series of experiments in which the paddle wheels were turned by slowly falling

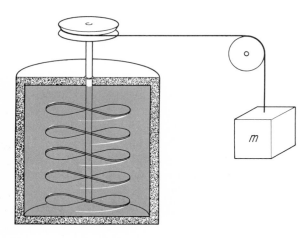

FIG. 4.1. Schematic diagram of the Joule apparatus.

weights. By this method the state of the system, a definite quantity of water, was changed so that the temperature rose from room temperature to a slightly higher temperature. It is important to note that the paddles form part of the boundary in this type of experiment, so that the state of the system is changed by moving the boundary. Joule also did experiments with mercury in place of water, and with iron disks rubbing each other under the liquid in place of paddles stirring the liquid. (He also attempted such experiments in which the temperature was raised by the performance of electrical work, but demonstrated instead that the system of electrical units in use at that time was quantitatively inaccurate.) He found that the performance of a definite amount of adiabatic work always produced the same change of state of the system, no matter what contrivance was used to perform the work or what the nature of the system was. If we now assume that this result is true for all thermodynamic systems under all conditions, we can define the energy of a thermodynamic system and proceed to the formulation of the first law.

DEFINITION OF INTERNAL ENERGY

Joule's experiments justify the assumption that a definite difference in energy between two states of a system is a meaningful concept, and further that this energy difference can be measured by the amount of work which "disappears" from the surroundings in order to change one state to the other under adiabatic conditions. This can be expressed mathematically as

$$E_2 - E_1 = -W_{\text{adiabatic}}, \tag{4.1}$$

where E_1 and E_2 represent the *internal energies** of states 1 and 2, respectively, and $(-W_{\text{adiabatic}})$ represents the amount of work which disappears from the surroundings during the adiabatic transformation. We use the adjective "internal" to distinguish the thermodynamic

---

* We have written the symbols for the internal energies as though absolute values of internal energy could be determined. Actually, only differences in internal energy can be measured; just as in mechanics, energy is always measured relative to an arbitrary zero. A standard state is chosen and the internal energy of this state is taken to be zero. A common choice of standard state conditions in thermodynamic calculations is chemical elements at 25°C, one atmosphere pressure, with each element in its most stable form under these conditions.

energy of Eq. (4.1) from ordinary mechanical energy, since we are in general completely ignorant about the microscopic structure of a thermodynamic system.

Before we can claim that Eq. (4.1) completely defines a quantity which is a function only of the state of a system and not of its past history, we must ask whether this definition will include *all* states of a system. So far as is known, any pair of states of a thermodynamic system can be connected by the performance of adiabatic work, and we therefore assume the general truth of this. The definition of internal energy is therefore based on the following two generalizations of experience:

> (a) Any two states of a thermodynamic system can be connected by the performance of adiabatic work.
>
> (b) The amount of adiabatic work needed to connect two given states depends *only* on the states and not on the particular contrivance for performing the work.

(4.2)

It should be noted that we have not claimed anything about the direction of the transformation from one state to another by adiabatic work. In Joule's experiments the temperature of the system increased as the fluid was stirred. There is no way by which this process can be reversed adiabatically and the temperature caused to decrease, so that the system would proceed from state 2 (high temperature) back to state 1 (low temperature) by an adiabatic process. All that concerns us now is that the connection between the two states is possible in at least one direction. The second law of thermodynamics places restrictions on the directions in which changes of state can be carried out adiabatically, as we shall see later, but it is always true that if an adiabatic transformation cannot be carried out in one direction it can be carried out in the other.

DEFINITION OF HEAT

We would like to believe that the quantity E defined by Eq. (4.1) depends only on the state of the system and not on the particular process by which that state was attained, but there are many ways other than adiabatic transformations by which a change in state can be brought about. For example, the same temperature change of the system used in Joule's experiment (call it system A) could have been brought about by putting the system in thermal contact with a second system B at a higher temperature. In this transformation no work would disappear from the surroundings,* but instead there would be a change in the state of system B. We can postulate that the change in internal energy of system A is the same as that caused by the adiabatic transformation, and that this energy has been transferred from B to A during the time the two systems were in thermal contact, but this postulate needs experimental verification. What is needed is a demonstration that the exact amount of energy represented by the change of system A from state 1 to state 2 has disappeared from B. We could test if this were so by putting B into an adiabatic envelope and performing Joule's experiment on it until its original state was restored. If the postulate is correct we should find that the same amount of work would disappear from the surroundings to restore B to its original state as disappeared in taking A from state 1 to state 2 adiabatically. Experiment confirms that this is true, and so the postulate is justified. The energy transferred from B to A during the thermal contact is called *heat*, and is denoted by the symbol Q.

The two methods of changing the state of a system can be combined, of course, and the state can be changed by successively carrying out adiabatic and diathermal transformations, or by doing work at the same time that the system is in thermal contact with another system. In such cases we can generalize the definition of heat by writing

$$E_2 - E_1 = Q - W, \qquad (4.3)$$

where $-W$ is the work which disappears from the surroundings, and $E_2 - E_1$ must be determined by a separate adiabatic experiment according to Eq. (4.1).

First Law

The foregoing discussion has really completely formulated the first law of thermodynamics, which we now summarize. On the basis of Joule's experiments and diathermal experiments of the sort just

---

* We assume the volume is kept constant.

discussed, we assert that:

(a) For every thermodynamic system there exists a quantity E called internal energy, which is a function only of the state of the system and not of the processes by which the state was attained.

(b) The internal energy difference between two states is measured by the adiabatic work required to transform the system from one state to the other.

(c) In non-adiabatic processes the difference between the actual work and the internal energy change is defined to be heat.

$$(4.4)$$

These three statements can be summarized by the two equations,

$$\Delta E = -W_{\text{adiabatic}}, \qquad (4.5)$$

$$\Delta E = Q - W. \qquad (4.6)$$

The notation, $\Delta E \equiv E_2 - E_1$, implies the statement that E is a *state function*, such notation being used only for state functions and never for quantities like Q and W which depend on the process by which the state was attained. The differential forms of Eqs. (4.5) and (4.6) are

$$dE = -dW_{\text{adiabatic}}, \qquad (4.7)$$

$$dE = dQ - dW. \qquad (4.8)$$

In these last two equations dQ and dW are not exact differentials in the mathematical sense because Q and W are not functions of the state of the system alone. The notation dQ and dW merely means quantities of infinitesimal order, not exact differentials.

Equation (4.6) is sometimes put forward as the complete first law of thermodynamics, but this is clearly not so, at least in the formulation given here. Only ΔE and W have been given operational definitions independent of Eq. (4.6), and we have given no way of measuring Q without invoking Eq. (4.6) somewhere in the procedure. Of course, if Q could be given a definition independent of Eq. (4.6), then Eq. (4.6) would indeed be a statement of the first law, but such a definition is extremely difficult to formulate in a satisfactory way.

In view of the fundamental nature of the law of conservation of energy, it might be expected that the first law would have been subjected to a wide variety of direct experimental tests of the sort just outlined. This is not the case, and the *direct* experimental evidence for the first law is rather scanty. The reason is historical: the acceptance of the first law and of the idea of the mechanical nature of heat was so rapid and complete shortly after Joule's experiments that such experimental efforts apparently did not seem worthwhile. As a result, the experimental evidence for the first law is largely indirect, in that its many consequences have been repeatedly and abundantly verified.

REMARKS ON HEAT

The treatment just given lays stress on the primary role of the internal energy of a system and places heat in a subordinate role. It stresses the ultimate manner in which a quantity of heat is to be measured; i.e., by measurement of the adiabatic work needed to restore to its original state a system which has lost a quantity of energy by a diathermal process. The unit of heat is then, very naturally, the same as the unit of work. In modern practice this is the joule. Formerly, the unit of heat was the calorie, one definition of the calorie being the amount of heat necessary to raise the temperature of one gram of water from 14.5°C to 15.5°C. The type of experiment done by Joule showed the relationship between the size of the unit of work and the calorie, the relationship being called the "mechanical equivalent of heat." From the present point of view a better name would be the "caloric equivalent of work." The first name indicates the historical fact that calorimetric experiments were performed long before Joule's experiments linked the concept of heat to the concept of work. From the present viewpoint the "mechanical equivalent of heat" is merely a statement about the specific heat of water, and it is not a fundamental physical quantity of the same class as the gravitational constant or the speed of light.

We can also show that the definition of heat given here has characteristics which correspond with the old intuitive ideas of heat obtained from calorimetric experiments. These characteristics are:

1. The flow of heat across the boundary of a system changes its state.
2. Heat cannot cross an adiabatic boundary.
3. Heat flows from a higher to a lower temperature.
4. Heat is conserved in adiabatic processes in which no net work is done (such as calorimetric mixing experiments).

The first of these follows from the known existence of diathermal walls. The second follows directly from Eqs. (4.5) and (4.6). The third was illustrated but not proved in our discussion of the definition of heat, in that energy flowed from system B at the higher temperature to system A at the lower temperature. It is not difficult to construct a proof that if energy flows from B to A, it will also flow from B to any other system at the same temperature as A, by showing that a violation of the zeroth law can be constructed if this statement is not valid. The fourth characteristic follows directly from Eq. (4.6).

It should be obvious that it makes no sense to talk about the amount of heat in a system or the amount of work in a system, since heat and work are not state functions. Since energy is a state function it does make sense to say that a system has a definite amount of internal energy (relative to some standard state), and that the amount of energy can be changed by allowing a certain amount of energy in the form of heat to pass across the boundary or by having the system bring about the appearance or disappearance of a certain amount of work in its surroundings.

Heat Capacities

When energy in the form of heat passes into a body, the temperature in general changes. The amount of heat depends on the particular process. Both the amount of heat Q and the change in temperature Δt can be measured, and their ratio, called the average heat capacity $\bar{C}$, is given by

$$\bar{C} = \frac{Q}{\Delta t}. \qquad (4.9)$$

In the limit as $\Delta t \to 0$, this ratio becomes the heat capacity,

$$C = \frac{dQ}{dt}, \qquad (4.10)$$

which is defined only when the process is specified. The measured heat capacity is a function of temperature and also other thermodynamic variables such as p and V, so that a further specification of the heat capacity is necessary. This is indicated by subscripts; for example, C_p and C_V indicate that the pressure or volume, respectively, is held constant at a particular value as heat is added to the system. The heat capacity of a particular kind of system is proportional to the mass of the system, and it is therefore convenient to express the heat capacity of the system in terms of the heat capacity per unit mass: the heat capacity per gram is called the specific heat $\bar{c}$, and the heat capacity per mole is called the molar heat capacity $\tilde{C}$.

<h2 style="text-align:center">PROBLEMS</h2>

1. Calculate the work done during the cycle diagrammed in Fig. P4.1. What is the sign of W if the cycle is carried out by proceeding clockwise around the circle as drawn? By proceeding counter-clockwise?

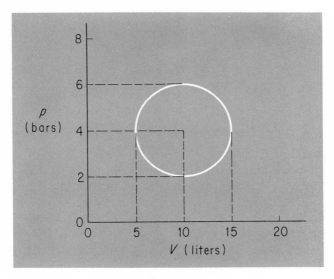

FIG. P4.1

2. The first law of thermodynamics is occasionally stated in the following way: "It is impossible to devise any process which will operate in a cycle (i.e., the system returns to its initial state) and which will have no other effect in the surroundings than the production of work." Prove that this statement follows from Eq. (4.6).

3. A volume of gas is confined in an insulated cylinder with an insulated weightless piston, as shown in Fig. P4.3. There is 10,000 dynes of sliding friction between the piston and the cylinder walls. The piston is allowed to move outward, raising a 100 g weight against the force of (standard) gravity through a distance of 10 cm.

(a) What is the amount of *thermodynamic* work which appears in the surroundings?

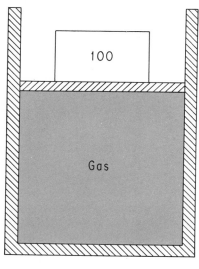

100

Gas

FIG. P4.3

(b) If the system is considered to be the cylinder, piston, and gas together, what is the change in internal energy of the system?

(c) If the piston and cylinder have negligible heat capacity, what is the change in internal energy of the gas alone?

4. Calculate the energy change for the melting of 1 mole of ice at 0°C and 1 atm pressure. The heat absorbed is 333 joule/g (the so-called latent heat of fusion), and the densities of ice and liquid water at 0°C and 1 atm are 0.917 g/cm³ and 1.000 g/cm³, respectively.

5. (a) Calculate the work in joules that is produced when 100 g of liquid water vaporizes at 100°C against an applied pressure of 1 atm (which is equal to the vapor pressure of water at 100°C). At 100°C and 1 atm the density of liquid water is 0.958 g/cm³, and that of steam is 0.598 kg/m³.

(b) What percentage error would be incurred by neglecting the volume of the liquid compared to that of the vapor? By neglecting the volume of the liquid and assuming the vapor to be an ideal gas? The molecular weight of steam is 18.016 g/mole.

(c) Calculate the energy change in joules for this change in state. The heat absorbed is 2257 joule/g (the so-called latent heat of vaporization).

6. A system is transformed from state A to state C, as shown in Fig. P4.6.

(a) Which process produces more work in the surroundings, process ABC or $AB'C$? In which process is more heat withdrawn from the surroundings? How much more?

(b) The system is carried through a complete cycle, $AB'CBA$. How much work is produced? How much heat is withdrawn? What is the net change in internal energy of the system?

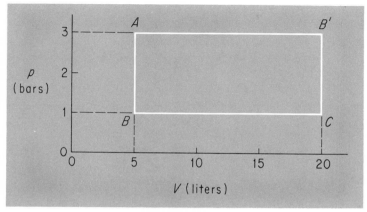

FIG. P4.6

7. (a) A system initially with a volume of 22.4 liters is compressed adiabatically until its volume is 11 2 liters. During this process 1350 joules of work is performed on the system, and the temperature rises from 0°C to 160°C. How much does the internal energy change during this process?

(b) The same initial system is heated at constant volume to 160°C, whereby 1320 joules of heat must be added. What is the change in internal energy of the system during this process?

(c) The system is now compressed at this constant temperature of 160°C to a volume of 11.2 liters, whereby 2550 joules of heat flow out of the system. What is the change in internal energy? How much work is done on the system?

8. Show that for a system of constant heat capacity whose energy along a given isotherm is constant, the energy depends only on temperature.

9. An electric motor doing work at the rate of 50 watts operates for one minute. During this time it is used to drive a friction device submerged in 100 g of water held in an adiabatic container, whereby the temperature of the water rises 6°C. When the experiment is repeated with 200 g of water in the container, the motor must operate for one minute and fifty seconds to bring about the same temperature change.

(a) What is the heat capacity of the container?

(b) What is the specific heat of water as calculated from these measurements?

10. Refer to Problem 2a of Chapter 3 for the specification of the thermometers involved in the following problem.

(a) In Laboratory I, thermometer I is used in an experiment in which 10 g of copper is raised in temperature at constant pressure from 0° to 25°. It is found that 500 joules of heat must be supplied to the copper to effect this change in temperature. What is the average specific heat of the copper at constant pressure according to these data?

(b) In Laboratory II, thermometer II is used in an experiment in which 30 g of copper is heated from 0° to 20° at constant pressure. The experimenter uses the average specific heat calculated by Laboratory I and the difference in temperature which he himself measures to calculate the amount of heat he has added to the copper. How many joules of heat does he calculate? How many joules of heat did he actually add?

11. By direct measurement (Fig. P4.11) it is found that $Q_{AB} = 7$ and $Q_{AD} = 1$ joule. The value of E_A is arbitrarily chosen to be zero.

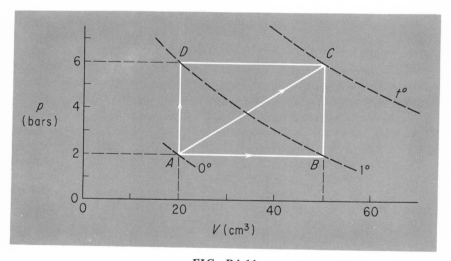

FIG. P4.11

(a) Find E_B and E_D. Calculate C_p and C_V on the assumption that they are constants, independent of temperature, volume, or pressure.

(b) Under the same assumption about C_p and C_V, calculate the temperature of the isotherm marked $t°$, on the same scale as the isotherms already marked.

(c) Calculate E_C and Q_{AC}. What is the average heat capacity along the line AC?

Chapter 5

SECOND LAW

STATEMENT OF THE SECOND LAW

One way of stating the second law of thermodynamics is similar to the statement given by William Thomson in 1851–1852, and is as follows:

It is impossible to make any transformation whose only final result is the exchange of a non-zero amount of heat with less than two heat reservoirs and the appearance of a positive amount of work in the surroundings.

Thomson based his statement on the 1824 work of Sadi Carnot, who had noticed that a steam engine (or any other heat engine) could not operate unless it absorbed heat at a high temperature and rejected it at some lower temperature. This is not the most elegant way of stating the second law, but has the advantage of being easy to understand.

Several phrases in the above statement need clarification. First, a *heat reservoir* is a system which can exchange heat with other systems without itself changing temperature. A heat reservoir can be visualized as a body of very large heat capacity, all of which is at the same temperature. The only purpose of this idealization is to avoid complications in the analysis which would arise if temperature changes in the reservoirs had to be taken into account. No real loss of generality results from this simplifying idealization. In the statement of the second law, the "two heat reservoirs" are understood to be at different temperatures. Two reservoirs at the same temperature are to be considered as one reservoir.

Second, the phrase "only final result" ensures that the system undergoing the transformation proceeds through a complete *cycle*. A cycle is a process in which the system is removed from its original state during the process but is returned to that state at the end of the process. All thermodynamic variables of the system must have exactly the same values after the transformation as they had before the transformation.

We shall also need the concept of a *reversible process* (first introduced by Carnot). A reversible process is one carried out in such a way that it can be exactly reversed at any time by making only infinitesimal changes in the surroundings. Such a process is clearly an idealization which can only be approximated in practice. In this chapter the only use we shall make of this concept is to take advantage of the fact that if a reversible cycle is carried out in reverse, all heat and work quantities pertaining to the cycle merely change sign.* Later we shall make extensive use of reversible processes in calculations. The usefulness of the concept for this purpose arises from the fact that every intermediate state of the system during the process is well-defined thermodynamically, or in other words is an equilibrium state.

We shall call a system undergoing a cycle an "engine," partly for historical reasons and partly just to avoid long circumlocutions. The "engine" of course can be perfectly arbitrary, and is not to be thought of as a collection of hardware with steam puffing about. Reasoning by the use of various hypothetical engines was characteristic of methods of solving thermodynamic problems a number of years ago and is still used occasionally. Such methods are usually awkward, and our object in this chapter is to define a new state function, entropy, so that problems can be solved analytically. To arrive at the definition of entropy from the foregoing statement of the second law we need to consider a few cycles, but after that almost all reasoning will be by analytical methods.

SYMBOLIC DIAGRAM OF A CYCLE

To represent an engine we shall use a diagram as shown in Fig. 5.1. The reservoirs, which have temperatures t_1 and t_2, are indicated as flat slabs. The system (or engine) S exchanges heat with the reservoirs and work appears or disappears in the surroundings. The direction of

---

* For heat flow to be reversible, the heat must flow under conditions of no temperature gradient. This idealization can be approached arbitrarily closely.

heat flow is shown both by the direction of the arrows and by the positive and negative signs in parentheses before the symbols Q. We have indicated that heat is absorbed from the reservoir at t_1 and rejected to the reservoir at t_2. We shall shortly prove that this is the only possible combination of directions if work appears in the surroundings. The appearance of work is shown as the lifting of a weight, and is also indicated by the direction of the arrow representing work W. If an amount of work W is performed during an integral number of engine

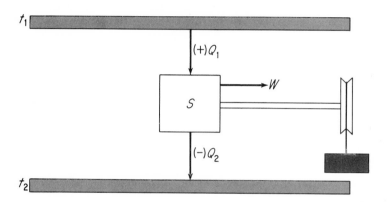

FIG. 5.1. Symbolic diagram of a cycle.

cycles, the total heat absorbed by the engine is $Q_1 + Q_2$; that is, the Q's are algebraic quantities carrying their own signs.

In the following discussion we shall keep the convention used in Chapter 3 that if two systems are connected by a diathermal wall, heat will flow from the higher temperature to the lower temperature. In the symbolic diagrams, the reservoir with the higher temperature is usually placed on top. Sometimes the hotter reservoir is called the *source* and the cooler reservoir the *refrigerator*.

CONSEQUENCES OF THE SECOND LAW ALONE

There are several consequences of the second law whose proofs follow more or less directly from the statement as we have given it, and hence will be called corollaries. The set of five corollaries given in this section depend *only* on the second law and do not involve the first law.

Corollary I

> *An engine operating in a cycle between two heat reservoirs will produce positive work only if heat is absorbed at the high temperature and rejected at the lower.*

The four conceivable arrangements for the flow of heat are shown in Fig. 5.2. The proof consists in showing that (a), (b), and (c) violate the second law, and is performed in two steps. The first step consists in showing that heat cannot be absorbed at the lower temperature. This is true because heat could always be made to flow from t_1 to t_2 by connecting the reservoirs by a diathermal wall; any amount of heat

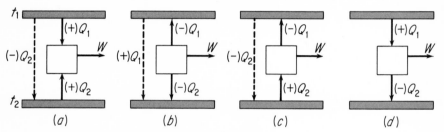

FIG. 5.2. Four conceivable heat flows in an engine.

withdrawn from t_2 by the engine could be returned to the reservoir by heat flow through the diathermal wall—making the net amount of heat exchanged with t_2 equal to zero. The second reservoir is then superfluous and the second law is violated; that is, the original engine plus the reservoir at t_2 constitutes a new engine which violates the second law. This argument eliminates (a) and (c).

The second step consists in showing that heat must be absorbed at some temperature, eliminating the possibility of (b). Any amount of heat transferred to t_1 by the engine could be compensated by permitting this amount of heat to flow from t_1 to t_2 through a diathermal wall. The upper reservoir is then superfluous and the second law is violated.

The only remaining possibility is (d), and no arrangement of diathermal walls will permit the net amount of heat exchanged with either reservoir to be zero. This completes the proof.

Corollary II

> *No engine operating between two heat reservoirs can have a higher efficiency than a reversible engine operating between the same two reservoirs.*

The efficiency, ϵ, of an engine operating between two reservoirs and withdrawing an amount of heat Q from the source is defined to be

$$\epsilon = \frac{W}{Q}, \tag{5.1}$$

where W is the amount of work which appears in the surroundings.

To prove the corollary we consider two engines, one reversible (R) and one irreversible (I), both operating between the reservoirs

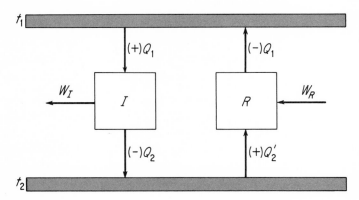

F I G. 5.3. Irreversible (I) and reversible (R) engines operating between the same two reservoirs.

t_1 and t_2, as shown in Fig. 5.3. We assume that the irreversible engine produces more work from a given amount of heat Q withdrawn from the source at t_1 in an integral number of cycles than does the reversible engine.* Thus, we assume that $\epsilon_I > \epsilon_R$. If this were so, then the irreversible engine could run the reversible engine backwards and also produce positive work. The combination would exchange no net amount of heat with t_1, since the reversible engine running backwards would give to the hotter reservoir the same amount of heat as was withdrawn by the irreversible engine. The hotter reservoir is therefore

---

* It may appear that there is some loss in generality in assuming that the two engines withdraw the same amount of heat from the source when they operate in the forward (work-producing) direction. This is only an apparent limitation; we can imagine that the total amount of heat withdrawn by the reversible engine running forward is Nq, where q is the heat withdrawn per cycle and N is an integer, and similarly the heat withdrawn by the irreversible engine is $N'q'$. As long as we can arrange that $N/N' = q'/q$ to any desired accuracy, the amounts of heat withdrawn by the two engines are equal.

superfluous and the second law is violated. Hence the assumption that $\epsilon_I > \epsilon_R$ must be incorrect and we conclude that

$$\epsilon_I \leqslant \epsilon_R. \tag{5.2}$$

Corollary III

> *All reversible engines operating between the same two reservoirs have the same efficiency.*

The proof of this corollary is similar to that given for Corollary II, and is left as an excercise.

Corollary IV

> *If two reversible engines operate with a common source temperature and different refrigerator temperatures, the engine operating over the larger temperature difference has the higher efficiency.*

In Fig. 5.4, engine A operates between t_1 and t_2 while engine B operates between t_1 and t_3, and $t_1 > t_2 > t_3$. Suppose that $\epsilon_A \geqslant \epsilon_B$. If this were true, we could adjust the engines so that $Q_{A1} = Q_{B1}$ and then we would have $W_A \geqslant W_B$. Under these conditions it would be possible for engine A to run engine B backwards and produce positive or zero work in the surroundings. Thus the combination of A, B, and reservoir t_1 is a system operating in a cycle which extracts heat from t_3, transfers heat to t_2, and produces positive or zero work. This can be shown to violate the second law, for a third engine could be introduced

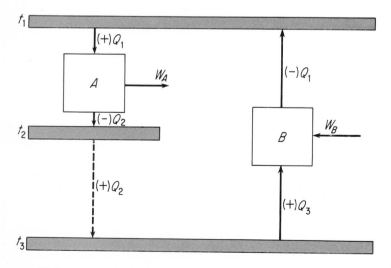

FIG. 5.4. Reversible engines with a common source and different refrigerator temperatures.

which would operate between t_2 and t_3 and produce positive work. This third engine could be adjusted to make zero the net amount of heat exchanged with either t_2 or t_3, and thereby reduce to one the number of reservoirs with which net heat is exchanged while positive work is produced. Our initial assumption must then be false and we conclude that $\epsilon_B > \epsilon_A$.

The same conclusion is obtained if the engines work with a common refrigerator temperature and different source temperatures. The engine operating over the larger temperature interval has the greater efficiency.

These last two corollaries have an important implication. They show how an "absolute" temperature scale can be based on the second law, without any dependence on the specific properties of any substance. A standard reservoir temperature could be chosen arbitrarily, and then all other temperatures could be referred to this chosen temperature by means of the efficiencies of reversible engines operated between the standard temperature and the temperature to be measured. This efficiency would depend only on the two temperatures, not upon the material of which the engines were made, or *any* characteristic of the cycle except reversibility. Thomson realized this in 1848 and suggested setting up an absolute temperature scale based on the efficiency of reversible engines before he accepted the truth of Joule's experiments. We mention this here to emphasize that the existence of a thermodynamic or absolute temperature scale is independent of the first law and depends only on the second law.

It is also worth noting that all the proofs given would be valid whether heat were a conserved quantity—as the old caloric theory maintained—or whether it had the characteristics demanded by the first law. The second law is a statement about the *direction* in which a process can proceed and therefore about one aspect of the nature of heat, but has nothing to do with the other aspect of heat which is summarized by the first law—that of the equivalence of a certain amount of heat to a certain amount of adiabatic work. In fact the two laws as we have presented them would be completely independent except for the minor point of logic that we have used the word "heat" in the statement of the second law, but have chosen to tie the precise definition of heat to the first law. Historically, the second law was realized about 25 years before the first.

There is one final corollary requiring only the second law which we shall present before discussing corollaries which depend on both the first and second laws.

Corollary V

> *No change in state of a system connected to a single heat reservoir can produce more work in the surroundings than the same change in state carried out reversibly.*

This can be shown by allowing a system to change in any manner from state 1 to state 2 and then returning it to its original state by a reversible process. This is shown schematically in Fig. 5.5. The net

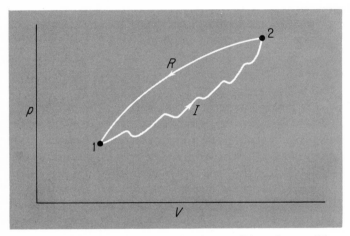

FIG. 5.5. Schematic diagram of an irreversible and reversible change in state of a system.

work produced must be less than or equal to zero according to the second law; that is,

$$W_I + W_R \leqslant 0,$$

which can be written as

$$\int_1^2 dW_I + \int_2^1 dW_R \leqslant 0. \tag{5.3}$$

Since for a reversible process

$$\int_2^1 dW_R = -\int_1^2 dW_R, \tag{5.4}$$

we can convert Eq. (5.3) to

$$\int_1^2 dW_I \leqslant \int_1^2 dW_R, \tag{5.5}$$

which proves the corollary.

Consequences of the First and Second Laws

The succeeding corollaries depend on both the first and second laws.

Corollary VI

For any reversible engine working between two heat reservoirs, t_1 and t_2, the ratio of the amount of heat absorbed at t_1 to the amount of heat absorbed at t_2 is given by

$$\frac{Q_1}{Q_2} = -\frac{\phi(t_1)}{\phi(t_2)},$$

where $\phi(t_1)$ and $\phi(t_2)$ are functions of t_1 and t_2 alone. Hence it is possible to write

$$\frac{Q_1}{Q_2} = -\frac{T_1}{T_2},$$

where T_1 and T_2 are temperatures on the thermodynamic temperature scale.

From the first law applied to the reversible engine shown in Fig. 5.6, we have

$$W = Q_1 + Q_2, \tag{5.6}$$

where Q_1 is of course a positive quantity and Q_2 is a negative quantity. The efficiency of this engine is then

$$\epsilon_R = \frac{W}{Q_1} = \frac{Q_1 + Q_2}{Q_1} = 1 + \frac{Q_2}{Q_1}. \tag{5.7}$$

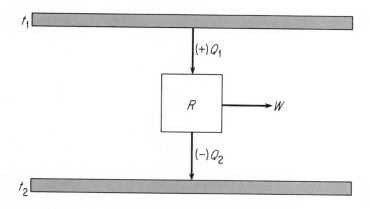

FIG. 5.6. Reversible engine.

From Corollaries III and IV we have concluded that ϵ_R is a function only of t_1 and t_2. Hence we can write

$$\frac{Q_1}{Q_2} = -f(t_1, t_2). \tag{5.8}$$

The same functional relationship must also hold for engines working

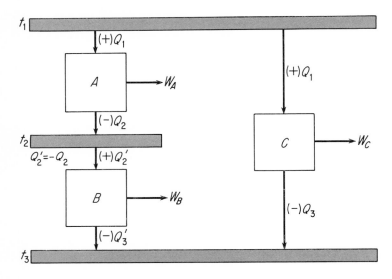

FIG. 5.7. Arrangement of reversible engines for defining the thermodynamic temperature scale, with Q_2' adjusted to equal $-Q_2$.

between any two temperatures. Hence, for the arrangement shown in Fig. 5.7 we have

$$\frac{Q_1}{Q_3} = -f(t_1, t_3), \tag{5.9}$$

$$\frac{Q_2'}{Q_3'} = -\frac{Q_2}{Q_3} = -f(t_2, t_3). \tag{5.10}$$

In the last step, the first law requires that $Q_3' = Q_3$. From the last three relations it follows that

$$f(t_1, t_2) = \frac{f(t_1, t_3)}{f(t_2, t_3)}. \tag{5.11}$$

Since the left-hand side of this expression is independent of t_3, then the right-hand side must also be independent of t_3; that is, t_3 must enter

only in such a fashion that it will cancel out between the numerator and
the denominator, so that

$$-\frac{Q_1}{Q_2} = f(t_1, t_2) = \frac{\phi(t_1)\phi(t_3)}{\phi(t_2)\phi(t_3)} = \frac{\phi(t_1)}{\phi(t_2)}. \tag{5.12}$$

Here $\phi(t_1)$ depends only on t_1 and $\phi(t_2)$ depends only on t_2. We see
then that the ratios of functions of temperatures can be determined by
measuring the ratio of the amounts of heat absorbed and rejected by a
reversible engine operating between the temperatures. Once a functional
form for $\phi(t)$ is chosen and a numerical value chosen for either $\phi(t_1)$
or $\phi(t_2)$, then the entire scale is determined. These choices are at our
disposal. If we choose a simple proportionality for the functional form,
and choose $\phi(t_1)$ as our standard with a numerical value denoted by
T_1, then we can write simply

$$\frac{Q_1}{Q_2} = -\frac{T_1}{T_2}. \tag{5.13}$$

The scale so defined is known as the thermodynamic temperature
scale. We repeat that this scale is completely independent of the
properties of any substance. When $T_1 = 273.16$ at the triple point of
water, the scale is called the Kelvin scale.

Notice that the first law has entered into the definition of the
thermodynamic temperature scale. This is convenient but not strictly
necessary, and occurs because we have elected to consider the heat
rejected by a reversible engine as well as the heat absorbed. The second
law is indifferent to the heat rejected, and it is necessary to invoke the
first law in order to say anything about the heat rejected. It is quite
possible to set up an absolute temperature scale without invoking the
first law, but it is less convenient than the present definition. The point
is that the *existence* of an absolute temperature scale involves only
the second law, even though the actual definition adopted here involves
the first law as well, for the sake of convenience.

Corollary VII

*If the thermodynamic temperature scale is defined so that T_1 is
positive, then all T's are positive.*

The proof follows from Corollaries I and VI. Corollary I established that Q_1 and Q_2 must have opposite signs, so that (Q_2/Q_1) is a
negative number. By Corollary VI we have, for any arbitrary T_2,

$$T_2 = T_1\left(-\frac{Q_2}{Q_1}\right), \tag{5.14}$$

and hence T_2 is positive if T_1 is positive. In other words, all temperatures accessible from T_1 have the same sign as T_1.

Corollary VIII

> *Whenever a system undergoes a cyclic transformation, the integral of dQ/T around the cycle is at most equal to zero; i.e.,*

$$\oint \frac{dQ}{T} \leqslant 0.$$

This result is usually called the *inequality of Clausius*. Here we are considering any system, S, which executes a complete cycle. We suppose that during this cycle the system exchanges heat with a series of n reservoirs having thermodynamic temperatures $T_1, T_2, \cdots,$ $T_i, \cdots, T_n$. The amount of heat absorbed from the reservoir T_i is Q_i. We shall first prove that

$$\sum_{i=1}^{n} \frac{Q_i}{T_i} \leqslant 0,$$

and then pass to the limit of an integral to complete the proof. Since the arguments leading to the proof of this corollary can be a bit subtle, we start first with a system which exchanges heat with only two reservoirs. The system absorbs an amount of heat Q_1 from reservoir T_1 and rejects an amount of heat Q_2 to reservoir T_2. We wish to prove that

$$\frac{Q_1}{T_1} + \frac{Q_2}{T_2} \leqslant 0.$$

To do this, we introduce two reversible engines, R_1 and R_2, which operate between T_1, T_2 and a third reservoir T_0, as shown in Fig. 5.8. We have introduced the third reservoir T_0 such that $T_0 < T_1, T_2$. Reversible engine R_1 operates backwards so that it rejects an amount of heat $Q_1' = -Q_1$ at T_1. Reversible engine R_2 operates so that it absorbs an amount of heat $Q_2' = -Q_2$ at T_2. The whole arrangement consisting of $(S + R_1 + R_2 + T_1 + T_2)$ then corresponds to one system doing work while withdrawing an amount of heat $(Q_{01} + Q_{02})$ from T_0. By the second law

$$W_{R1} + W_{R2} + W_S \leqslant 0. \tag{5.15}$$

By the first law, however, the net heat absorbed by the composite system equals the work done, so that

$$Q_{01} + Q_{02} = W_{R1} + W_{R2} + W_S \leqslant 0. \tag{5.16}$$

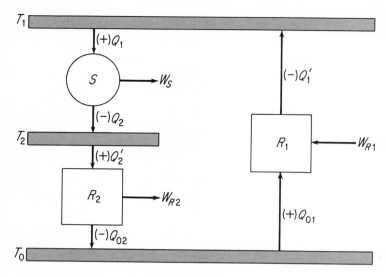

FIG. 5.8. Arrangement of engines for proving the inequality of Clausius.

From Corollary VI we have

$$\frac{Q_{01}}{Q_1'} = -\frac{T_0}{T_1}, \tag{5.17}$$

$$\frac{Q_{02}}{Q_2'} = -\frac{T_0}{T_2}. \tag{5.18}$$

Solving Eqs. (5.17) and (5.18) for Q_{01} and Q_{02}, adding, and substituting $Q_1' = -Q_1$ and $Q_2' = -Q_2$, we obtain

$$T_0\left(\frac{Q_1}{T_1} + \frac{Q_2}{T_2}\right) \leqslant 0, \tag{5.19}$$

or since $T_0 > 0$ by Corollary VII,

$$\frac{Q_1}{T_1} + \frac{Q_2}{T_2} \leqslant 0, \tag{5.20}$$

which was to be proven.

In the more general case where the system exchanges heat with n reservoirs at temperatures $T_1, \cdots, T_n$, we have to introduce n reversible engines and a reservoir at T_0, where T_0 is at a lower temperature than any of the other reservoirs. The ith reversible engine operates between the reservoirs at T_i and T_0, absorbing an amount of heat Q_i' at T_i and an amount Q_{0i} at T_0. As in the preceding case the second law requires that the work done shall be equal to or less than zero,

$$dW_S + \sum_{i=1}^{n} dW_{Ri} \leq 0. \tag{5.21}$$

The total heat absorbed from the reservoir at T_0 will be $\sum_{i=1}^{n} Q_{0i}$, which according to the first law is equal to the work done by the composite system, so that

$$\sum_{i=1}^{n} Q_{0i} \leq 0. \tag{5.22}$$

By Corollary VI we have

$$Q_{0i} = -Q_i' \frac{T_0}{T_i}. \tag{5.23}$$

Since Q_i' is equal to $-Q_i$, where Q_i is the heat absorbed by the system S at T_i, we have

$$T_0 \sum_{i=1}^{n} \frac{Q_i}{T_i} \leq 0, \tag{5.24}$$

or since $T_0 > 0$,

$$\sum_{i=1}^{n} \frac{Q_i}{T_i} \leq 0. \tag{5.25}$$

If we proceed to the limit where the system exchanges heat with a continuous distribution of reservoirs, the above equation becomes

$$\oint \frac{dQ}{T} \leq 0. \tag{5.26}$$

This is an extremely important result, for it is the basis of the definition of the state function entropy.

Corollary IX

Whenever a system undergoes a reversible cycle, then

$$\oint \frac{dQ_R}{T} = 0.$$

For any reversible cycle, we have $\oint (dQ_R/T) \leq 0$. However, if the cycle is reversible, we can make it proceed in the opposite direction, so that the sign of dQ_R is reversed. The inequality of Clausius then requires that $\oint (-dQ_R/T) \leq 0$, or $\oint (dQ_R/T) \geq 0$. The only way both inequalities can hold is

$$\oint \frac{dQ_R}{T} = 0, \tag{5.27}$$

which proves the corollary.

It is important to note that in the inequality $\oint (dQ/T) \leq 0$, the temperature is not necessarily the temperature of the system. It is the temperature of the reservoir, or reservoirs, with which the system exchanged heat. This may or may not be equal to the temperature of the system. In the case of the equality $\oint (dQ_R/T) = 0$, however, the temperature is that of both the reservoir and the system, since an exchange of heat between two systems can be reversible only if their temperatures are equal.

ENTROPY

In the case of the first law, we were able to express the law in mathematical form by working with an energy function which was a state function and hence independent of the path. In order to express the second law in mathematical form, we introduce an entropy function S defined in differential form as

$$dS \equiv \frac{dQ_R}{T}, \tag{5.28}$$

where dQ_R means a reversible change. We now have to show that this entropy function is a state function. From Corollary IX we have

$$\oint dS = \oint \frac{dQ_R}{T} = 0. \tag{5.29}$$

We now show that $\oint dS = 0$ implies that S is a state function. Let us take an arbitrary system and let it undergo a reversible transformation from some state A to another state B along path I, as shown in Fig. 5.9, and then back to A along the reversible path II. For such a process we have

$$\oint dS = {}_{\mathrm{I}}\!\int_A^B \frac{dQ_R}{T} + {}_{\mathrm{II}}\!\int_B^A \frac{dQ_R}{T} = 0,$$

or

$${}_{\mathrm{I}}\!\int_A^B \frac{dQ_R}{T} = - {}_{\mathrm{II}}\!\int_B^A \frac{dQ_R}{T} = {}_{\mathrm{II}}\!\int_A^B \frac{dQ_R}{T}. \tag{5.30}$$

The integral, therefore, is independent of the reversible path chosen and the value depends only on the two states of the system. It is then possible to write

$$S(B) - S(A) = \int_A^B \frac{dQ_R}{T}, \tag{5.31}$$

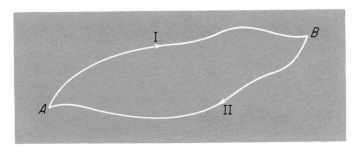

FIG. 5.9. Schematic diagram of two reversible paths connecting states A and B.

where $S(A)$ and $S(B)$ are the entropies of the system when it is in states A and B, respectively. The quantity dS is therefore a perfect differential, and the following two equations can be taken as the mathematical statement of the second law:

$$dS \equiv \frac{dQ_R}{T}, \qquad \oint dS = 0. \tag{5.32}$$

This statement defines only entropy differences, just as the mathematical statement of the first law defined only energy differences.

The foregoing definition implicitly assumes that all states of a system can be connected by reversible processes, just as the definition of the first law assumed that the states could be connected by adiabatic work processes. If systems should be found for which this is not true, the laws of thermodynamics are not thereby demolished, but such systems cannot be discussed by classical thermodynamic methods. Such systems simply lie outside of thermodynamics.

We have now accomplished what we set out to do—namely to define the state function entropy. As mentioned in the early paragraphs of this chapter, such a function enables us to treat problems analytically, and no recourse to hypothetical engines is necessary. The importance of the entropy function and some of the properties of entropy will be considered in the next chapter.

EXAMPLES OF REVERSIBLE CYCLES

In all proofs involving heat engines so far considered in this chapter, we have referred to reversible cycles without specifying any particular kind of reversible cycle. It is convenient at this point, but not necessary, to imagine that the engine is undergoing a particular kind of reversible cycle. We therefore present two examples of reversible cycles, out of the many which are known.

(a) Carnot Cycle

This particular cycle was first used by Carnot as a "thought aid" in his theoretical reasoning. It consists of the following four distinct reversible processes, which are indicated in Fig. 5.10.

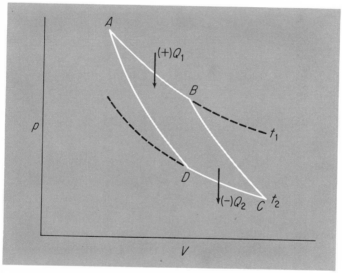

FIG. 5.10. Schematic diagram of Carnot cycle.

1. An isothermal expansion from a volume V_A to a volume V_B.
2. An adiabatic expansion from V_B to V_C.
3. An isothermal compression from V_C to V_D.
4. An adiabatic compression from V_D back to V_A.

The cycle can, of course, be started at any point and proceed in either direction. In the direction indicated above, the engine would perform work and would absorb an amount of heat Q_1 at the temperature t_1, and reject an amount of heat Q_2 at the temperature t_2. The amount of work produced in the surroundings is equal to $Q_1 + Q_2$ by the first law.

(b) *Stirling Cycle*

This cycle also consists of four distinct reversible processes, as does the Carnot cycle. Two of the processes are isothermal as before, but the two adiabatic processes of the Carnot cycle are replaced by two other processes, which are carried out with the aid of a *regenerator*. These are indicated in Fig. 5.11 as isochores or isometrics (curves of constant volume or density), which is what they would be for an ideal gas.

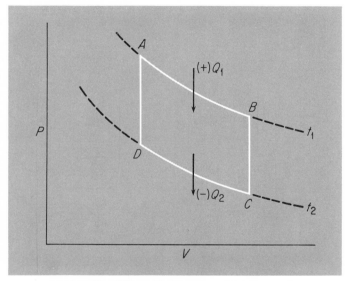

FIG. 5.11. Schematic diagram of Stirling cycle.

Along the isotherms AB and CD the engine exchanges amounts of heat Q_1 and Q_2 with reservoirs at t_1 and t_2, respectively. Along the path BC the engine passes through intermediate temperatures by being put in contact with a series of heat reservoirs which are not supplied with energy from any outside source; these reservoirs constitute the regenerator. The working substance of the engine is cooled by successive contact with parts of the regenerator which are at temperatures ranging from t_1 to t_2. Along the path DA the working substance is heated by coming in contact with the same parts of the regenerator but in reverse order. The regenerator is therefore in exactly the same state after the completion of the cycle as it was before, and is thus to be considered part of the engine, *not* part of the heat reservoir system.

In order for the cycle to be reversible without more than two reservoirs, the non-isothermal processes must be of such a nature that the working substance of the engine has the same specific heat at the same temperature on the cooling part of the cycle as on the heating part of the cycle. This might present a practical problem in building such an engine using a real fluid rather than an ideal gas, but there is no problem so far as the principle is concerned, and that is what concerns us here. One can always find two processes to connect the two isothermal processes without exchanging a net amount of heat with the regenerator during a complete cycle, and also so the flow of heat between the regenerator and the working substance takes place reversibly.

From a practical standpoint the Stirling cycle is often preferred over the Carnot cycle because it gives more work per cycle for a given engine stroke (i.e., for a given maximum volume change over the whole cycle). It is the cycle used in the particularly efficient Philips gas liquifier, the working fluid being helium gas.

Although different kinds of cycles can be interesting for engineering purposes, the only feature of importance for our purposes is that of reversibility.

Problems

1. Prove Corollary III.

2. Prove the analogue of Corollary IV for two reversible engines with a common refrigerator temperature and different source temperatures; that is, prove that the engine operating over the smaller temperature difference cannot have a higher efficiency. Is it possible to prove that the two engines cannot have equal efficiencies without invoking the first law? Why?

3. (a) Prove that it is impossible for any engine to absorb heat at a low temperature and reject heat at a high temperature unless work disappears from the surroundings. (This is called the Clausius statement, sometimes paraphrased that heat cannot flow from a low temperature to a high temperature by itself.)

(b) If the Clausius statement is taken as the formulation of the second law, prove that the statement of the second law given in this chapter then follows as a corollary.

4. Which causes the greater increase in the efficiency of a reversible engine—raising the source temperature by ΔT or lowering the refrigerator temperature by ΔT?

5. If a substance is described by only two mechanical variables (e.g., a fluid by p and V), prove that two reversible adiabatic curves of such a substance cannot intersect.

6. Three reversible engines are connected as shown in Fig. P5.6. What is the relationship among the efficiencies of the three engines?

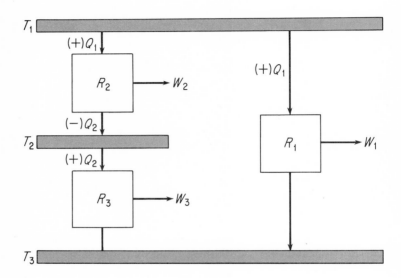

FIG. P5.6

7. In Figure 5.7, prove that the first and second laws require that $Q'_3 = Q_3$.

8. (a) Consider two large equivalent bodies with constant heat capacity C_p and negligible thermal expansion. Show that when they are placed in contact and surrounded by an adiabatic envelope the final temperature at equilibrium is $\frac{1}{2}(T_1 + T_2)$, where T_1 and T_2 are the initial temperatures of the two bodies.

(b) Now consider the two bodies being brought to temperature equilibrium by means of an infinitesimal reversible engine working between them. Show that the final temperature is $(T_1 T_2)^{1/2}$.

(c) Derive expressions for the work produced in processes (a) and (b).

9. It takes 10 kilowatts to keep the interior of a certain house at 20°C when the outside temperature is 0°C. This heat flow is usually obtained directly by burning gas or oil. Calculate the power required if the 10 kilowatts heat flow were supplied by operating a reversible engine with the house

as the upper reservoir and the outside surroundings as the lower reservoir, so that the power were used only to perform the work needed to operate the engine.

10. A system is taken reversibly around the cycle $ABCD$ shown in Fig. P5.10. The temperature on the Celsius scale is indicated at each corner.

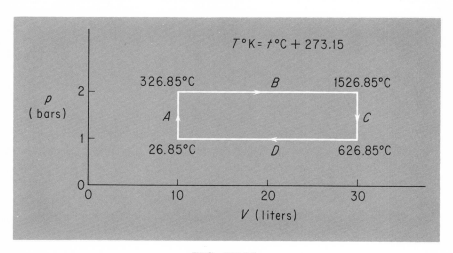

FIG. P5.10

The pressure and volume of the system are as indicated on the scale of the diagram. The heat capacities of the system are

$$C_p = 8.381 \text{ joule/°K}, \qquad C_V = 5.048 \text{ joule/°K}.$$

(a) Calculate the value of $\int dQ_R$ along each part of the cycle. The sum of these is $\oint dQ_R$. What is its significance according to the first law?

(b) Calculate the value of $\int (dQ_R/T)$ along each part of the cycle. The sum of these is $\oint (dQ_R/T)$. What is its significance according to the second law?

(c) If °C were converted to °K by adding a conversion constant other than 273.15, what would happen to the value of the integral $\oint (dQ_R/T)$? Discuss the significance of this according to the second law and the definition of an absolute temperature scale.

Chapter 6

ENTROPY

Before proceeding to the development of analytical techniques for applying the two laws of thermodynamics to physical and chemical systems, we wish to survey some of the properties of the new state function, entropy, in order to develop some intuitive "feel" for the concept. This was not so necessary for the internal energy function since there is at least an analogy to the function in ordinary mechanics. However, the mechanical interpretation of entropy requires statistical mechanics, which is outside the scope of this book. Nevertheless, entropy was formulated before statistical mechanics was, and it is quite possible to develop a familiarity with entropy apart from any mechanical model.

DIFFERENTIAL EQUATION FOR ENTROPY

The first law for a reversible change in state is

$$dE = dQ_R - dW_R. \tag{6.1}$$

On substituting $dQ_R = TdS$ and solving for dS, we obtain

$$dS = \frac{1}{T} dE + \frac{1}{T} dW_R. \tag{6.2}$$

Depending on the kind of system with which we are dealing—gaseous, chemical, magnetic, electrical—the expression for an infinitesimal amount of reversible work, dW_R, will have different forms. To choose an example, if the system can do work by expanding against an external pressure, then

$$dW_R = pdV, \tag{6.3}$$

50

where p is the pressure of the system.* Then the differential equation for the entropy of this system is

$$dS = \frac{1}{T}\,dE + \frac{p}{T}\,dV. \qquad (6.4)$$

This is a fundamental equation, containing both laws of thermodynamics, and is a recipe for calculating changes in entropy for given changes in internal energy and volume. It is a fundamental equation in the sense that if the entropy is known as a function of E and V, then all the other thermodynamic properties can be calculated by differentiation, no undetermined constants of integration occurring. Such equations are also called characteristic equations. Actually one of the independent variables, energy, is not a convenient independent variable to use in specifying the state of the system because it cannot easily be measured. In the next chapter we shall show how to change such equations so as to involve more convenient independent variables.

It is important to notice that all differentials in Eq. (6.4) are exact. They represent state functions. This is not true in the statement of the first law alone, in which the differential of heat does not represent an actual function. The fact that the differentials are exact is the reason that powerful mathematical techniques can be used to solve subsequent problems, in place of laborious schemes based on various hypothetical engine cycles.

ADDITIVITY OF ENTROPY FOR COMPOSITE SYSTEMS

If a system is composed of a number of parts, it is often true (but not always) that the entropy of the system is the sum of the entropies of its parts. The entropy will be additive if the energy is additive and if the total work involved in a transformation of the system is the sum of the amounts of work involved for each of the parts individually. This is not true if, for instance, the energy depends on the extent of the surfaces of the parts of the system. Thus if we wish to discuss surface phenomena

---

* Imagine the system confined in a cylinder closed with a frictionless piston. The work done for an infinitesimal displacement, $d\ell$, of the piston is $dW = F\,d\ell$, where F is the external force. Since $F = p_{ext}A$, where p_{ext} is the external pressure and A is the area of the piston, we can write $dW = p_{ext}A\,d\ell = p_{ext}\,dV$, since $A\,d\ell = dV$. For a reversible displacement we must have $p_{ext} = p$, where p is the pressure of the system, and so $dW_R = p\,dV$.

thermodynamically, we should not assume additivity of energy and entropy. This difficulty is sometimes circumvented by counting the surfaces as separate phases.

EXPERIMENTAL DETERMINATION OF ENTROPY

Several rather simple methods of measuring entropy changes follow directly from the definition. We recall that only changes can be measured and absolute values of entropy are meaningless. This situation is completely analogous to that for energy, and, just as in the case of energy, it is often convenient to refer entropy changes to some standard state where entropy is arbitrarily assigned some convenient number (usually zero). With these introductory remarks, we present below several possible methods of measuring entropy changes.

(a) *From Heat Capacity Measurements*

If a system is heated reversibly from T to $T + dT$, the heat capacity along the particular path is

$$C \equiv \frac{dQ_R}{dT} = T\left(\frac{dS}{dT}\right).$$ (6.5)

The entropy change from state 1 to state 2 can be obtained by integration if C is known,

$$\Delta S = \int_1^2 \frac{C}{T}\, dT.$$ (6.6)

Since entropy is a state function, the integral must be independent of the path. On the other hand, the heat capacity depends on the path. The presence of the factor $(1/T)$ in the integrand makes the integral path-independent. The integral

$$Q = \int_1^2 C\, dT$$ (6.7)

is of course dependent on the path. The factor $(1/T)$ is therefore called an integrating factor for heat.

Constant volume and constant pressure processes are usually considered since they are often easy to carry out experimentally, and two arbitrary states can usually be connected by a combination of such processes. For example, in Fig. 6.1 the states 1 and 2 can be connected either by path aa' or path bb', both of which are combinations

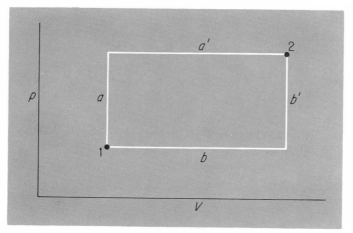

FIG. 6.1. Schematic diagram of a change in state carried out by a combination of constant volume and constant pressure processes.

of constant volume and constant pressure processes. The entropy change calculated along either path is the same.

For constant volume or constant pressure processes we have

$$C_V = T\left(\frac{\partial S}{\partial T}\right)_V \quad \text{and} \quad C_p = T\left(\frac{\partial S}{\partial T}\right)_p, \tag{6.8}$$

so that

$$\Delta S_V = \int \frac{C_V}{T}\, dT = \int C_V d\ln T, \tag{6.9}$$

and

$$\Delta S_p = \int \frac{C_p}{T}\, dT = \int C_p d\ln T. \tag{6.10}$$

Notice that the integrals in Eqs. (6.9) and (6.10) correspond to different changes in state.

(b) *From Isothermal Heats of Transition and Reaction*

If a phase transition or chemical reaction is carried out reversibly and isothermally, we have from the definition of entropy that

$$\Delta S = \frac{Q_R}{T}. \tag{6.11}$$

In particular, for processes at constant volume or constant pressure,

$$\Delta S = \frac{Q_{R,V}}{T} = \frac{\Delta E}{T} \quad \text{(const. } V\text{)}, \tag{6.12}$$

$$\Delta S = \frac{Q_{R,p}}{T} \quad \text{(const. } p\text{)}. \tag{6.13}$$

Thus, measurements of the thermodynamic temperature and the amount of heat which flows into or out of a system as an isothermal phase transition or chemical reaction takes place are sufficient to calculate the entropy change for the change in state.

(c) From Reversible Adiabatic Changes

It is an almost trivial result that $\Delta S = 0$ for any reversible adiabatic change. This follows directly from the definition of entropy.

This list is not exhaustive, and in subsequent chapters we shall derive other relations by which entropy changes can be obtained from experimental measurements.

OTHER PROPERTIES OF ENTROPY

Most of the things we have said about entropy so far are true because entropy is a state function. Let us now examine some other properties of entropy.

(a) Non-Conservation of Entropy

Unlike energy, entropy is not conserved, even though both are state functions. The fact that in mechanics a conservative system is sometimes defined as a system in which the amount of work to move a body from one position to another is independent of the path may lead one to think that all state functions are conserved. This is not so; the fact that internal energy is a conservative state function, whereas entropy is not, points up the fact that the analogy between thermodynamic and mechanical systems is not complete from any simple viewpoint. The methods of statistical mechanics are needed to make the analogy more nearly complete, as we have already remarked.

To illustrate the non-conservation of entropy we can use the Joule paddle wheel device (discussed in Chapter 4 in connection with the first law). This is an example of an "entropy generator." The experiment can be set up as shown in Fig. 6.2. The fluid A being stirred in the container is kept at a constant temperature T by placing it in contact with a heat reservoir through a diathermal wall. As the paddle wheels rotate, the temperature remains constant because heat flows out of the container into the reservoir. This heat flow occurs reversibly

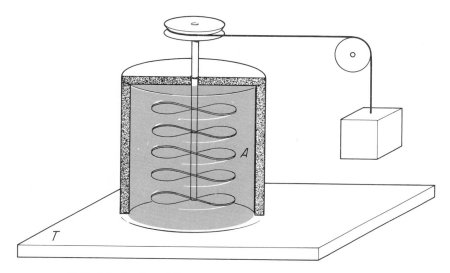

FIG. 6.2. Joule paddle wheel device as an "entropy generator."

since at any instant there is only an infinitesimal difference in temperature between the fluid and the reservoir. The entropy change of the reservoir is

$$\Delta S = \int \frac{dQ_R}{T} = \frac{Q_R}{T}. \tag{6.14}$$

This is also the total entropy change for the composite system of fluid plus reservoir, since the state of the fluid A in the container is unchanged at the end of the process. Furthermore $\Delta E_A = 0$, so that $Q_R = W$ and the total entropy increase is

$$\Delta S = \frac{W}{T}. \tag{6.15}$$

Thus a continuous performance of work on this system generates entropy continuously. Note that the entropy of the system of weights turning the paddle wheels does not change during the process. Also, the entropy generated has not been created out of nothing—it has been created by the disappearance of work from the surroundings.

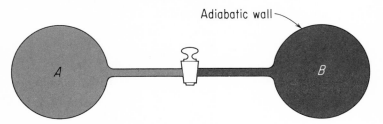

FIG. 6.3. Entropy increase in an isolated system (Joule free expansion experiment).

From the foregoing one might think that it is necessary for a system to have some communication with the surroundings in order for the entropy of the system to increase. This is not so. The entropy of an isolated system can also increase—in fact, we shall shortly prove that it can never decrease. An example here may help to make that result more meaningful. A good example is the Joule free expansion experiment illustrated in Fig. 6.3. Here a gas at equilibrium is initially contained in bulb *A*, and bulb *B* is evacuated. The stopcock is then opened and the gas is allowed to expand into *B* and the system allowed to attain equilibrium again. The complete system is surrounded by an adiabatic wall.*

It is impossible to calculate the entropy change *during* the course of the expansion because the system is not in equilibrium and the entropy is not defined except at the beginning and the end of the process. We do know that the internal energy of the system remains unchanged because no heat and no work are exchanged with the surroundings. To calculate the entropy change from the initial to the final equilibrium states, we must imagine that these states can be connected by some reversible path so that the relationship $dS = dQ_R/T$ holds. This reversible path can be chosen for convenience in calculation, and so we choose a reversible expansion with the requirement that the energy of the system remain unchanged during the entire expansion. Any other reversible path could be chosen as long as the initial and final states are the same as those actually observed in the irreversible expansion. For the reversible process chosen for calculation, we can use Eq. (6.4) with $dE = 0$, which is

$$dS = \frac{p}{T}\, dV \quad \text{(const. } E\text{)}.$$

* It is better to assume that the bulbs themselves serve as adiabatic walls—then the complete system is simply the gas.

This can be formally integrated to yield

$$\Delta S = \int_{V_1}^{V_2} \frac{p}{T}\, dV \quad \text{(const. } E\text{).}$$
$$(6.16)$$

It is easy to see that $\Delta S > 0$ since all quantities in the integrand are positive and $V_2 > V_1$. To obtain a numerical value for ΔS we would have to know the equation of state of the gas, and that comes from outside thermodynamics. The essential point here is only that the entropy of an isolated system can increase, and this result follows from basic thermodynamics alone.

(b) *Entropy Changes in Irreversible Processes*

The preceding two examples have illustrated the fact that entropy is not conserved. Both were examples in which the process was irreversible. This connection between entropy increase and irreversible processes is not accidental, but is an illustration of a general theorem— *the total entropy change is positive in all irreversible processes.* This follows directly from the inequality of Clausius (Corollary VIII of Chapter 5),

$$\oint \frac{dQ}{T} \leqslant 0.$$
$$(6.17)$$

Let us carry out *any* change in state and then restore the system to its original state by a *reversible* process. Then Eq. (6.17) becomes

$$\int_1^2 \frac{dQ}{T} + \int_2^1 \frac{dQ_R}{T} \leqslant 0.$$
$$(6.18)$$

But for a reversible process

$$\int_2^1 \frac{dQ_R}{T} = -\int_1^2 \frac{dQ_R}{T},$$

and so Eq. (6.18) becomes

$$\int_1^2 \frac{dQ_R}{T} \geqslant \int_1^2 \frac{dQ}{T}.$$
$$(6.19)$$

The left-hand side is by definition the entropy change, and so

$$\Delta S \geqslant \int_1^2 \frac{dQ}{T}.$$
$$(6.20)$$

For infinitesimal changes in state Eq. (6.20) can be written

$$dS \geqslant \frac{dQ}{T}. \qquad (6.21)$$

The equality sign holds only for reversible processes, as was shown in Chapter 5. Note again that T in Eq. (6.21) refers to the temperature of the reservoir and *not* to the temperature of the system. During an irreversible process the temperature of the system is not even defined.

(c) *Entropy of an Isolated System*

An isolated system exchanges neither heat nor work with the surroundings. On setting $dQ = 0$, we obtain from Eq. (6.21)

$$dS \geqslant 0. \qquad (6.22)$$

Thus *the entropy of an isolated system can never decrease.* A concrete example of this was the Joule free expansion experiment; here we see that the result is completely general. The interest in this result arises because we can always imagine any system to be isolated by redrawing the boundaries far enough away that no heat flows across these (imaginary) boundaries. The "immediate surroundings" of the original system are now included as part of the isolated system. This result can further be used to indicate whether certain processes are possible or not: *if a process requires a net decrease in entropy, the process is impossible.* That is, we could calculate the value of ΔS for processes at constant E (corresponding to an isolated system) and dismiss as impossible all processes for which $\Delta S < 0$.

(d) *Entropy Criterion for Equilibrium*

The conclusion just reached—that a process which demands a decrease in entropy is impossible—can also be used as a criterion for equilibrium in isolated systems. Suppose we consider a system in a certain definite state, and calculate the entropy change for *all* imaginable processes for which E is constant. If for all these we find that $\Delta S < 0$, we conclude that no process at all is possible and the system must therefore be in equilibrium. This is summarized by saying that at equilibrium the entropy is a maximum. This maximum principle can be used to deduce a great many interesting results about systems in equilibrium, such as the famous phase rule of Gibbs.

This maximum principle is often not convenient to apply since E can be a difficult independent variable to hold constant. Other functions can be defined for which the natural independent variables are p, V, or T, and the maximum principle for entropy can be shown to be equivalent to minimum principles for these new functions. This will be shown in Chapter 11. These minimum principles are often more convenient to apply than the maximum principle for entropy.

EXAMPLES OF ENTROPY CHANGES IN IRREVERSIBLE PROCESSES

To illustrate the foregoing results, let us calculate the entropy changes in some typical simple irreversible processes. We shall first allow a system to undergo an irreversible change in state in such a way that the entropy of the immediate surroundings does not change. We shall then carry out the same change in state reversibly. The entropy change of the system is the same in both cases because entropy is a state function, but the entropy change in the surroundings is different in the two processes. If we consider the system plus its immediate surroundings to be an isolated system, we shall then find for this composite system that $\Delta S > 0$ for the irreversible process and $\Delta S = 0$ for the reversible process.

(a) *Joule Free Expansion*

We have already found that the Joule free expansion of a gas involves an entropy change of

$$\int_{V_1}^{V_2} \frac{p}{T} \, dV$$

for the system. In the irreversible free expansion, the entropy change of the surroundings was zero since the system was isolated. The total entropy change of the composite system—gas plus immediate surroundings—was therefore

$$\Delta S \text{ (total)} = \Delta S \text{ (system)} + \Delta S \text{ (surroundings)}$$

$$= \int_{V_1}^{V_2} \frac{p}{T} \, dV + 0 > 0. \tag{6.23}$$

In the reversible process, the entropy change of the system was again

$$\int_{V_1}^{V_2} \frac{p}{T} \, dV,$$

but the entropy of the surroundings changed by the amount

$$\Delta S \text{ (surroundings)} = -\int_1^2 \frac{dQ_R}{T},$$

where dQ_R is the heat which flows from the surroundings into the system. But $dE = 0$ for the system during the expansion, so $dQ_R = dW$ and therefore

$$\Delta S \text{ (surroundings)} = -\int_1^2 \frac{dW}{T} = -\int_{V_1}^{V_2} \frac{pdV}{T}. \qquad (6.24)$$

Hence the total entropy change for the reversible process is

$$\Delta S \text{ (total)} = \int_{V_1}^{V_2} \frac{pdV}{T} - \int_{V_1}^{V_2} \frac{pdV}{T} = 0. \qquad (6.25)$$

Note that the entropy changes for the system alone or the surroundings alone are *not* zero, but that the total entropy change of the system plus surroundings is zero.

(b) *Adiabatic Stirring (Joule's Experiment)*

We have already used the Joule paddle wheel device to show that entropy can be generated. We should now like to calculate how much the entropy of the system changes when its state is changed by carrying out the stirring adiabatically. This may help to give an idea of the "size" of entropy units (calories/degree or, preferably, joules/degree). Imagine that 1000 g of water at 14.5°C is stirred adiabatically until the temperature rises to 15.5°C. The entropy of the water thus changes in this process, but the entropy of the immediate surroundings does not change (only weights have fallen in the surroundings). To calculate the entropy change of the system we imagine carrying out the same change in state by allowing heat to flow reversibly from the surroundings to the system. Then we calculate that

$$\Delta S \text{ (system)} = \int_1^2 \frac{dQ_R}{T} = \int_{T_1}^{T_2} \frac{C_p dT}{T} = C_p \ln \frac{T_2}{T_1}. \qquad (6.26)$$

Inserting numbers ($\bar{c}_p = 1.000$ cal/g-deg; degrees Celsius are converted to degrees Kelvin by adding 273.15), we find

$$\Delta S \text{ (system)} = (1000 \text{ g})(1.000 \text{ cal/g-deg})(2.303) \log \frac{288.65}{287.65}$$

$$= 3.47 \text{ cal/deg.}$$

In the reversible process,

$$\Delta S \text{ (surroundings)} = \int_1^2 \left(-\frac{dQ_R}{T} \right) = -3.47 \text{ cal/deg.}$$

Thus for the irreversible process the total entropy change is

$$\Delta S \text{ (total)} = 3.47 + 0 = 3.47 \text{ cal/deg,}$$

and for the reversible process,

$$\Delta S \text{ (total)} = 3.47 - 3.47 = 0.$$

(c) *Irreversible Heat Flow*

As our final example we consider two large bodies at temperatures T_1 and T_2, respectively, where $T_1 > T_2$. For the irreversible process we allow a quantity of heat Q to flow from T_1 to T_2. (To simplify the calculations we shall assume that the bodies are such that this does not change their temperatures appreciably. This can be accomplished by imagining the bodies to be very large and Q to be small, or by imagining that the two bodies consist of phases in equilibrium, so that a finite amount of heat can flow without change in temperature. For instance, the body at T_1 could be an equilibrium mixture of steam and water, and the body at T_2 could be an equilibrium mixture of ice and water.) To calculate the entropy change of the system we have to devise a reversible process for bringing about the same change in state. To do this we set up a heat reservoir in the immediate surroundings at a temperature T_0, and connect reversible engines between T_1 and T_0 and between T_2 and T_0. We then reversibly remove a quantity of heat Q from T_1 and supply a quantity of heat Q to T_2. The entropy change of the system consisting of the two bodies is therefore

$$\Delta S \text{ (system)} = -\frac{Q}{T_1} + \frac{Q}{T_2}, \qquad (6.27)$$

which is greater than zero because $T_1 > T_2$. The entropy change of the immediate surroundings (reservoir T_0 plus the two reversible engines) is

$$\Delta S \text{ (surroundings)} = \frac{Q}{T_1} - \frac{Q}{T_2} = -\Delta S \text{ (system)}.$$

So in the reversible process we again have $\Delta S(\text{total}) = 0$. In the irreversible process, however, the entropy change of the surroundings is zero, but that of the system is still as given in Eq. (6.27) because entropy is a state function. Thus for the irreversible process

$$\Delta S \text{ (total)} = \left(-\frac{Q}{T_1} + \frac{Q}{T_2} \right) + 0 > 0. \tag{6.28}$$

This example can also be used to illustrate the inequality $dS \geqslant dQ/T$ of Eq. (6.21) if we imagine each of the bodies as a separate system. The entropy change of the body at T_1 is

$$\Delta S_1 = -\frac{Q}{T_1}, \tag{6.29}$$

and that of the body at T_2 is

$$\Delta S_2 = \frac{Q}{T_2}. \tag{6.30}$$

Notice that the temperature in the denominator is the same as the temperature of the system, since ΔS must be calculated for the reversible process, which means that the temperature of the source (in this case the source is a reversible engine) can be only infinitesimally different from the temperature of the system. In the irreversible process, however, each system acts as the source for the *other* system. So the ratio Q/T for the system at T_1 is

$$-\frac{Q}{T_2}, \tag{6.31}$$

and that for the system at T_2 is

$$\frac{Q}{T_1}. \tag{6.32}$$

Comparing Eq. (6.29) with Eq. (6.31), we find

$$-\frac{Q}{T_1} = \Delta S_1 > -\frac{Q}{T_2}, \tag{6.33}$$

since $T_2 < T_1$. Similarly, from Eqs. (6.30) and (6.32) we find

$$\frac{Q}{T_2} = \Delta S_2 > \frac{Q}{T_1}. \tag{6.34}$$

So we see that our fundamental inequality, $dS \geqslant dQ/T$, holds for each system individually, as it should. This little example also serves to emphasize that the temperature of the *reservoir* is the one to use in the right-hand side of the inequality, not the temperature of the system.

The properties and uses of the entropy function should become clearer as we develop the techniques for its use and give examples and problems. One important idea to remember is that entropy has no simple mechanical analogy but yet has certain characteristics which can be comprehended without recourse to statistical mechanics.

PROBLEMS

1. State whether the entropy of the system increases, decreases, or remains the same in the following changes of state:

(a) One gram of water evaporates to steam at the same p and T.

(b) One gram of water freezes to ice at the same p and T.

(c) One mole of a gas (not necessarily ideal) is compressed reversibly and adiabatically.

(d) One mole of a gas (not necessarily ideal) is compressed reversibly and isothermally.

(e) One mole of a gas (not necessarily ideal) expands irreversibly and adiabatically into a vacuum chamber and thereby increases its volume.

2. Calculate the entropy change for each of the following changes of state:

(a) Ten grams of steam at 100°C and 1 atm condenses to liquid water at the same temperature and pressure. The latent heat of vaporization of water is 2257 joule/g.

(b) Ten grams of water at 100°C and 1 atm is cooled to 0°C at constant pressure. The average specific heat of water between 0° and 100°C is 4.184 joule/g-°C.

(c) Ten grams of water at 0°C and 1 atm freezes to ice at the same temperature and pressure. The latent heat of fusion of ice is 333 joule/g.

3. A 50 kg bag of sand at 25°C falls 10 m under standard gravity and comes to an abrupt stop by landing on a rigid pavement. Neglecting any energy transfer to the pavement, calculate the entropy increase of the bag of sand.

4. Consider a system consisting of two 10 g balls of putty at 25°C. Initially one putty ball is at rest and the other is traveling at a velocity of 100 cm/sec. The moving ball strikes the stationary ball head-on and makes a perfectly inelastic collision so that the two balls stick together and travel on at a reduced velocity. Neglecting any energy transfer to the surroundings, calculate the entropy change in the system due to the collision.

5. (a) The heat capacity of oxygen gas (O_2) can be represented to about 1 per cent accuracy from 300°K to 5000°K by the following empirical equation

$$\tilde{C}_p = 34.6 + (1.08 \times 10^{-3})T - \frac{7.85 \times 10^5}{T^2},$$

where $\tilde{C}_p$ is in joule/mole-°K and T is in °K. Calculate the entropy change on heating 1 mole of O_2 from 1000°K to 2000°K at 1 atm, and from 2000°K to 3000°K at 1 atm.

(b) The specific heat of beryllium metal (Be) can be represented at low temperatures (0°–20°K) by a Debye-Sommerfeld equation

$$\tilde{c}_V = (2.5 \times 10^{-5})T + (1.38 \times 10^{-7})T^3,$$

where $\tilde{c}_V$ is in joule/g-°K and T is in °K. Calculate the entropy difference between 10 g of Be at 0°K and at 10°K; between 10 g of Be at 10°K and at 20°K.

6. The normal melting point of tin is 231.9°C, but molten tin can be supercooled a few degrees. At 1 atm pressure 100 g of molten tin is supercooled to 230.0°C, and then freezes spontaneously and adiabatically, whereby some solid forms and the temperature rises to 231.9°C. This process is quite irreversible. Devise a reversible process for bringing about the same change in state, and calculate the amount of solid formed and the entropy change. The latent heat of fusion of tin is 60.6 joule/g and the specific heat of molten tin is 0.23 joule/g-°C.

7. At 1 atm pressure, 1 g of ice at 0°C is dropped into 100 g of liquid water at 100°C and the mixture allowed to come to equilibrium. What is the entropy change for this irreversible process? The latent heat of fusion of ice is 333 joule/g and the specific heat of water (assumed constant) is 4.18 joule/g-°C.

8. Calculate the entropy of H_2O relative to the entropy of the liquid at 25°C from −5°C to 200°C at 1 atm pressure from the following data:
 specific heat of ice = 2.09 joule/g-°C
 specific heat of water = 4.18 joule/g-°C
 specific heat of steam = $(1.91 + 0.000035\ T°K)$ joule/g-°C
 melting point of ice = 0°C
 boiling point of water = 100°C
 latent heat of fusion of ice = 333 joule/g
 latent heat of vaporization of water = 2257 joule/g.
Make a graph of $S - S_{25}$ against log T.

9. Take the specific heat of water to be 4.18 joule/g-°C and the latent heat of fusion of ice to be 333 joule/g in the following problems.

(a) 100 g of water at 100°C is placed in thermal contact with 1 kg of ice at 0°C and the system allowed to come to equilibrium. Calculate the entropy change for the original 100 g of water, for the original 1 kg of ice, and for the total system. Verify that the inequality $\Delta S \geqslant \int dQ/T$ holds for this irreversible process.

(b) 100 g of water at 50°C is placed in thermal contact with 1 kg of ice at 0°C and the system allowed to come to equilibrium. Calculate the entropy change for the original 100 g of water, for the original 1 kg of ice, and for the total system. Verify that the inequality $\Delta S > \int dQ/T$ holds for this irreversible process.

(c) From the results of (a) and (b), calculate the entropy change for the change in state: 100 g H_2O (100°C) → 100 g H_2O (50°C).

10. According to Trouton's rule, the molar entropies of vaporization of many liquids at their boiling points under 1 atm pressure are approximately constant. Test this rule for the following substances.

Substance	Mol. wt. g/mole	Latent heat joule/g	Boiling point °C
nitrogen	28.0	204	−196
argon	39.9	164	−186
water	18.0	2257	100
benzene	78.1	402	80
ethyl alcohol	46.1	857	78
mercury	200.6	296	357
potassium chloride	74.6	2270	1420

11. Show that the entropy increase for the process described in Problem 8(a) of Chapter 5 is

$$\Delta S = 2C_p \ln \frac{(T_1 + T_2)}{2(T_1 T_2)^{1/2}}.$$

Chapter 7

ANALYTICAL METHODS,
WITH EXAMPLES

In the preceding chapters the discussion has been kept general, with little mention of particular systems. This was done in order to emphasize that the laws of thermodynamics are independent of the particular properties of various systems and processes. Such an approach necessarily limits the number of specific examples which can be given to illustrate a point. Now that the basis of the subject has been essentially completed, we can devote much of the remainder of the book to applications of the two laws.

In this chapter we shall deal with two main topics, the introduction of new thermodynamic functions and the technique of cross differentiation. Neither topic adds anything new to the fundamentals of the subject. The functions we shall introduce are simply combinations of the internal energy function with other state functions. The particular combinations are chosen to make certain kinds of problems particularly simple to handle. The technique of cross differentiation permits relationships among various thermodynamic variables to be found rather easily, such as the Maxwell relations. These relationships follow directly from the fact that the thermodynamic functions are state variables. Hence they add nothing new to the fundamentals of thermodynamics, but follow from the basic postulates.

COMBINED STATEMENT OF FIRST
AND SECOND LAWS

We have already expressed the first and second laws in a combined form in Eq. (6.4), which was

$$dS = \frac{1}{T} dE + \frac{p}{T} dV, \qquad (7.1)$$

which can also be written as

$$dE = TdS - pdV. \tag{7.2}$$

We now wish to point out that these equations are true whether or not the process is reversible so that $dS = dQ/T$ and whether or not $pdV = dW$. Since both energy and entropy are state functions, their values are independent of the process by which the state was attained; we can therefore employ the equations with impunity, knowing always that the above relationships among the variables must hold provided that the initial and final states are thermodynamically well-defined.

Equations (7.1) and (7.2) are of course applicable only when the work involved is that of simple compression or expansion. In Chapter 10 we will extend the equations to handle other kinds of work, and will give some examples.

DEFINITIONS OF NEW STATE FUNCTIONS

The first and second laws have assured us of the existence of two functions, the internal energy and the entropy, which depend only on the state of a system and not at all on the process by which the state was achieved. This is an extremely important property. It means that if we wish to calculate the difference in internal energy or entropy between two states of a system, we can do so using any physically attainable reversible process we please, no matter how idealized, in order to make the calculation as simple as possible. This calculated difference must then be the same as the difference obtained for any real process connecting the two states, no matter how complicated, because energy and entropy are state functions. This is not true of heat and work, which are not state functions. It is hardly an exaggeration to say that the study of thermodynamics consists to a large extent of a search for useful state functions.

The differential equations (7.1) and (7.2) have E, S, and V as the variables, p and T occurring only as coefficients. These are not always the most convenient state functions to have as variables in solving problems; indeed in most problems the natural variables involve p, V, or T, since these are the quantities ordinarily measured more or less directly in the laboratory. It is therefore useful to define some new state functions whose differential equations involve experimentally convenient variables.

(a) *Enthalpy*

The equation for E has V as one of the independent variables; in some problems it is more convenient to have p instead. This is accomplished by defining a new function H, called the *enthalpy* (accent on the second syllable), as follows:

$$H \equiv E + pV. \tag{7.3}$$

Since E, p, and V are all state functions, H is also a state function. For a reversible process, the first law is $dE = dQ_R - pdV$. When we differentiate Eq. (7.3) and substitute for dE from the first law, we obtain

$$dH = dQ_R + Vdp. \tag{7.4}$$

Inserting the second law in the form $dQ_R = TdS$, we also obtain

$$dH = TdS + Vdp. \tag{7.5}$$

Enthalpy is usually a convenient function for problems involving heat quantities, such as heats of reaction or heat capacities, when pressure is an important variable. Heat is a rather cumbersome quantity to handle in thermodynamic problems because it is not a state function, and we are therefore not at liberty to devise ingenious idealized paths at will. It is therefore helpful to connect the heat quantities of interest with state functions, for which we can invent idealized processes with impunity. For instance, from Eq. (7.4) and the previous definition of heat capacity given by Eq. (4.10), we find that the heat capacity at constant pressure is

$$C_p = \left(\frac{dQ}{dT}\right)_p = \left(\frac{\partial H}{\partial T}\right)_p. \tag{7.6}$$

Thus C_p is the derivative of a state function, and is itself a state function. Similarly, for constant pressure processes the last term of Eq. (7.4) vanishes and we can integrate to obtain

$$\Delta H = Q_p, \tag{7.7}$$

where we have added an obvious subscript to Q. Thus for constant pressure processes we can study heat effects by studying the state function H.

Constant volume processes are not as common experimentally as are constant pressure processes, but if we are interested in constant volume processes the equations analogous to Eqs. (7.6) and (7.7) are

$$C_V = \left(\frac{\partial E}{\partial T}\right)_V,$$
(7.8)

$$\Delta E = Q_V.$$
(7.9)

In other words, energy and enthalpy play analogous roles in processes at constant volume and constant pressure, respectively.

As a preliminary example of the use of the enthalpy function, we consider the relation between C_p and C_V. We start by differentiating Eq. (7.3) to obtain

$$dH = dE + p\,dV + V\,dp.$$
(7.10)

Now for most simple fluids it is necessary to specify only two variables to specify the state of the system. Choosing V and T as the independent variables, we can therefore express dE as

$$dE = \left(\frac{\partial E}{\partial T}\right)_V dT + \left(\frac{\partial E}{\partial V}\right)_T dV,$$

or

$$dE = C_V dT + \left(\frac{\partial E}{\partial V}\right)_T dV.$$
(7.11)

Substituting this into Eq. (7.10) we obtain

$$dH = C_V dT + V\,dp + \left[p + \left(\frac{\partial E}{\partial V}\right)_T\right] dV,$$
(7.12)

and by dividing by dT and restricting ourselves to constant pressure so that $dp = 0$, we get the result:

$$C_p = C_V + \left[p + \left(\frac{\partial E}{\partial V}\right)_T\right]\left(\frac{\partial V}{\partial T}\right)_p.$$
(7.13)

Notice that so far we have used only the first law. If we use the second law we can go further and express $(\partial E/\partial V)_T$ in terms of more easily measured quantities, but we will postpone this until later in the chapter. It happens that for many gases $(\partial E/\partial V)_T$ is negligible compared to p, in which case Eq. (7.13) gives the difference between C_p and C_V in terms of quantities which can be obtained from an equation of state. Thus if we measured C_p and the equation of state of a simple gas, we would not have to measure C_V, which in fact is rather difficult to measure directly for gases.

(b) *Helmholtz Function*

This function is designed for problems in which T and V are the convenient independent variables, and is defined as

$$A \equiv E - TS. \qquad (7.14)$$

Note that A is a state function because E, T, and S are. We can write the combined statement of the first and second laws in terms of differentials of this function. For, by definition,

$$dA = dE - TdS - SdT, \qquad (7.15)$$

and substituting for dE from Eq. (7.2), we obtain

$$dA = -SdT - pdV. \qquad (7.16)$$

Now the explicit independent variables are T and V. The Helmholtz function is especially convenient for processes occurring at constant volume or constant temperature. In the latter case $dA = -pdV$, and the Helmholtz function is equal to the reversible work. For this reason it is occasionally called the work function, and indeed the symbol for the Helmholtz function comes from the German word for work (*Arbeit*).

(c) *Gibbs Function*

This function is designed for problems in which T and p are the convenient independent variables (hence most chemical problems), and is defined as

$$G \equiv E + pV - TS = H - TS. \qquad (7.17)$$

The Gibbs function is a state function just as the enthalpy and the Helmholtz function are, and the differential of the Gibbs function can be derived completely analogously to the differential of the Helmholtz function. Thus,

$$dG = -SdT + Vdp. \qquad (7.18)$$

From the independent variables which now appear we expect that the Gibbs function is convenient for processes occurring at constant pressure or constant temperature.

The definitions of the above functions may appear to be somewhat arbitrary and to a certain extent this is true. Other functions have been invented and used. As long as the explicit independent variables of the function fit the natural independent variables of the system studied, the function will be found to be convenient in making calculations on the system. There is a general recipe for generating desired new functions, which is called the Legendre transformation. If the state of a system is described by a function of two variables $f(x, y)$ which satisfies the relation,

$$df = u\,dx + v\,dy, \tag{7.19}$$

and we wish to change the description to one involving a new function $g(u, y)$ satisfying a similar relation in terms of du and dy, then the way to do this is to define

$$g \equiv f - ux. \tag{7.20}$$

It is readily verified that g satisfies the relation

$$dg = -x\,du + v\,dy. \tag{7.21}$$

CHARACTERISTIC FUNCTIONS

In terms of the state functions so far defined, we have written four differential statements of the first and second laws, namely

$$dE = TdS - pdV, \tag{7.22}$$
$$dH = TdS + Vdp, \tag{7.23}$$
$$dA = -SdT - pdV, \tag{7.24}$$
$$dG = -SdT + Vdp. \tag{7.25}$$

These are differential equations for E in terms of S and V, H in terms of S and p, and so on. The functions $E(S, V)$, $H(S, p)$, $A(T, V)$, and $G(T, p)$ are sometimes called "characteristic functions" because they have the property that if they are known as functions of the appropriate variables, then all the thermodynamic properties of a system can be calculated by differentiation alone. For instance, if A is known as a function of T and V for a system, we can calculate all the other thermodynamic properties of the system by differentiation, and no new constants or functions will appear in the calculation. However, if E were known as a function of T and V, we could not obtain the rest of the thermodynamic properties without performing integrations, and this introduces unknown constants of integration. For E to be a characteristic function, it must be given as a function of S and V.

There are of course other characteristic functions than the four just mentioned. Any of Eqs. (7.22)–(7.25) could be algebraically rearranged to produce other characteristic functions. For instance, $E(S, V)$ could be solved (in principle) to give $S(E, V)$, and we could then say that S is the characteristic function for energy and volume, just as E is the characteristic function for entropy and volume.

As an example we shall calculate the thermodynamic properties of a system for the case where the Helmholtz function is given in terms of T and V. The reader can readily carry out similar programs for other characteristic functions. The properties to be found are the energy, entropy, pressure, various specific heats, and the elastic properties (the compressibility, the expansivity, and the pressure coefficient), in terms only of A and its derivatives with respect to temperature and volume.

From the differential equation for $A(T, V)$, Eq. (7.24), we immediately obtain

$$p = -\left(\frac{\partial A}{\partial V}\right)_T , \qquad (7.26)$$

$$S = -\left(\frac{\partial A}{\partial T}\right)_V . \qquad (7.27)$$

Thus, pressure and entropy are determined. Since $E = A + TS$ by definition, we obtain

$$E = A - T\left(\frac{\partial A}{\partial T}\right)_V . \qquad (7.28)$$

If we differentiate this with respect to T, we obtain C_V,

$$C_V = \left(\frac{\partial E}{\partial T}\right)_V = -T\left(\frac{\partial^2 A}{\partial T^2}\right)_V . \qquad (7.29)$$

The calculation of C_p is a little more trouble. We go back to Eq. (7.13), which was

$$C_p = C_V + \left[p + \left(\frac{\partial E}{\partial V}\right)_T\right]\left(\frac{\partial V}{\partial T}\right)_p . \qquad (7.30)$$

In this equation only $(\partial V/\partial T)_p$ is not readily available in terms of derivatives of A, so we must first find an expression for this derivative in which V and T rather than T and p are the independent variables. This can be done by writing the identity

$$dp = \left(\frac{\partial p}{\partial T}\right)_V dT + \left(\frac{\partial p}{\partial V}\right)_T dV. \qquad (7.31)$$

Now take $p = $ constant, so that $dp = 0$, and solve algebraically to obtain the identity

$$\left(\frac{\partial V}{\partial T}\right)_p = -\frac{\left(\frac{\partial p}{\partial T}\right)_V}{\left(\frac{\partial p}{\partial V}\right)_V}. \tag{7.32}$$

From this we now immediately obtain

$$\left(\frac{\partial V}{\partial T}\right)_p = -\frac{\left[\frac{\partial}{\partial T}\left(\frac{\partial A}{\partial V}\right)_T\right]_V}{\left(\frac{\partial^2 A}{\partial V^2}\right)_T}. \tag{7.33}$$

Substitution for this and the other quantities then yields

$$C_p = \frac{T\left[\frac{\partial}{\partial T}\left(\frac{\partial A}{\partial V}\right)_T\right]_V^2}{\left(\frac{\partial^2 A}{\partial V^2}\right)_T} - T\left(\frac{\partial^2 A}{\partial T^2}\right)_V. \tag{7.34}$$

The compressibility κ_T is defined as

$$\kappa_T \equiv -\frac{1}{V}\left(\frac{\partial V}{\partial p}\right)_T. \tag{7.35}$$

This is evaluated by inverting the derivative and then substituting from Eq. (7.26) for p,

$$\kappa_T = -\frac{1}{V\left(\frac{\partial p}{\partial V}\right)_T} = \frac{1}{V\left(\frac{\partial^2 A}{\partial V^2}\right)_T}. \tag{7.36}$$

The expansivity α_p is defined as

$$\alpha_p \equiv \frac{1}{V}\left(\frac{\partial V}{\partial T}\right)_p, \tag{7.37}$$

which has already been essentially evaluated in Eq. (7.33). The result is

$$\alpha_p = -\frac{\left[\frac{\partial}{\partial T}\left(\frac{\partial A}{\partial V}\right)_T\right]_V}{V\left(\frac{\partial^2 A}{\partial V^2}\right)_T}. \tag{7.38}$$

Finally, the pressure coefficient α_V is defined as

$$\alpha_V \equiv \frac{1}{p}\left(\frac{\partial p}{\partial T}\right)_V, \tag{7.39}$$

which is readily evaluated as

$$\alpha_V = \frac{\left[\dfrac{\partial}{\partial T}\left(\dfrac{\partial A}{\partial V}\right)_T\right]_V}{\left(\dfrac{\partial A}{\partial V}\right)_T}. \tag{7.40}$$

We thus see that if the Helmholtz function for a system has been determined over a range of temperatures and volumes then all the thermodynamic properties over that range can be calculated. However, the Helmholtz function for a particular system cannot be determined by thermodynamics. It must be determined on the basis of some theory of matter or it must be determined by measurements on the system itself. But once it is determined in some way, then thermodynamics permits all the other thermodynamic properties to be calculated in a routine manner.

CROSS DIFFERENTIATION—MAXWELL'S RELATIONS

The technique of cross differentiation is merely a mathematical formulation of the statement that a state function depends only on the state of a system and is independent of the process by which the state was attained. From this it follows that the order of differentiation of a state function with respect to one variable and then with respect to another variable is immaterial, the final result being the same. That is, if $F(x, y)$ is a state function of the variables x and y, then

$$\left[\frac{\partial}{\partial y}\left(\frac{\partial F}{\partial x}\right)_y\right]_x = \left[\frac{\partial}{\partial x}\left(\frac{\partial F}{\partial y}\right)_x\right]_y. \tag{7.41}$$

The expression for dF in terms of its partial derivatives is

$$dF = \left(\frac{\partial F}{\partial x}\right)_y dx + \left(\frac{\partial F}{\partial y}\right)_x dy, \tag{7.42}$$

or

$$dF = M(x, y)\, dx + N(x, y)\, dy, \tag{7.43}$$

where $M(x, y) = (\partial F/\partial x)_y$ and $N(x, y) = (\partial F/\partial y)_x$. Substituting these expressions back into Eq. (7.41) we obtain the desired result:

$$\left(\frac{\partial M}{\partial y}\right)_x = \left(\frac{\partial N}{\partial x}\right)_y. \tag{7.44}$$

We can use this result to obtain the four Maxwell relations, which relate entropy derivatives to elastic constants. We have previously written down four differential statements of the first and second laws in terms of the state functions E, H, A, and G. These are Eqs. (7.22)–(7.25), and by applying Eq. (7.44) to them we obtain the following relations among the coefficients:

$$\left(\frac{\partial T}{\partial V}\right)_S = -\left(\frac{\partial p}{\partial S}\right)_V, \qquad \text{M-1} \qquad (7.45)$$

$$\left(\frac{\partial T}{\partial p}\right)_S = \left(\frac{\partial V}{\partial S}\right)_p, \qquad \text{M-2} \qquad (7.46)$$

$$\left(\frac{\partial S}{\partial V}\right)_T = \left(\frac{\partial p}{\partial T}\right)_V, \qquad \text{M-3} \qquad (7.47)$$

$$\left(\frac{\partial S}{\partial p}\right)_T = -\left(\frac{\partial V}{\partial T}\right)_p. \qquad \text{M-4} \qquad (7.48)$$

These are the Maxwell relations. A number of other Maxwell-like relations can easily be derived by first algebraically solving Eqs. (7.22)–(7.25) for one of the other state functions, such as S or V, and then applying cross differentiation. The four relations given above are usually the most useful, however.

EXAMPLES OF THE USE OF THE MAXWELL RELATIONS

We shall now give four examples to illustrate how the Maxwell relations can be used to advantage in thermodynamic calculations.

(a) Calculation of Entropy Changes

Consider the entropy change accompanying a change in the volume and temperature of a simple fluid,

$$dS = \left(\frac{\partial S}{\partial T}\right)_V dT + \left(\frac{\partial S}{\partial V}\right)_T dV, \qquad (7.49)$$

$$= \frac{C_V}{T} dT + \left(\frac{\partial S}{\partial V}\right)_T dV. \qquad (7.50)$$

Substitution from the third Maxwell relation (M-3) gives

$$dS = \frac{C_V}{T} dT + \left(\frac{\partial p}{\partial T}\right)_V dV, \tag{7.51}$$

$$= C_V d \ln T + p\alpha_V \, dV. \tag{7.52}$$

Thus if C_V is known as a function of T and V and the equation of state is known, then the entropy change can be calculated by integration. For a change in state from T_1, V_1 to T_2, V_2, the entropy change $S_2 - S_1$ is

$$S_2 - S_1 = \int_{T_1}^{T_2} C_V \, d \ln T + \int_{V_1}^{V_2} p\alpha_V \, dV, \tag{7.53}$$

the first integration being carried out at a constant volume of V_1 and the second integration at a constant temperature of T_2 (or the second integral being evaluated first at T_1 and then the first integral evaluated at V_2). Actually, it is not necessary to have a complete knowledge of C_V as a function of T and V if the equation of state is known. This is shown by the next example.

Before proceeding to show how the dependence of C_V on V can be calculated from the equation of state, we should point out that the method used in this first example is applicable to the calculation of the change of any state function, and is not restricted to the calculation of entropy changes. Furthermore, the independent variables do not have to be T and V as in this example, but can be T and p or p and V.

(b) Dependence of Heat Capacities on p and V

The Maxwell relations can also be used to relate the change in heat capacity with pressure or volume to the elastic properties of the system. For example,

$$C_V = T \left(\frac{\partial S}{\partial T}\right)_V, \tag{7.54}$$

so that

$$\left(\frac{\partial C_V}{\partial V}\right)_T = T \left[\frac{\partial}{\partial V}\left(\frac{\partial S}{\partial T}\right)_V\right]_T. \tag{7.55}$$

But S is a state function, so we can interchange the order of differentiation and use the third Maxwell relation (M-3) to get

$$\left(\frac{\partial C_V}{\partial V}\right)_T = T \left[\frac{\partial}{\partial T}\left(\frac{\partial S}{\partial V}\right)_T\right]_V = T \left[\frac{\partial}{\partial T}\left(\frac{\partial p}{\partial T}\right)_V\right]_V,$$

$$= T \left(\frac{\partial^2 p}{\partial T^2}\right)_V. \tag{7.56}$$

A very similar derivation can be given to obtain the analogous result for C_p,

$$\left(\frac{\partial C_p}{\partial p}\right)_T = -T\left(\frac{\partial^2 V}{\partial T^2}\right)_p, \tag{7.57}$$

the proof of which is left as an exercise.

Equations (7.56) and (7.57) state that if we know C_V or C_p at one point on an isotherm, we can obtain their values at any other point on the isotherm if equation of state data are available. For instance, we can always integrate Eq. (7.56), by numerical methods if necessary,

$$C_{V_2} - C_{V_1} = T\int_{V_1}^{V_2}\left(\frac{\partial^2 p}{\partial T^2}\right)_V dV \quad (T \text{ constant}), \tag{7.58}$$

a similar result holding for C_p.

(c) *Calculation of Temperature Changes*

The Maxwell relations are also useful in the calculation of temperature changes accompanying a change in state. We shall illustrate three types of processes: (1) constant entropy processes, (2) constant energy processes, and (3) constant enthalpy processes. The general calculation procedure is the same for all three cases: first a differential expression is written for the quantity held constant, and this is equated to zero. The resulting equation is then solved algebraically for dT, and a Maxwell relation is used to obtain a final expression involving only heat capacities and the equation of state.

(1) *Constant Entropy Processes.* An experimental example of a constant entropy process is a reversible adiabatic change in state. Clearly T will always be one of the independent variables chosen, but whether the second variable is V or p depends on the problem. For this illustration we first choose V as the other variable and write

$$dS = \left(\frac{\partial S}{\partial T}\right)_V dT + \left(\frac{\partial S}{\partial V}\right)_T dV = 0, \tag{7.59}$$

from which we obtain

$$\left(\frac{\partial T}{\partial V}\right)_S = -\frac{\left(\frac{\partial S}{\partial V}\right)_T}{\left(\frac{\partial S}{\partial T}\right)_V}. \tag{7.60}$$

Since $C_V = T(\partial S/\partial T)_V$, and from the Maxwell relation (M-3), $(\partial S/\partial V)_T = (\partial p/\partial T)_V$, we obtain

$$\left(\frac{\partial T}{\partial V}\right)_S = -\frac{T}{C_V}\left(\frac{\partial p}{\partial T}\right)_V = -\frac{pT\alpha_V}{C_V}. \tag{7.61}$$

This result could also have been quickly obtained by starting with the Maxwell relation (M-1), but this is left as an exercise for the reader. Equation (7.61) can be integrated by one means or another if C_V and the equation of state are known, but if ΔT and ΔV are small, we can write Eq. (7.61) approximately as

$$(\Delta T)_S \approx -\frac{T}{C_V}\left(\frac{\partial p}{\partial T}\right)_V \Delta V. \tag{7.62}$$

If we had chosen p instead of V as one of the independent variables, we would have proceeded as follows.

$$dS = \left(\frac{\partial S}{\partial T}\right)_p dT + \left(\frac{\partial S}{\partial p}\right)_T dp = 0. \tag{7.63}$$

Substituting for C_p and using (M-4), we obtain

$$\left(\frac{\partial T}{\partial p}\right) = \frac{T}{C_p}\left(\frac{\partial V}{\partial T}\right)_p = \frac{VT\alpha_p}{C_p}, \tag{7.64}$$

or if ΔT and Δp are small,

$$(\Delta T)_S \approx \frac{T}{C_p}\left(\frac{\partial V}{\partial T}\right)_p \Delta p. \tag{7.65}$$

This result could also have been obtained by starting with the Maxwell relation (M-2).

(2) *Constant energy processes.* An adiabatic process in which no work is performed is an example of a constant energy process. Perhaps the best-known case is the Joule free expansion discussed in connection with the calculation of entropy changes in Chapter 6. We choose the second independent variable to be V, because V is a natural independent variable for E, and write

$$dE = \left(\frac{\partial E}{\partial T}\right)_V dT + \left(\frac{\partial E}{\partial V}\right)_T dV = 0. \tag{7.66}$$

Solving for the ratio $(\partial T/\partial V)_E$, which is called the Joule coefficient and denoted by η, we obtain

$$\eta \equiv \left(\frac{\partial T}{\partial V}\right)_E = -\frac{1}{C_V}\left(\frac{\partial E}{\partial V}\right)_T, \tag{7.67}$$

where we have used $C_V = (\partial E/\partial T)_V$. So far we have used only the first law, but to express $(\partial E/\partial V)_T$ in terms of quantities obtainable from an equation of state we must use the second law as well. From $dE = T\,dS - p\,dV$ we obtain

$$\left(\frac{\partial E}{\partial V}\right)_T = T\left(\frac{\partial S}{\partial V}\right)_T - p, \tag{7.68}$$

and using the Maxwell relation (M-3) for $(\partial S/\partial V)_T$ we obtain an expression for η in terms of C_V and the equation of state

$$\eta C_V = p - T\left(\frac{\partial p}{\partial T}\right)_V = p - pT\alpha_V. \tag{7.69}$$

If ΔT and ΔV are small, then Eq. (7.69) can be written approximately as

$$(\Delta T)_E \approx \frac{1}{C_V}\left[p - T\left(\frac{\partial p}{\partial T}\right)_V\right]\Delta V. \tag{7.70}$$

It is interesting at this point to compare this result with Eq. (7.62) for $(\Delta T)_S$. Note that the only difference is the presence of the term $p\Delta V/C_V$. The numerator of this term represents the work which appeared in the surroundings in the isentropic process (none appeared in the constant energy process). Since all the quantities in this additional term are positive, we see that the temperature drop is greater in the isentropic process. We would expect this, since the work which appeared in the surroundings did so at the expense of the internal energy of the system.

(3) *Constant enthalpy processes.* Before going through the routine of the derivation, which is closely analogous to those already given, we wish to describe an experimental arrangement for carrying out an isenthalpic process since we have not yet given any example of such a process. Perhaps the best-known isenthalpic process is the Joule-Thomson expansion, which consists of allowing a gas to expand through a throttle valve (a porous plug was used in the original experiments). If the flow is sufficiently slow, the gas has a well-defined pressure and temperature upstream from the valve, and a well-defined pressure and temperature downstream. The process is carried out as a steady flow process, under adiabatic conditions, and the initial and final pressures and temperatures measured. At first sight it would appear that we could not employ thermodynamic reasoning on such a flow process, but we can do so by carrying out the expansion sufficiently slowly and choosing our boundaries properly. We choose an imaginary boundary

which encloses a fixed mass of gas of volume V_1 upstream from the valve, and allow the boundary to move with the flow until this same mass of gas appears downstream, where it now occupies a volume V_2. The change of state of the fixed mass of gas can thus be symbolized as $(p_1, V_1, T_1) \rightarrow (p_2, V_2, T_2)$. The experimentally measured quantities are

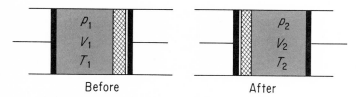

Before   After

FIG. 7.1. Schematic diagram of the Joule-Thomson expansion. All boundaries are adiabatic.

$(p_2 - p_1)$ and $(T_2 - T_1)$. We now imagine carrying out the same change in state with the idealized piston and porous plug arrangement shown in Fig. 7.1. Since $Q = 0$, we have $\Delta E = -W$, or in detail,

$$E_2 - E_1 = -(p_2 V_2 - p_1 V_1). \tag{7.71}$$

This can be written as

$$E_2 + p_2 V_2 = E_1 + p_1 V_1,$$

or

$$H_2 = H_1. \tag{7.72}$$

In other words, the enthalpy is constant for this change in state.

We now proceed in the same manner as in the calculation of the Joule coefficient, except that p is the second independent variable instead of V, since p is a natural independent variable for H. The measurement is conveniently summarized by the ratio $(\partial T/\partial p)_H$, which is called the Joule-Thomson coefficient and denoted by μ. We write

$$dH = \left(\frac{\partial H}{\partial T}\right)_p dT + \left(\frac{\partial H}{\partial p}\right)_T dp, \tag{7.73}$$

and since $dH = 0$ we obtain

$$\mu \equiv \left(\frac{\partial T}{\partial p}\right)_H = -\frac{1}{C_p}\left(\frac{\partial H}{\partial p}\right)_T, \tag{7.74}$$

where we have used Eq. (7.6), $C_p = (\partial H/\partial T)_p$. So far we have used only the first law, but to express $(\partial H/\partial p)_T$ in terms of quantities obtainable from an equation of state we must use the second law. From $dH = TdS + Vdp$ we obtain

$$\left(\frac{\partial H}{\partial p}\right)_T = T\left(\frac{\partial S}{\partial p}\right)_T + V, \tag{7.75}$$

and using the Maxwell relation (M-4) we obtain an expression for μ in terms of C_p and the equation of state

$$\mu C_p = T\left(\frac{\partial V}{\partial T}\right)_p - V = VT\alpha_p - V. \tag{7.76}$$

If ΔT and Δp are small, then Eq. (7.76) can be written approximately as

$$(\Delta T)_H \approx \frac{1}{C_p}\left[T\left(\frac{\partial V}{\partial T}\right)_p - V\right]\Delta p. \tag{7.77}$$

Again it is interesting to compare the result with the corresponding $(\Delta T)_S$ of Eq. (7.65). The only difference is the presence of the term $V\Delta p/C_p$ in Eq. (7.77). Since C_p and $(\partial V/\partial T)_p$ are always positive, the sign of $(\Delta T)_S$ is always the same as the sign of Δp; in other words, a decrease in pressure always cools the gas in the isentropic process. This is not true for the isenthalpic process, for $(\Delta T)_H$ can be positive, negative, or zero, depending on the magnitude of the extra $V\Delta p$ term compared to the term in $T(\partial V/\partial T)_p\Delta p$. All three cases have been observed experimentally. Similar remarks apply to the Joule coefficient η, but η has not been studied experimentally as extensively as has μ.

Although the procedures for the calculation of the various temperature changes have been analytical, the mathematical steps have physical interpretations which are worth a few comments for the insight they can give on characteristic thermodynamic techniques. The actual processes as carried out experimentally are often irreversible, and the thermodynamic calculation cannot attempt to follow such a process in detail. Instead the initial and final states are noted, and an alternate reversible process for the same change in state is devised. The calculation is shorter in proportion to the ingenuity shown in the selection of the alternate process. For instance, Eq. (7.66) corresponds to a two-step reversible process which will bring about the same change in state as the highly irreversible Joule free expansion. One step is at constant volume and the other at constant temperature. One characteristic technique is thus the use of idealized alternate reversible processes.

Reversible processes are used because every state is thermodynamically well-defined during the entire course of the process. Another characteristic technique is of course the use of state functions, without whose existence the invention of ingenious alternate processes would be futile.

(d) *Relationship between Heat Capacities*

As a further example of the use of Maxwell's relations, we shall show how one heat capacity can be determined from another heat capacity plus equation of state data. We have already carried this problem as far as possible with just the first law, in connection with the definition of the enthalpy, and obtained Eq. (7.13), which was

$$C_p - C_V = \left[p + \left(\frac{\partial E}{\partial V} \right)_T \right] \left(\frac{\partial V}{\partial T} \right)_p.$$

Notice that the left-hand side of this equation involves only heat quantities and the right-hand side involves work quantities (per temperature increase dT at constant p). The term in p is the work involved in pushing back the external atmosphere when the volume increases by dV; the term in $(\partial E/\partial V)_T$ can be interpreted as a sort of internal work. If $(\partial E/\partial V)_T$ is zero, then this equation can be used to calculate the mechanical equivalent of heat from data on the specific heats and equation of state of gases. This was first done by J. R. Mayer some years before Joule's paddle wheel experiments, but the indirect calculation made little impression on contemporary physicists. The formulation of the first law had to await the direct, painstaking work of Joule to be convincing.

To complete the derivation we need to use the second law to evaluate $(\partial E/\partial V)_T$. We use Eq. (7.68) and the Maxwell relation $(M\text{-}3)$, after which we obtain

$$C_p - C_V = T \left(\frac{\partial p}{\partial T} \right)_V \left(\frac{\partial V}{\partial T} \right)_p = pVT\alpha_V\alpha_p. \tag{7.78}$$

The same result could have been obtained a little more directly by using the second law from the beginning and writing

$$dS = \left(\frac{\partial S}{\partial T} \right)_V dT + \left(\frac{\partial S}{\partial V} \right)_T dV.$$

Dividing by dT and applying the condition of constant p, we obtain

$$\left(\frac{\partial S}{\partial T} \right)_p = \left(\frac{\partial S}{\partial T} \right)_V + \left(\frac{\partial S}{\partial V} \right)_T \left(\frac{\partial V}{\partial T} \right)_p, \tag{7.79}$$

or

$$C_p = C_V + T\left(\frac{\partial S}{\partial V}\right)_T \left(\frac{\partial V}{\partial T}\right)_p. \qquad (7.80)$$

Use of the Maxwell relation (*M*-3) then gives Eq. (7.78).

The only slight danger in starting a derivation immediately with the second law is that a desired result may not really depend on the second law at all. The result will of course still be correct, but an erroneous idea of the basis of the result will be obtained. An example of this will be given in the next section.

FURTHER EXAMPLES

To conclude this chapter we give two more examples. The first of these involves one of the four Maxwell relations, and is a proof of the identity of the thermodynamic and the ideal gas temperature scales. The second example is the derivation of the ideal gas adiabatic equation of state, and is given as an illustration of a result which is independent of the second law even though many existing derivations invoke this law.

(a) *Identity of Ideal Gas and Thermodynamic Temperature Scales*

We have given the equation of state of an ideal gas as $pV = nR\theta$ in Eq. (3.4). We have also mentioned that for many gases the quantity $(\partial E/\partial V)_T$ is very small, and the idealization that $(\partial E/\partial V)_T = 0$ is usually also incorporated into the definition of an ideal gas. The complete definition of an ideal gas is therefore

$$pV = nR\theta, \qquad (7.81)$$

$$\left(\frac{\partial E}{\partial V}\right)_\theta = 0, \qquad (7.82)$$

where we have used the symbol θ instead of T in Eq. (7.82) to make the definition self-contained. Equation (7.81) defines the ideal gas temperature scale; Eq. (7.82) states that the internal energy of an ideal gas depends only on the temperature and is independent of volume (and pressure) at constant temperature. As far as thermodynamics is concerned, these are independent statements and one cannot be derived from the other.

The thermodynamic temperature scale is independent of the properties of any particular substance. The ratio of two temperatures on this scale is defined to be

$$\frac{T_1}{T_2} = -\frac{Q_1}{Q_2},$$ (7.83)

where Q_1 and Q_2 are the heats absorbed and rejected by a reversible engine working between these two temperatures. This is not an experimentally convenient scale, because it is difficult both to construct a reversible engine and to accurately measure heats absorbed or rejected. We accordingly wish to see how the numbers assigned to temperatures on this scale compare with those on the ideal gas temperature scale, which is an experimentally practical scale. If we rewrite the definition of an ideal gas in terms of the thermodynamic scale, Eqs. (7.81) and (7.82) become

$$pV = nf(T),$$ (7.84)

$$\left(\frac{\partial E}{\partial V}\right)_T = 0,$$ (7.85)

where $f(T)$ is some function of T. The problem is thus to find the function $f(T) = R\theta$, since this will give the desired relationship.

Equation (7.85) suggests that we begin with $dE = TdS - pdV$ and write

$$\left(\frac{\partial E}{\partial V}\right)_T = T\left(\frac{\partial S}{\partial V}\right)_T - p = 0.$$

We now use the Maxwell relation (M-3) and a mathematical identity to obtain

$$\left(\frac{\partial E}{\partial V}\right)_T = T\left(\frac{\partial p}{\partial T}\right)_V - p = T^2\left[\frac{\partial\left(\frac{p}{T}\right)}{\partial T}\right]_V = 0,$$

or in other words the following relation is true for an ideal gas:

$$\left[\frac{\partial\left(\frac{p}{T}\right)}{\partial T}\right]_V = 0.$$ (7.86)

Hence p/T is independent of temperature at constant volume, or

$$\frac{p}{T} = g(V),$$ (7.87)

where $g(V)$ is some unknown function of volume. Substituting for p from Eq. (7.84) and rearranging, we obtain

$$\frac{f(T)}{T} = \frac{Vg(V)}{n}. \tag{7.88}$$

Now the only way that a function of temperature alone can be equal to a function of volume alone is for both functions to be constant. If we call this constant R', we have

$$\frac{f(T)}{T} = R',$$

or the relation between the two temperature scales is, since $f(T) = R\theta$,

$$R'T = R\theta. \tag{7.89}$$

If now T and θ are defined so as to agree at one temperature (say the triple point of water is chosen as 273.16 on each scale), then R' and R are identical, and T and θ are identical at *all* temperatures.

An ideal gas thus obeys the equation of state

$$pV = nRT, \tag{7.90}$$

where T is now the thermodynamic temperature rather than the ideal gas temperature. In other words, Eq. (7.90) is equivalent to both Eqs. (7.81) and (7.82). We have just proved the equivalence in one direction; it is left as an exercise for the reader to prove the equivalence in the other direction; that is, to prove $(\partial E/\partial V)_T = 0$ starting with Eq. (7.90).

The equivalence of the thermodynamic and ideal gas temperature scales is of great practical importance, for it provides a good experimental method for the accurate realization of thermodynamic temperatures. Gas thermometers are the best devices known for the determination of thermodynamic temperatures in the range of temperature where gas thermometers can be used at all. (They cannot be used at very low or very high temperatures because of practical limitations of construction and accuracy of measurement.) The equivalence is of no great importance as far as thermodynamic theory is concerned, however, and the theory would not suffer if ideal gases did not exist at all. If a practical way could be found to construct a reversible cycle and accurately measure the heat quantities involved, then the gas thermometer might be superseded and end up merely as a historical curiosity.

(b) *Adiabatic Equation of State*

The ordinary equation of state expresses a relation among p, V, and T; the adiabatic equation of state is a special relation among these variables for adiabatic changes of state. The problem is to predict the adiabatic equation of state given the ordinary equation of state. For an adiabatic change it would seem sensible to start the derivation with the condition $dS = 0$, so we write

$$dS = \left(\frac{\partial S}{\partial T}\right)_V dT + \left(\frac{\partial S}{\partial V}\right)_T dV = C_V\, d\ln T + \left(\frac{\partial p}{\partial T}\right)_V dV = 0. \quad (7.91)$$

Now $(\partial p/\partial T)_V$ can be evaluated as a function of T and V if the equation of state is known, and C_V can be completely evaluated from the equation of state if it is known as a function of T at just one V. We could substitute these relations back into Eq. (7.91) and have a differential equation in T and V. This solves the problem in principle, since such a differential equation can always be integrated (by numerical methods if nothing else works).

But to have an analytical answer, let us specialize to the ideal gas. Then from Eq. (7.90) we find

$$(\partial p/\partial T)_V = nR/V,$$

so that Eq. (7.91) becomes

$$C_V\, d\ln T + nR\, d\ln V = 0. \quad (7.92)$$

To integrate, C_V must be known as a function of T (it is not a function of V for an ideal gas), and it is often a good first approximation to take C_V as a constant, so that the integral of Eq. (7.92) is

$$VT^{\tilde{C}_V/R} = \text{constant}. \quad (7.93)$$

This is the ideal gas adiabatic equation of state explicit in V and T for constant $\tilde{C}_V \equiv C_V/n$. It can be made explicit in p and V or in p and T by substitution from $pV = nRT$, a manipulation which is left as an exercise for the reader.

Apparently Eq. (7.93) depends on the second law in a very fundamental way, since we have invoked the second law several times in the derivation. Surprisingly, a closer examination shows that Eq. (7.93) is independent of the second law. To demonstrate this, we start over, beginning with the first law alone and using θ instead of T (since the definition of T depends on the second law). For an adiabatic reversible compression or expansion the first law becomes

$$dE = -pdV. \tag{7.94}$$

Now we imagine carrying out the same change in state in two steps, one step at constant volume and the other step at constant temperature. The energy change is then

$$dE = \left(\frac{\partial E}{\partial \theta}\right)_V d\theta + \left(\frac{\partial E}{\partial V}\right)_\theta dV = C_V d\theta - \eta C_V dV, \tag{7.95}$$

where the second step involves only the definitions of C_V and the Joule coefficient η, plus the first law to relate $(\partial E/\partial V)_\theta$ to η. Eliminating dE between Eqs. (7.94) and (7.95), we obtain

$$C_V d\theta - \eta C_V dV = -pdV, \tag{7.96}$$

which is a completely general relationship in the form of a differential equation. To integrate it we would have to express C_V, η, and p as functions of θ and V. We now see how the second law enters into the general derivation: it is needed to obtain C_V and η in terms of the equation of state, and if we substitute for η from Eq. (7.69) we immediately recover Eq. (7.91), the original starting point. The only way to use Eq. (7.96) without invoking the second law is to have experimental information on C_V and η. This is exactly the situation for the ideal gas, for by definition $(\partial E/\partial V)_\theta = 0$ and so $\eta = 0$ and C_V is a function of θ alone. Thus Eq. (7.96) becomes, without any use of the second law,

$$C_V d\theta = -\frac{nR\theta}{V} dV, \tag{7.97}$$

which is the same as Eq. (7.92) which supposedly depended on the second law. The integration to obtain Eq. (7.93) with θ in place of T is then straightforward.

No great harm is done by using the first and second laws together when only one or the other is sufficient, except to obscure the often overlooked fact that the first and second laws are essentially independent of each other, and that many results really depend on only one of the laws and not on both.

Problems

1. The Helmholtz function of one mole of a certain gas is given by
$$A = -(a/V) - RT \ln (V - b) + f(T),$$
where a and b are constants and $f(T)$ is a function of temperature only. Derive an expression for the pressure of the gas.

2. The Gibbs function of one mole of a certain gas is given by
$$G = RT \ln p + A + Bp + \tfrac{1}{2}Cp^2 + \tfrac{1}{3}Dp^3,$$
where A, B, C, D are functions of temperatures only. Find the equation of state of the gas.

3. Suppose that G is known as a function of p and T for a system. Derive the expressions for the other thermodynamic functions of the system (V, S, H, E, A, C_p, C_V, κ_T, α_p, α_V) in terms of G and its derivatives with respect to p and T only.

4. The internal energy of a certain gas depends on volume as well as on temperature, and obeys the relation
$$\left(\frac{\partial E}{\partial V}\right)_T = \frac{a}{V^2},$$
where a is a constant. Prove that C_V for this gas depends only on temperature.

5. Prove Eq. (7.57),
$$\left(\frac{\partial C_p}{\partial p}\right)_T = -T\left(\frac{\partial^2 V}{\partial T^2}\right)_p.$$
Use this result to show that C_p for an ideal gas depends only on temperature.

6. Prove that
$$C_p - C_V = -T\left(\frac{\partial p}{\partial V}\right)_T \left(\frac{\partial V}{\partial T}\right)_p^2 = \frac{VT\alpha_p^2}{\kappa_T},$$
$$C_p - C_V = -T\left(\frac{\partial p}{\partial T}\right)_V^2 \left(\frac{\partial V}{\partial p}\right)_T = p^2 VT\alpha_V^2 \kappa_T.$$
Find $C_p - C_V$ for an ideal gas.

7. The temperature at which the Joule-Thomson coefficient is zero is called the Joule-Thomson inversion temperature. Show that at this temperature the following relation holds
$$T = V\left(\frac{\partial T}{\partial V}\right)_p.$$
Use this result to show that the Joule-Thomson coefficient is always zero for an ideal gas.

8. Prove that $(\partial E/\partial V)_T = 0$ for a system whose equation of state is $pV = nRT$.

9. Construct an alternate proof of the identity of the thermodynamic and ideal gas temperature scales by using the ideal gas as the working substance for a Carnot engine.

10. Show that

$$\frac{1}{S^2}\left(\frac{\partial S}{\partial p}\right)_G = \frac{1}{S}\left(\frac{\partial V}{\partial G}\right)_p - \frac{V}{S^2}\left(\frac{\partial S}{\partial G}\right)_p.$$

11. Calculate the entropy change that occurs when an ideal gas at 25°C undergoes a Joule free expansion to three times its initial volume.

12. One mole of a certain gas obeys the equation of state

$$\frac{pV}{RT} = 1 + \frac{B(T)}{V},$$

where $B(T)$ is a function of temperature alone.

(a) One mole of this gas at temperature T and volume V_0 is expanded isothermally and *reversibly* to twice its initial volume. Calculate ΔA, ΔS, ΔE, W, and Q for this process.

(b) The same change in state as in (a) is brought about *irreversibly* by expanding the gas into a vacuum. Calculate ΔA, ΔS, ΔE, W, and Q for this process.

13. The temperature at which the Joule coefficient is zero is called the Joule inversion temperature. For a gas obeying the equation of state of Problem 12, show that the Joule inversion temperature is that temperature for which $B(T)$ is a maximum. If a certain gas has its $B(T)$ given by the equation

$$B(T) = b_1 - (b_2/T) - (b_3/T^3),$$

where b_1, b_2, and b_3 are positive constants, show that such a gas has no Joule inversion temperature.

14. The three points in Fig. P7.14 represent three points in the p-V diagram of one mole of an ideal gas, with $V_2 = V_1$ and $p_3 = p_1$.

(a) Find the difference in entropy between state 3 and state 1, and between state 2 and state 1.

(b) If $T_2 = T_3$, what is the value of $(S_3 - S_2)$?

(c) If $T_2 = T_3$, what are the values of $(A_3 - A_2)$ and of $(G_3 - G_2)$?

15. A manuscript is submitted for publication to a journal. The author claims to have determined the equation of state of a certain solid to be

$$V = V_0 - Ap + BT,$$

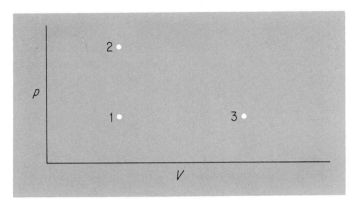

FIG. P7.14

and the internal energy to be

$$E = CT - BpT,$$

where A, B, C, and V_0 are constants. Check whether the existence of such a substance is compatible with the first and second laws by testing these two equations for thermodynamic consistency. Would you recommend that the journal editor publish the manuscript? Hint: derive a thermodynamic relation for $(\partial E/\partial p)_T$ in terms of derivatives of V with respect to p and T, and see whether the solid obeys the relation.

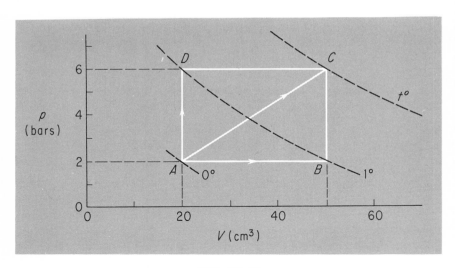

FIG. P7.17

16. Prove that, for *any* fluid,

$$\left(\frac{\partial p}{\partial V}\right)_S = \frac{C_p}{C_V}\left(\frac{\partial p}{\partial V}\right)_T.$$

17. Figure P7.17 refers back to Problem 11 of Chapter 4, where the given quantities were $Q_{AB} = 7$ joules, $Q_{AD} = 1$ joule, and $E_A = 0$.

(a) Calculate the enthalpies H_A, H_B, H_C, and H_D.

(b) Using the thermodynamic relation between C_p and C_V given by Eq. (7.78), and approximating derivatives by finite difference ratios, i.e., $(\partial p/\partial T)_V = (\Delta p/\Delta t)_V$, prove that the absolute temperature of the isotherm marked $0°$ is $\frac{1}{2}°$ absolute.

(c) Calculate $S_B - S_D$, the entropy difference between states B and D.

Chapter 8

APPLICATIONS TO SIMPLE
SYSTEMS: GASES, LIQUIDS,
AND SOLUTIONS

In the preceding chapter several consequences of the first and second laws were discussed and some analytical methods for applying thermodynamics to physical systems were developed. In this chapter we shall apply some of these methods to some simple representative physical systems. We shall begin this chapter with a discussion of the equation of state of a real gas, and shall then show how to use such an equation to predict one set of properties of a substance from another set of properties. This will illustrate one aspect of thermodynamics: relations among thermodynamic variables dictated by the first and second laws are used as a kind of recipe or machine for generating a set of calculated properties from a set of measured properties. We shall then discuss some applications dealing with phase equilibria, the study of the conditions under which two or more phases can coexist. The illustrations will include such phenomena as the coexistence line, the effect of external pressure on vapor pressure, and some of the properties of gaseous and liquid solutions, particularly the effect of a non-volatile solute on the freezing point and boiling point. Pressure and temperature are the logical independent variables for these problems, and hence the Gibbs function is the most convenient function to use in the discussion of phase equilibria. This chapter will therefore also serve to illustrate some of the properties of this function. The two kinds of applications mentioned—the calculation of one set of properties from another set and the determination of the conditions of equilibrium—are the only kinds of results obtainable from thermodynamics.

EQUATION OF STATE OF A REAL GAS

The equation of state of a real gas is shown schematically in Fig. 8.1, in which isotherms of pressure vs. volume are plotted. Several features which are common to all gases are worth noting. First, in the region of comparatively large molar volumes the behavior of the

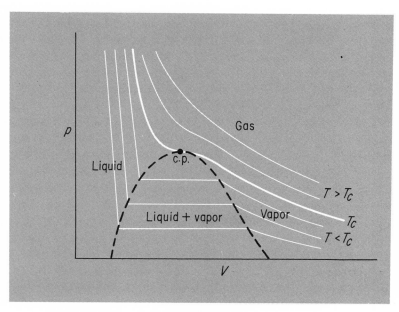

FIG. 8.1. Schematic representation of the equation of state of a real gas.

gas is well approximated by the ideal gas equation. The isotherms in this region are therefore close to being equilateral hyperbolas, $pV = nRT$. Second, there is a temperature above which the gas cannot be liquefied (though it may be solidified at very high pressure). This temperature is called the critical temperature and is denoted by T_c in Fig. 8.1. Below T_c the gas can be liquefied if the pressure is high enough. Gases at temperatures less than T_c are often called vapors. Third, in the two-phase region marked "liquid + vapor" the volume of the system can be changed without changing the pressure. This pressure, which depends only on temperature in the two-phase region, is called the vapor pressure. The dashed curve marks the boundary of the region where liquid and vapor can coexist. Points at the left side of the dashed curve give the volumes of the saturated liquid, and points at the right side give the volumes of the saturated vapor. When the volume is decreased below that of the saturated liquid, the pressure rises rapidly—another way of remarking that liquids are much less compressible than vapors. Fourth, the critical isotherm just touches the two-phase region at one point, called the critical point. At this point the volumes of the saturated liquid and saturated vapor have become the same, and the two phases are in fact indistinguishable. The volume and pressure· at the critical point are called the critical volume, V_c, and the critical pressure, p_c. This completes the comments on the pV diagram itself and we shall now discuss analytical representation of the isotherms.

We have remarked that the equation of state of a substance is not necessarily represented by an analytical function, and in fact no simple function seems likely to be devised to represent the properties of a fluid over its *entire* range of existence with sufficient accuracy for computational purposes. There are, however, many equations which adequately represent the behavior quantitatively over certain limited regions of pressure and temperature, or which represent the behavior qualitatively over large regions. Two of the most important of these equations will be mentioned. As far as thermodynamics is concerned all this is immaterial; all that is needed is an accurate set of corresponding values of pressure, volume, and temperature. The analytical form merely makes a computation easier.

The first equation, the older one, was devised by J. D. van der Waals, and has the form

$$\left(p + \frac{n^2a}{V^2}\right)(V - nb) = nRT. \tag{8.1}$$

The quantities a and b are supposed to be constants for a particular gas. Their original interpretation was that b corrected the total volume for the finite volume of the molecules, and a corrected the pressure for the effect of the attractive forces between the molecules. It is now known that this is true only in a rough approximation, but the equation retains an importance because it mimics the qualitative behavior of real gases surprisingly well, and never seems to predict a physically absurd behavior. Quantitatively, it is not very accurate, and can be

used only over very limited regions for a given choice of a and b.
Isotherms of this equation are shown in Fig. 8.2, where it is seen that
the equation imitates the real gas behavior shown in Fig. 8.1 quite well
except for the oscillation in the two-phase region. Even this can be
remedied, as we shall show shortly. The equation also approaches ideal

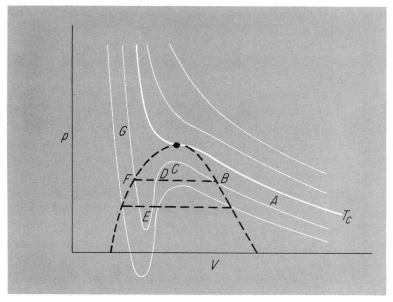

FIG. 8.2. Schematic representation of the van der Waals
equation of state.

gas behavior at large volumes, as it should; it can be seen by inspection
that the terms containing a and b become negligible as V is made very
large.

The oscillatory section of the van der Waals isotherm is an interesting feature. To make this section conform to the actual equilibrium
situation, it should be replaced by a horizontal line. The question is,
how to decide where to draw the line. A procedure for deciding this
was suggested by Maxwell, who pointed out that the line should be
drawn so that the area of the loop $BCDB$ was the same as that of the
loop $DEFD$. Otherwise, if an engine could be constructed to operate
around the cycle $BCDEFB$, it would violate the second law by producing

net work from a single heat reservoir at the temperature of the isotherm. The van der Waals equation plus the Maxwell construction together mimic all the qualitative features of real equilibrium fluids, but the sections BC and FE also correspond to realizable experimental conditions. If a vapor is carefully compressed isothermally starting from point A, it may not condense on reaching point B, but continue up towards point C, the pressure supported by the vapor then being higher than the coexistence pressure. Such a state is unstable with respect to condensation, and the introduction of a few "condensation nuclei," such as dust, droplets, or ions, will cause condensation to occur very rapidly until the system ends up on the horizontal line BDF. This situation is analogous to the case of a mixture of hydrogen and oxygen, which may be unstable with respect to a chemical reaction that can be initiated by a spark or a bit of catalyst. A similar phenomenon can happen with the liquid. It is sometimes possible to reduce the pressure on a liquid from G past F without any vapor formation. With considerable care it is even possible to go to negative pressures (i.e., the liquid is under tension). This corresponds to the portion of the lowest isotherm which lies below the volume axis in Fig. 8.2. The section CDE having a positive slope is not experimentally realizable, however, because it is mechanically unstable with respect to infinitesimal changes in pressure. That is, an increase in pressure would increase the volume, which would further increase the pressure, and so on until the maximum point C was reached.

As the temperature is raised, the oscillatory section becomes narrower and narrower and the amplitude of the oscillation decreases, so that the points corresponding to C, D, and E become closer and closer. There finally occurs a temperature at which the slope of the curve never becomes positive, but does equal zero at one point. At this point the curvature is also zero, so that a horizontal inflection point exists. This corresponds to the critical point, so that

$$\left(\frac{\partial p}{\partial V}\right)_{\text{crit.}} = 0, \tag{8.2a}$$

$$\left(\frac{\partial^2 p}{\partial V^2}\right)_{\text{crit.}} = 0. \tag{8.2b}$$

The location of the critical point can be found in terms of the constants a and b by applying the conditions of Eq. (8.2) to the van der Waals equation and solving the resulting two simultaneous equations. It can also be found by noting that the van der Waals equation is a cubic in V and that the three roots of the cubic coincide at the critical point, so that $(V - V_c)^3 = 0$. If this is expanded and the coefficients compared with those of the van der Waals equation, the critical constants can be easily identified. Either procedure yields the following relations:

$$b = \tfrac{1}{3}\tilde{V}_c, \tag{8.3}$$

$$a = \tfrac{9}{8}RT_c\tilde{V}_c, \tag{8.4}$$

$$p\tilde{V}_c/RT_c = \tfrac{3}{8}. \tag{8.5}$$

Note that Eq. (8.5) indicates that the critical constants should bear the same relation to one another for all gases. This rule holds approximately for a number of gases, although the value of the constant is not quite the predicted value of $\tfrac{3}{8}$. This is typical of predictions from the van der Waals equation: qualitatively they are almost always correct, but quantitatively they are almost never so.

The second equation which we shall mention is the virial equation of state,

$$p\tilde{V} = RT\left(1 + \frac{B}{\tilde{V}} + \frac{C}{\tilde{V}^2} + \cdots\right), \tag{8.6}$$

which is written as an infinite series. The coefficients B, C, etc. depend only on T and are called virial coefficients. Another form often used is

$$p\tilde{V} = RT + B'p + C'p^2 + \cdots, \tag{8.7}$$

and the coefficients B', C', etc. also depend only on temperature. Provided both Eqs. (8.6) and (8.7) are infinite series and not just finite polynomials, the coefficients can be shown mathematically to be in a definite relation to each other: $B = B'$, $C = (B')^2 + RTC'$, etc.

At first sight it might appear as if the virial equation of state were merely an illustration of the common procedure in physical problems of representing complicated functions by infinite series. But it happens that the equation rests on a sound theoretical basis, and each virial coefficient has a definite physical interpretation in terms of the interactions between the molecules which make up the gas. In practice the full infinite series cannot be used, because only a finite number of experimental points exist and because it is very difficult to carry out a completely theoretical calculation of the higher virial coefficients. Only the first few terms of the series are actually used, so that it is used only at moderately high pressures and densities, where the convergence of the series is rapid. We should remark again, however, that all this is immaterial so far as thermodynamics is concerned.

There are many other equations of state besides the two so far mentioned, many of which may be more convenient in certain circumstances for the empirical representation of data. The two just mentioned, however, have some importance outside the realm of thermodynamic calculations: the virial equation because it is fundamentally related to the molecular properties of matter, and the van der Waals equation because it combines simplicity of form with correct qualitative behavior.

ILLUSTRATIONS INVOLVING REAL GASES

By way of illustration we shall calculate the effect of pressure and volume on the heat capacities of a real gas, and the Joule-Thomson coefficient for a real gas.

(a) *Heat Capacities*

For this example we use the van der Waals equation of state. We recall that for an ideal gas both C_p and C_V depend on temperature alone. Let us first investigate $(\partial C_V / \partial V)_T$, which by Eq. (7.56) is equal to $T(\partial^2 p / \partial T^2)_V$. Writing the van der Waals equation in the form

$$p = \frac{RT}{\tilde{V} - b} - \frac{a}{\tilde{V}^2}, \tag{8.8}$$

we readily see that $(\partial^2 p / \partial T^2)_V = 0$. Hence C_V is a function of temperature alone for a van der Waals gas, just as for an ideal gas. The situation is quite different for C_p, however. From Eq. (7.57) we have

$$\left(\frac{\partial \tilde{C}_p}{\partial p}\right)_T = -T \left(\frac{\partial^2 \tilde{V}}{\partial T^2}\right)_p, \tag{8.9}$$

so that we need to use Eq. (8.8) to find $(\partial^2 \tilde{V} / \partial T^2)_p$. Differentiating Eq. (8.8) with respect to temperature at constant pressure, we obtain

$$0 = \frac{R}{\tilde{V} - b} - \frac{RT}{(\tilde{V} - b)^2}\left(\frac{\partial \tilde{V}}{\partial T}\right)_p + \frac{2a}{\tilde{V}^3}\left(\frac{\partial \tilde{V}}{\partial T}\right)_p. \tag{8.10}$$

We can solve this for $(\partial \tilde{V} / \partial T)_p$ and then differentiate again, producing a rather complicated expression involving both $(\partial^2 \tilde{V} / \partial T^2)_p$ and $(\partial \tilde{V} / \partial T)_p$.

The latter can be eliminated by substitution from Eq. (8.10), and the final result is

$$\left(\frac{\partial \tilde{C}_p}{\partial p}\right)_T = \frac{4a}{RT^2}\left(\frac{\tilde{V}-b}{\tilde{V}}\right)^3\left[\frac{3}{2}\left(\frac{\tilde{V}-b}{\tilde{V}}\right)-1\right]\left[1-\frac{2a}{RT\tilde{V}}\left(\frac{\tilde{V}-b}{\tilde{V}}\right)^2\right]^{-3}.$$

(8.11)

If we eliminate a and b in favor of T_c and $\tilde{V}_c$ by Eqs. (8.3) and (8.4), we obtain the alternate form

$$\left(\frac{\partial \tilde{C}_p}{\partial p}\right)_T = \frac{9}{2}\frac{T_c\tilde{V}_c}{T^2}\left(1-\frac{\tilde{V}_c}{3\tilde{V}}\right)^3\left[\frac{3}{2}\left(1-\frac{\tilde{V}_c}{3\tilde{V}}\right)-1\right]$$

$$\times\left[1-\frac{9}{4}\frac{T_c\tilde{V}_c}{T\tilde{V}}\left(1-\frac{\tilde{V}_c}{3\tilde{V}}\right)^2\right]^{-3}. \quad (8.12)$$

From this rather complicated expression it is apparent that C_p for a van der Waals gas is a function of the volume (or pressure) as well as the temperature. The sign of $(\partial \tilde{C}_p/\partial p)_T$ can be either positive or negative, and can even be infinity if the last bracket in Eqs. (8.11) or (8.12) is zero.

(b) *Joule-Thomson Coefficient*

For this example we use the virial equation of state. From Eq. (7.76) we have

$$\mu \tilde{C}_p = T\left(\frac{\partial \tilde{V}}{\partial T}\right)_p - \tilde{V}. \quad (8.13)$$

We differentiate Eq. (8.7) to find $(\partial \tilde{V}/\partial T)_p$, and obtain

$$\left(\frac{\partial \tilde{V}}{\partial T}\right)_p = \frac{R}{p} + \frac{dB'}{dT} + p\frac{dC'}{dT} + \cdots, \quad (8.14)$$

from which follows

$$\mu \tilde{C}_p = -\left(B' - T\frac{dB'}{dT}\right) - p\left(C' - T\frac{dC'}{dT}\right) + \cdots. \quad (8.15)$$

The Joule-Thomson coefficient can be positive or negative, depending in general on the relative values of $\tilde{V}$ and $T(\partial \tilde{V}/\partial T)_p$. For an ideal gas μ is zero, as shown by Eq. (8.15), but for any real gas μ depends in general on temperature and pressure. At a given pressure, the temperature at which μ changes from positive to negative values (i.e., μ becomes zero) is called the Joule-Thomson inversion point. The zero-pressure limit of the inversion point is called the Joule-Thomson inversion temperature.

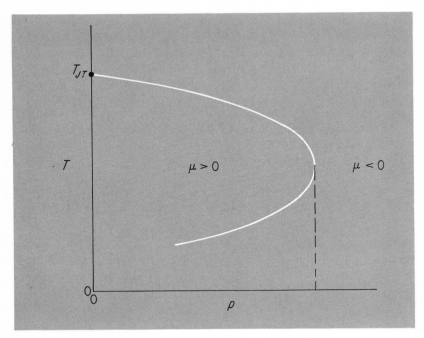

FIG. 8.3. Schematic diagram of the Joule-Thomson inversion curve.

A plot of the inversion points in a $T - p$ diagram traces out the inversion curve, which is shown schematically in Fig. 8.3. Of course, only the low-pressure upper part of the curve is described by Eq. (8.15); more virial coefficients must be included to describe the high-pressure behavior of real gases. In the region where $\mu > 0$ the gas temperature will drop in a Joule-Thomson expansion. It is apparent that above the inversion temperature, T_{JT}, the gas cannot be cooled by the expansion. This is 621°K for N_2 and 202°K for H_2. Hence if we want to liquefy H_2 by Joule-Thomson cooling, we must first cool the gas below 202°K. The figure also shows that there is a maximum pressure above which no Joule-Thomson cooling will occur no matter what the temperature is. This is marked by the dashed line, and is about 380 atm for N_2 and 164 atm for H_2.

As the pressure on a gas is reduced, the behavior of the gas becomes more nearly ideal, so that

$$\lim_{p \to 0} (p \tilde{V}) = RT, \tag{8.16}$$

as can be seen directly from Eq. (8.7), for example. If we wish information on the second virial coefficient B from p-V-T measurements, we must therefore work at moderately high pressures in order that the deviation from ideality we are interested in will be large enough to measure accurately. The situation is quite different for the Joule-Thomson coefficient, however. From Eq. (8.15) we see that

$$\lim_{p \to 0} \mu \tilde{C}_p = -B' + T \frac{dB'}{dT}, \qquad (8.17)$$

so that there is a Joule-Thomson effect even in the limit of very low pressures, where the behavior of a gas is usually otherwise ideal. Furthermore, the Joule-Thomson coefficient gives information on the second virial coefficient directly, whereas a p-V-T measurement gives such information only as a small difference between two quantities of similar magnitude, namely $p\tilde{V}$ and RT. The Joule-Thomson coefficient is therefore of considerable importance in the investigation of virial coefficients.

The Joule coefficient η is similar in some respects to the Joule-Thomson coefficient, but is of minor importance. One reason for this is that η goes to zero as p goes to zero, and does so as p^2 (or as $\tilde{V}^{-2}$). This can be easily verified by evaluating η for the virial equation of state.

The preceding examples are merely illustrations of the general result that all the thermodynamic properties of a simple fluid can be determined if the equation of state and one of the heat capacities (as a function of temperature) are known.

COEXISTING PHASES (CLAPEYRON EQUATION)

We now consider the case of two phases coexisting which may be solid + liquid, solid + vapor, or liquid + vapor. At equilibrium the pressure and temperature of one phase is equal to the pressure and temperature of the other phase. We inquire as to what relationship must exist between this equilibrium pressure and temperature because of the requirements of the first and second laws. To answer this, we imagine a change from one phase to the other to take place at constant pressure and temperature; for example, we imagine some liquid evaporates and forms vapor. Since we are considering pressure and temperature as independent variables, the Gibbs function is the most convenient function to use. If we start initially with all the material in phase 1 and reversibly convert it entirely to phase 2, keeping the pressure and temperature constant, the Gibbs function of the system cannot have changed (why?). Thus, initially the Gibbs function of the whole system would be $n\tilde{G}_1$, when n is the number of moles of material in the system and $\tilde{G}_1$ is the Gibbs function per mole for phase 1. At the end of the process the Gibbs function of the entire system would be $n\tilde{G}_2$, $\tilde{G}_2$ being the Gibbs function per mole of phase 2. Since the Gibbs function of the system does not change in the transformation described, we must have $\tilde{G}_1 = \tilde{G}_2$. This equality then must hold for all temperatures and pressures. If the temperature and pressure of the system of two coexisting phases are changed slightly, then the Gibbs functions of the two phases must change equally. Thus,

$$d\tilde{G}_1 = d\tilde{G}_2. \tag{8.18}$$

Using the statement of the first and second laws in terms of dG, we can write this as

$$-\tilde{S}_1 dT + \tilde{V}_1 dp = -\tilde{S}_2 dT + \tilde{V}_2 dp, \tag{8.19}$$

which can be rearranged into the form

$$\left(\frac{dp}{dT}\right)_{\text{coex.}} = \frac{\tilde{S}_2 - \tilde{S}_1}{\tilde{V}_2 - \tilde{V}_1}. \tag{8.20}$$

Using the definition of entropy we can write

$$\tilde{S}_2 - \tilde{S}_1 = (\tilde{H}_2 - \tilde{H}_1)/T, \tag{8.21}$$

or

$$\left(\frac{dp}{dT}\right)_{\text{coex.}} = \frac{\tilde{H}_2 - \tilde{H}_1}{T(\tilde{V}_2 - \tilde{V}_1)}. \tag{8.22}$$

This is usually written as

$$\left(\frac{dp}{dT}\right)_{\text{coex.}} = \frac{\Delta S}{\Delta V} = \frac{\Delta H}{T\,\Delta V}. \tag{8.23}$$

This equation is called the *Clapeyron equation*. The transformation from solid to vapor, solid to liquid, or liquid to vapor is always accompanied by an increase in enthalpy, so that ΔH is positive for these transformations. The same is not true for the sign of ΔV. For most substances these transformations are accompanied by an increase in volume, so that ΔV is usually positive, but there are few systems known for which the transformation from solid to liquid is accompanied by a decrease in volume (i.e., the liquid is denser than the solid). If ΔV is positive, then from Eq. (8.23) we see that dp and dT must have the same sign, because the right-hand side of the equation is positive.

That is, the temperature at which two phases coexist increases if the pressure is increased. For instance, the boiling point of water increases with an increase in pressure. The same is not true for the transformation from ice to water, however. The specific volume of water at ordinary pressures is less than the specific volume of ice at the same pressure and temperature. Thus ΔV is negative for the ice-to-water transition, and the freezing point of water decreases with an increase in pressure. The decrease in temperature per atmosphere can be calculated as follows. The heat of fusion of ice is approximately 6.02×10^3 joules/mole $= 6.02 \times 10^{10}$ ergs/mole. The molar volume of ice at 273°K is 19.6 cm³, and of water at 273°K is 18.0 cm³. Therefore,

$$\frac{dp}{dT} = \frac{6.02 \times 10^{10}}{(273)(18.0 - 19.6)} = -138 \text{ bar/°K} = -136 \text{ atm/°K},$$

where 1 bar $\equiv 10^6$ dyne/cm² and 1 atm $\equiv 1.01325$ bar, by definition. A pressure increase of 136 atmospheres decreases the melting point of ice by 1°K.

The Clapeyron equation can also be written down from the third Maxwell relation,

$$\left(\frac{\partial S}{\partial V}\right)_T = \left(\frac{\partial p}{\partial T}\right)_V. \tag{8.24}$$

At the coexistence line the pressure does not depend upon the volume but only upon the temperature. The right side of Eq. (8.24) is therefore $(dp/dT)_{\text{coex.}}$ at the coexistence line. The left side is $(\Delta S/\Delta V)$, or $(\Delta H/T \, \Delta V)$, at the coexistence line.

A third method of arriving at the Clapeyron equation is by consideration of a Carnot engine operating with a two-phase system as working fluid. This has some historical interest since both Clapeyron and James Thomson (brother of Lord Kelvin) derived the result in this manner. It will be evident that the two methods already used are more convenient than this last method, an illustration of the simplification possible through the use of the proper thermodynamic function.

In the coexistence region two closely-spaced isotherms would appear as shown schematically in Fig. 8.4. In the reversible cycle $ABCDA$, the adiabatic processes are given by AD and BC. Along AB, n moles of phase 1 are converted to phase 2, while along CD, n moles of phase 2 are converted to phase 1. From the first and second laws,

$$\epsilon = \frac{W}{Q} = \left(1 - \frac{T}{T + dT}\right) = \frac{dT}{T}. \tag{8.25}$$

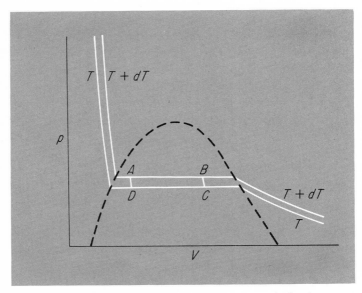

FIG. 8.4. Schematic diagram of a Carnot cycle in the co-existence region.

The work done is $(dp)(n\Delta\tilde{V})$, where $\Delta\tilde{V}$ is the volume change per mole transformed at the temperature T. The heat absorbed along AB is simply $n\Delta\tilde{H}$, where $\Delta\tilde{H}$ is the heat of transition per mole. Hence Eq. (8.25) can be written as

$$\frac{(dp)(n\Delta\tilde{V})}{n\Delta\tilde{H}} = \frac{dT}{T}, \qquad (8.26)$$

or

$$\left(\frac{dp}{dT}\right)_{\text{coex.}} = \frac{\Delta\tilde{H}}{T\,\Delta\tilde{V}}, \qquad (8.27)$$

as before. This derivation does have the advantage of clearly showing the condition for the Clapeyron equation to apply to a system, which is simply that the system have an equation of state with horizontal p–V sections of its isotherms.

Some further remarks about the Clapeyron equation can be made.

(1) The Clapeyron equation is applicable to any system which has an equation of state of the form $p = f(T)$; that is, p is not a function

of volume. It thus applies to pure substances in the coexistence region, and also to solutions which exhibit the same kind of behavior in this region. For example, at one atmosphere pressure ethyl alcohol and water form such a system at a composition of 95.5% by weight of alcohol and 4.5% of water. Such solutions are called azeotropes.

(2) A useful approximation can be made for a liquid-vapor system. Starting with Eq. (8.27), we assume the molar volume of the liquid to be negligible compared to that of the vapor, and that the vapor behaves as an ideal gas, so that

$$\Delta \tilde{V} \approx \frac{RT}{p}.$$

Then

$$\left(\frac{dp}{dT}\right)_{\text{coex.}} \approx \frac{p\,\Delta \tilde{H}}{RT^2},\qquad(8.28)$$

which can be written as

$$\left(\frac{d\ln p}{dT}\right)_{\text{coex.}} \approx \frac{\Delta \tilde{H}}{RT^2},\qquad(8.29a)$$

or

$$\left[\frac{d\ln p}{d(1/T)}\right]_{\text{coex.}} \approx -\frac{\Delta \tilde{H}}{R}.\qquad(8.29b)$$

This last form shows that a plot of $\ln p$ vs. $1/T$ will be nearly a straight line if $\Delta \tilde{H}$ is nearly independent of temperature. If the dependence of $\Delta \tilde{H}$ on T is known, then the above equations can be integrated to obtain an equation which describes the coexistence line. Conversely, if $\Delta \tilde{H}$ is known for one temperature and pressure and the coexistence line has been determined separately, it is possible to calculate $\Delta \tilde{H}$ as a function of temperature.

EFFECT OF EXTERNAL PRESSURE ON VAPOR PRESSURE (POYNTING RELATION)

It has been observed that when a liquid is subjected to a large external pressure, the vapor pressure of the liquid increases. This large external pressure can be exerted on the liquid in practice by the use of an inert gas. Effectively this means that to a first approximation only the liquid phase is experiencing the pressure, whereas the gas phase is not. We can idealize this situation as shown in Fig. 8.5, where two phases are separated by a membrane which is permeable to one phase but not to the other. For the specific case of liquid and vapor, phase 1 in Fig. 8.5 corresponds to liquid and phase 2 to vapor.

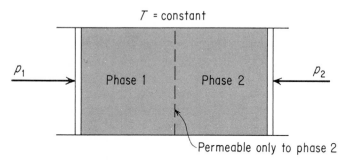

FIG. 8.5. Diagram for the derivation of the Poynting relation.

To find the effect on p_2 of a change dp_1 in the pressure p_1, we make use of the relation derived in the previous section,

$$d\tilde{G}_1 = d\tilde{G}_2.$$

Since $d\tilde{G} = -\tilde{S}dT + \tilde{V}dp$, and T is constant, this relation becomes

$$\tilde{V}_1 dp_1 = \tilde{V}_2 dp_2, \tag{8.30}$$

or

$$\frac{dp_2}{dp_1} = \frac{\tilde{V}_1}{\tilde{V}_2} = \frac{\rho_2}{\rho_1}, \tag{8.31}$$

where ρ is the density. This equation is usually known as the *Poynting relation*.

For the special case of phase 2 a vapor and phase 1 a liquid or solid, Eq. (8.31) can be integrated approximately by assuming that the vapor is an ideal gas and the density of the condensed phase is not affected by pressure. That is, we assume $\tilde{V}_2 = RT/p_2$ and $\tilde{V}_1 = $ constant. From the first assumption we obtain

$$RT d \ln p_2 = \tilde{V}_1 dp_1, \tag{8.32}$$

and integrating under the assumption of constant $\tilde{V}_1$ we find

$$RT \ln \frac{p_2'}{p_2} = \tilde{V}_1 (p_1' - p_1). \tag{8.33}$$

To give a specific interpretation to this result, p_2 could be the normal vapor pressure of the substance at temperature T (in which case $p_1 = p_2$), and p_2' would be the vapor pressure when the condensed phase is subjected to an external pressure p_1'.

SOLUTIONS—NONTHERMODYNAMIC BACKGROUND

Up to now we have considered only pure substances, such as gases, or vapors in equilibrium with their liquids. We now wish to consider some simple mixtures or solutions. It is well known that if some sugar, say, is dissolved in water, the properties of the resulting solution differ in a number of important respects from those of pure water. For instance, the solution boils at a higher temperature and freezes at a lower temperature. If the solution and pure water are separated by a membrane impermeable to sugar but permeable to water, then the pressures on the two liquids must be considerably different for equilibrium to exist. This phenomenon (osmotic pressure) is of great importance in biological processes. We now wish to show how thermodynamics can be used to relate these properties of solutions to other properties, such as the vapor pressure.

To start, then, we must know something about the vapor pressures of mixtures and solutions. This information lies outside of thermodynamics proper, in the same way that an equation of state does. We shall give only the simplest forms of the empirical laws of mixtures and solutions. These simple "laws" are really only idealizations that are approached more or less closely by real substances, just as $pV = nRT$ is an idealization that is approached more or less closely by real gases. From these empirical "laws" we shall then deduce other solution properties by purely thermodynamic methods.

(a) *Gas Mixtures* (*Gibbs-Dalton Law*)

The Gibbs-Dalton "law" is an extension of the ideal gas "law" to mixtures. We shall discuss only mixtures of two gases, inasmuch as the extension to mixtures of many gases is straightforward. Suppose we have a mixture of n_A moles of gas A and n_B moles of gas B. Each gas when pure is described by the ideal gas equation of state, and we wish to know how the mixture behaves. We imagine the mixture to be placed in contact with pure gas A through an ideal membrane which is permeable only to A, and the pressure of pure A is adjusted to a value p_A

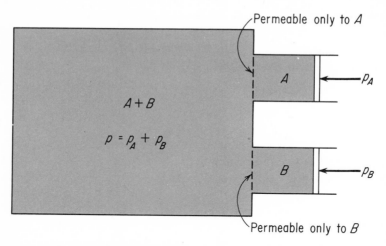

FIG. 8.6. Diagram for discussing the Gibbs-Dalton law.

such that the system is in equilibrium with respect to passage of A through the membrane. The temperature is everywhere the same. A similar arrangement is made for gas B, as shown in Fig. 8.6. The Gibbs-Dalton law can then be stated as follows:

$$p_A = \frac{n_A RT}{V}, \tag{8.34}$$

$$p_B = \frac{n_B RT}{V}, \tag{8.35}$$

$$p = p_A + p_B, \tag{8.36}$$

where p and V are the *total* pressure and volume, respectively, of the *mixture*. From these equations we readily deduce that

$$pV = (n_A + n_B)RT, \tag{8.37}$$

and

$$p_A = \left(\frac{n_A}{n_A + n_B}\right)p, \tag{8.38a}$$

$$p_B = \left(\frac{n_B}{n_A + n_B}\right)p. \tag{8.38b}$$

It is worth mentioning that there is no necessity for the mixture to follow the Gibbs-Dalton law, even though pure A and B individually may follow the ideal gas equation of state. This will be the case, for instance, if A and B react chemically when mixed. The equilibrium concept sketched in Fig. 8.6 holds in any case, however, and the pressure p_A and p_B are called the *partial pressures* of A and B, respectively (even if the mixture does not follow the Gibbs-Dalton law, and even if the pure gases are not ideal).

(b) Liquid Mixtures (Raoult's Law)

Raoult's "law" is an empirical equation relating the vapor pressure of a solution to its composition. Suppose we mix n_A moles of pure liquid A with n_B moles of pure liquid B to form a homogeneous solution. The vapor pressure of pure liquid A at the same temperature as the solution is denoted as p_A°, and that of pure liquid B as p_B°. Then Raoult's law can be written as

$$p_A = \left(\frac{n_A}{n_A + n_B}\right)p_A^\circ \equiv x_A p_A^\circ , \qquad (8.39)$$

$$p_B = \left(\frac{n_B}{n_A + n_B}\right)p_B^\circ \equiv x_B p_B^\circ , \qquad (8.40)$$

where p_A and p_B are the partial pressures of A and B in the vapor. The quantities x_A and x_B are called the *mole fractions* of A and B, and it is

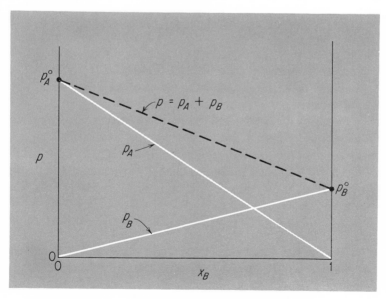

FIG. 8.7. Vapor pressure of a solution following Raoult's law.

apparent from the definition that

$$x_A + x_B = 1. \tag{8.41}$$

These relations are illustrated in Fig. 8.7 for the case where the vapor also obeys the Gibbs-Dalton law.

Some solutions obey Raoult's law fairly well, but many exhibit large deviations. It is found, however, that Raoult's law is a correct limiting law for all solutions as the solution becomes very dilute. Expressed mathematically, $p_A \to x_A p_A^\circ$ as $x_A \to 1$. Thus the relations which we derive thermodynamically from Raoult's law will still hold in the limit of very dilute solutions. Solutions obeying Raoult's law are called *ideal solutions*.

ILLUSTRATIONS INVOLVING SOLUTIONS

The preceding empirical limiting laws plus the first and second laws of thermodynamics lead to a number of consequences, of which we shall present three examples: the elevation of the boiling point, the depression of the freezing point, and the osmotic pressure of an ideal solution.

(a) *Boiling Point Elevation*

The boiling point of a liquid is defined as the temperature at which the vapor pressure is equal to the external pressure (usually 1 atmosphere). Let us consider a case where a non-volatile substance such as sugar is added to a liquid such as water. Since sugar does not exert any vapor pressure, and since by Raoult's law $p_{H_2O} = x_{H_2O} p_{H_2O}^\circ$, the vapor pressure of the water will decrease as sugar is dissolved, and we should expect a change in the boiling point. This is illustrated in Fig. 8.8. We can calculate this increase in boiling point (from T_0 to T in the figure) from Raoult's law and the Clapeyron equation. The change in vapor pressure of the solution with composition and temperature can be written as

$$dp_A = \left(\frac{\partial p_A}{\partial x_A}\right)_T dx_A + \left(\frac{\partial p_A}{\partial T}\right)_{x_A} dT, \tag{8.42}$$

where we have selected A to be the solvent liquid and B to be the non-volatile solute. By Raoult's law and the approximate Clapeyron equation (Eq. (8.28)) this becomes

$$dp_A = p_A^\circ dx_A + \frac{\Delta \tilde{H}_v}{RT^2} p_A dT, \tag{8.43}$$

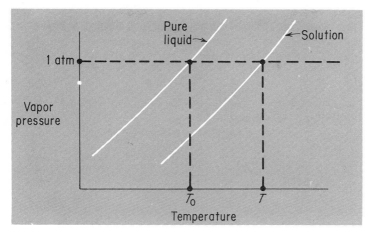

FIG. 8.8. Vapor pressure curves of pure liquid and solution, illustrating the elevation of the boiling point.

where $\Delta \tilde{H}_v$ is the heat of vaporization per mole. Since we want to vary T and x_A in such a way that the total pressure remains unchanged, we obtain

$$p_A^\circ \, dx_A = -\frac{\Delta \tilde{H}_v}{RT^2}\, p_A \, dT = -\frac{\Delta \tilde{H}_v}{RT^2}\, x_A p_A^\circ \, dT,$$

or

$$\frac{dx_A}{x_A} = -\frac{\Delta \tilde{H}_v}{RT^2}\, dT. \tag{8.44}$$

On integration we get

$$-\ln x_A = \frac{\Delta \tilde{H}_v}{R}\left(\frac{1}{T_0} - \frac{1}{T}\right), \tag{8.45}$$

where T_0 is the boiling point of the pure liquid and T the boiling point of the solution. This equation is accurate in general only for dilute solutions.

If $x_A \to 1$, we have a dilute solution with $x_B \ll 1$. Hence $T_0 \approx T$ and $\ln (1 - x_B) \approx -x_B$, so that Eq. (8.45) can be written in the approximate form

$$x_B \approx \frac{\Delta \tilde{H}_v}{R}\frac{\Delta T}{T_0^2}, \tag{8.46}$$

where $\Delta T = T - T_0$ is the boiling point elevation. In dilute solutions

$$x_B = \frac{n_B}{n_A + n_B} \approx \frac{W_B M_A}{W_A M_B},$$

where W_A, W_B, M_A, and M_B are the weights and molecular weights of the solvent A and the solute B. With these definitions Eq. (8.46) becomes

$$\Delta T \approx \frac{RT_0^2}{\Delta \bar{H}_v} \frac{W_B}{W_A M_B} , \qquad (8.47)$$

where $\Delta \bar{H}_v$ is the heat of vaporization per *gram* for the pure liquid. Finally, $W_B / W_A M_B$ is set equal to $m/1000$, where m is the number of moles of solute per 1000 grams of solvent, the so-called *molality*. We have then finally

$$\Delta T \approx \frac{RT_0^2}{\Delta \bar{H}_v} \frac{m}{1000} \equiv K_B m, \qquad (8.48)$$

where K_B is called the molal boiling-point elevation constant. For water $K_B = 0.520$ and for benzene $K_B = 2.67$. The elevation of the boiling point is a useful way to determine the molecular weight of a non-volatile solute, or the heat of vaporization of a solvent.

(b) *Freezing Point Depression*

In the same way that the boiling point of a liquid is elevated by the addition of a non-volatile solute, the freezing point is depressed. This can be understood from Fig. 8.9. Here we have plotted the natural logarithm of the vapor pressure of the pure solid, pure liquid, and solution as a function of the reciprocal of temperature. These should be nearly straight lines according to the approximate form of the Clapeyron equation given by Eq. (8.29b). The vapor pressure line for the solid cuts that for the pure liquid at the point $(1/T_0)$ corresponding to the freezing point of the pure liquid. It also cuts the vapor pressure line for the solution at the point $(1/T)$, corresponding to the new freezing point at which this solution is in equilibrium with pure solid. We assume that when the solution starts to freeze, it is *pure* solvent A which forms the solid phase, and not a solid mixture of both A and B. In other words, the present treatment will not apply to systems which form solid solutions on freezing.

According to Eq. (8.29b) the vapor pressure of the pure solid changes with temperature as follows,

$$\frac{d \ln p_s}{d(1/T)} = - \frac{\Delta \tilde{H}_s}{R}, \qquad (8.49)$$

where $\Delta \tilde{H}_s$ is the heat of sublimation of the solid per mole. The vapor pressure of the liquid solution changes both with temperature and with

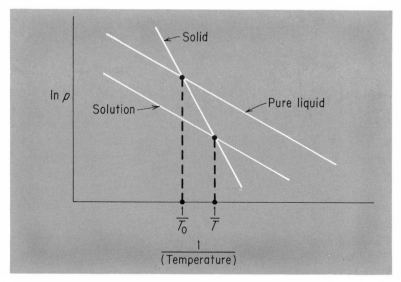

FIG. 8.9. Vapor pressure curves of pure solid, pure liquid, and solution, illustrating the depression of the freezing point.

mole fraction x_A of solvent, so we write

$$d \ln p_l = \left[\frac{\partial \ln p_l}{\partial x_A} \right]_T dx_A + \left[\frac{\partial \ln p_l}{\partial (1/T)} \right]_{x_A} d(1/T),$$

or

$$\frac{d \ln p_l}{d(1/T)} = \left[\frac{\partial \ln p_l}{\partial x_A} \right]_T \left[\frac{dx_A}{d(1/T)} \right] + \left[\frac{\partial \ln p_l}{\partial (1/T)} \right]_{x_A}, \qquad (8.50)$$

which by Raoult's law and the approximate Clapeyron equation becomes

$$\frac{d \ln p_l}{d(1/T)} = \frac{d \ln x_A}{d(1/T)} - \frac{\Delta \tilde{H}_v}{R}. \qquad (8.51)$$

Since the change in vapor pressure of both solid and solution must be equal to maintain equilibrium, we have from Eqs. (8.49) and (8.51),

$$\frac{d \ln x_A}{d(1/T)} - \frac{\Delta \tilde{H}_v}{R} = - \frac{\Delta \tilde{H}_s}{R}. \qquad (8.52)$$

Integrating this differential equation from pure solvent to the composition of the solution, we obtain

$$\int_1^{x_A} d \ln x_A = - \frac{(\Delta \tilde{H}_s - \Delta \tilde{H}_v)}{R} \int_{1/T_0}^{1/T} d(1/T),$$

which integrates to

$$\ln x_A = -\frac{\Delta \tilde{H}_f}{R}\left(\frac{1}{T} - \frac{1}{T_0}\right), \tag{8.53}$$

where $\Delta \tilde{H}_f = \Delta \tilde{H}_s - \Delta \tilde{H}_v$. This equation expresses the new freezing point in terms of the composition. The quantity $\Delta \tilde{H}_f$ is the latent heat of fusion of the solid per mole (why?).

If $x_A \to 1$, the mole fraction x_B of solute is small, so that $\ln x_A \approx -x_B$. The freezing point depression will then also be small, so that $T_0 \approx T$ and Eq. (8.53) can be written in the approximate form

$$x_B \approx \frac{\Delta \tilde{H}_f}{R}\frac{\Delta T}{T_0^2}, \tag{8.54}$$

where $\Delta T = T_0 - T$ is the freezing point depression. Following the same arguments as in the derivation of the boiling point elevation, we arrive at the useful form

$$\Delta T = K_f m, \tag{8.55}$$

where

$$K_f = \frac{RT_0^2}{1000\,\Delta \tilde{H}_f}. \tag{8.56}$$

The quantity K_f is called the molal freezing-point depression constant. It has the value 1.855 for water, 5.12 for benzene, and 40.0 for camphor.

In the above derivation, we have taken $\Delta \tilde{H}_s$ to be equal to $(\Delta \tilde{H}_f + \Delta \tilde{H}_v)$ without proof. We have also taken the vapor pressure of the solid to be equal to that of the solution at equilibrium. The proofs of these facts are left as an exercise.

(c) Osmotic Pressure

If a solution and pure solvent are placed in contact across a membrane permeable to solvent but not to solute, it is found that the hydrostatic pressures on the two phases must be different in order for equilibrium to exist (that is, to prevent solvent from flowing from one phase to the other). The pressure on the solution must be greater than that on the solvent, and the pressure difference is called the osmotic pressure π. We shall now calculate π in terms of the properties of the solvent and solution by means of Raoult's law and the Poynting relation. As with all our calculations for solutions in this chapter, the results will be valid in the limit of dilute solutions.

Ordinarily the solution has a vapor pressure p and the solvent a vapor pressure p_0, but the hydrostatic pressure on the solvent is now imagined to be decreased by an amount π, which is just sufficient to reduce the vapor pressure of the solvent to that of the solution.* (Why is equality of vapor pressures required to insure equilibrium?) From the approximate Poynting relation Eq. (8.33) applied to the solvent, we can write

$$RT \ln \frac{p}{p_0} = -\tilde{V}_0 \pi, \tag{8.57}$$

where $\tilde{V}_0$ is the molar volume of the solvent (assumed constant). By Raoult's law for a non-volatile solute, $p = x_A p_0$, and we can eliminate p between this equation and Eq. (8.57) to obtain a relation between π and the composition,

$$RT \ln x_A = -\tilde{V}_0 \pi. \tag{8.58}$$

As before we write $\ln x_A \approx -x_B$, so that Eq. (8.58) becomes

$$\pi \approx \frac{x_B RT}{\tilde{V}_0}. \tag{8.59}$$

This can be put in a form resembling the ideal gas equation of state by writing $x_B = n_B/(n_A + n_B) \approx n_B/n_A$, and noting that $n_A \tilde{V}_0 = V_0 \approx V$, where V is the volume of the solution which contains n_B moles of solute. Substituting these relations into Eq. (8.59) we then obtain

$$\pi \approx \frac{n_B RT}{V}, \tag{8.60}$$

a result which is strictly valid only for extremely dilute solutions, but which is usually a good approximation for only moderately dilute solutions.

PROBLEMS

1. Prove that for a van der Waals gas,

$$C_p - C_V = nR \left[1 - \left(\frac{2an}{RTV} \right) \left(\frac{V - nb}{V} \right)^2 \right]^{-1}.$$

2. Calculate ηC_V and μC_p for a van der Waals gas in the limit of very low pressures (very large volumes).

* Many authors define a slightly different osmotic pressure π' such that the pressure on the pure solvent is defined to be $p - \pi'$ rather than $p_0 - \pi$. The difference between these two osmotic pressures is obviously $\pi - \pi' = p_0 - p$, which is usually small compared to either π or π'.

3. Calculate ηC_V for a gas obeying the virial equation of state. How does ηC_V behave in the limit of very low pressures, for which the gas is nearly ideal?

4. Find $C_p - C_V$ for a gas obeying the virial equation of state.

5. Find C_V as a function of volume for a gas obeying the virial equation of state.

6. Integrate the approximate Clapeyron equation to find the boiling point of water at a pressure of 2 atm, if the boiling point at 1 atm is 100°C. The enthalpy of vaporization of water is $\Delta \tilde{H}/R = 4891°K$, which is approximately constant.

7. Calculate the vapor pressure of water at 100°C and 10 atm external pressure. The density of water at 100°C and 1 atm is 0.9588 g/cm³.

8. Calculate the vapor pressure of liquid bromine at 20°C under a pressure of 1000 atm of the inert gas argon. The vapor pressure of bromine at 1 atm is 175 torr and its density is 3.12 g/cm³. Bromine exists as Br_2 molecules in the vapor phase. Neglect the solubility of argon in liquid bromine.

9. One mole of liquid mercury (200.6 g) is placed in an evacuated vessel of 20,000 cm³ volume and the temperature raised to the normal boiling point of mercury (630.0°K). At this temperature the vapor pressure of the mercury (1 atm) is too small for all the liquid to evaporate in the fixed volume. However, all the liquid mercury can be made to evaporate by pumping inert gas into the vessel. Calculate the pressure of inert gas required, assuming that all gases and gas mixtures are ideal and that liquid mercury is incompressible and has a density of 12.8 g/cm³.

10. Show that for one of the two phases along a coexistence curve,

$$C_{\text{coex.}} = C_p - T\left(\frac{\partial V}{\partial T}\right)_p \left(\frac{dp}{dT}\right)_{\text{coex.}}.$$

From this show that the heat capacity of a saturated vapor is approximately

$$\tilde{C}_{\text{sat.}} = \tilde{C}_p - \frac{\Delta \tilde{H}}{T}.$$

Describe the process that corresponds to this equation and give a physical interpretation of the results.

11. The temperature at which pure ice is in equilibrium with air-saturated water at 1 atm of air pressure is 0.0100°C lower than the triple point of water, where ice, liquid, and vapor are all in equilibrium at a pressure of 4.6 torr of vapor. How much of this freezing point depression can be attributed to the pressure increase alone? How much must then be attributed to the solubility

of air in the liquid water, assuming all gases and vapors to be ideal? What
then is the molality of the saturated solution of air in water? The densities
of water and ice are 1.000 and 0.917 g/cm³, respectively; the latent heat of
fusion of ice is 333 joule/g; the molal freezing point depression constant for
water is 1.855°C/mole.

12. The sublimation pressure of solid white phosphorus between 0°
and 44°C is reported to be

$$\log_{10} p = -\frac{3297.1}{T} + 9.6511,$$

where p is in torr. Calculate an approximate expression for the vapor pressure
of liquid phosphorus from the following data: the melting point of white
phosphorus is 44.1°C and its latent heat of fusion is 657 joule/g-atomic-
weight; phosphorus vapor consists of P_4 molecules at these temperatures;
the atomic weight of phosphorus is 31.0.

13. The vapor pressure of camphor is as follows:

t, °C	18.9	30.8	55.0	62.0	78.0
p, torr	0.46	1.04	3.12	4.22	6.4

Make a plot of log p against $1/T$ and estimate the latent heat of vaporization
of camphor from its slope.

14. The vapor pressure of solid and liquid iodine is given as follows:

t, °C	20	40	60	80	100	110
p, torr	0.202	1.03	4.31	15.1	45.5	74.9

	114.15 (mp)	120	140	160	180
	90.1	111	217	394	679

Calculate the latent heat of *fusion* of iodine at 114.15°C.

15. When one mole of a non-volatile solute is dissolved in 1000 g of
ethyl alcohol (C_2H_5OH), the boiling point is raised by 1.20°C. The boiling
point of pure alcohol is 78°C. From this information calculate the latent
heat of vaporization of ethyl alcohol.

16. A solution of 4.00 g of sulfur in 100 g of carbon disulfide (molal
boiling point elevation, 2.40°C/mole) is observed to boil 0.381°C higher than
pure carbon disulfide. What is the molecular weight of sulfur in carbon
disulfide solution? How many atoms are there in the sulfur molecule in this
solution?

17. Prove that for two phases in equilibrium the vapor pressures of the
two phases must be equal.

18. How many grams of methyl alcohol (CH_3OH) must be added to 10 kg of water to lower the freezing point of the solution to $-10°C$?

19. Calculate the osmotic pressure at 25°C of a 5.00 weight percent solution of ordinary sugar (sucrose, $C_{12}H_{22}O_{11}$) in water. The density of the solution is 1.017 g/cm³. Find the height of a column of the solution which would just balance the osmotic pressure. What is the freezing point of this solution?

20. Osmotic pressure is sometimes used to estimate the molecular weight of very high molecular weight molecules. One gram of serum albumin dissolved in 1000 cm³ of water gives a solution height of 3.90 mm at 25°C. What is the molecular weight of serum albumin? The density of the solution can be taken as 1.00 g/cm³. What is the freezing point of this solution?

Chapter 9

THERMOCHEMISTRY AND AN INTRODUCTION TO CHEMICAL EQUILIBRIUM

In this chapter we shall consider problems in which chemical reactions and other kinds of transformations can occur. Such transformations usually involve the absorption or evolution of heat and often are studied from this viewpoint alone. Part of the reason for this is that the first law alone is adequate for such a study. The first law enables a connection to be made between the heat quantities of interest and the state functions energy and enthalpy. As was pointed out in Chapter 7, the fact that heat is not a state function makes it a difficult quantity to handle in thermodynamic calculations, and it is a big advantage to be able to operate with state functions instead. The most important and extensive applications of this class of problems, involving heats of reaction and transition, pertain to chemical systems. Hence the whole field is sometimes lumped together under the name of *thermochemistry*.

The use of the second law in discussing such transformations allows one to go much further, and answer questions such as the following. Is it possible for a certain transformation to occur at all under given external conditions? If not, what changes in external conditions are necessary to make the transformations thermodynamically possible? Such questions are really questions about the state of equilibrium of the system. Since an important criterion for equilibrium involves the second law (the entropy criterion discussed in Chapter 6), it is to be expected that a complete discussion of states of equilibrium must involve the second law.

We shall first discuss thermochemistry, which involves only the first law, and then make use of the second law to introduce the basic ideas involved in treating chemical equilibrium, but only treat reactions in ideal gases and ideal solutions. The general treatment of physical and chemical equilibrium in arbitrary systems is best based on the thermodynamics of open systems, which is taken up in Chapters 12 and 13.

THERMOCHEMISTRY

We first take up the calculation of the heat of any reaction from the heats of reaction for a number of simpler or more easily studied reactions. These heats of reaction usually refer to isothermal conditions. A few remarks on their experimental determination are then made. Finally, the effect of temperature on the heat of reaction is discussed.

(a) Heats of Transition and Reaction

Let us take a hypothetical example which will typify a whole class of problems involving heats of transition and reaction. Suppose we want to know the heat effect accompanying the change in state symbolized by the equation

$$aA + bB = cC + dD, \qquad (T, p \text{ constant}), \qquad (9.1)$$

where A, B, C, and D are just general symbols which can be used to represent various substances, and a, b, c, and d are their stoichiometric coefficients. There can be any number of symbols on the left and right sides of the equation; we have written two on each side just for concreteness. Thus Eq. (9.1) might represent a simple physical process like the melting of one mole of ice at 0°C and 1 atm, in which case it would be written

$$H_2O(s) = H_2O(l), \qquad (0°C, 1 \text{ atm}).$$

Note the symbols in parentheses indicating solid, gas, and liquid states. Or Eq. (9.1) might represent a rather complex chemical reaction like the reduction of iron oxide by graphite at 25°C and 1 atm,

$$Fe_2O_3(s) + 3C(\text{graphite}) = 2Fe(s) + 3CO(g), \qquad (25°C, 1 \text{ atm}).$$

Notice that this reaction, although it might be possible, takes place far too slowly at 25°C for any direct heat measurements to be made.

Returning now to the general form of Eq. (9.1), let us suppose that we are unable to carry out the direct transformation of $A + B$ to $C + D$ in such a way as to make an accurate heat measurement. For concreteness, suppose further that we are interested in the transformation as it occurs at constant pressure. In this case, we know that Q_p behaves like a state function, since $Q_p = \Delta H$, and we can therefore devise any roundabout process we please for carrying out the transformation, since H is a state function. Here is one typical roundabout scheme which can be adapted and extended to cover all sorts of complicated situations. Let us add some reactive substance X to the $A + B$ mixture, which then reacts sufficiently rapidly for us to make an accurate heat measurement:

$$aA + bB + xX = yY + zZ, \qquad \Delta H_1. \qquad (9.2)$$

We now do the same for $C + D$, as follows:

$$cC + dD + xX = yY + zZ, \qquad \Delta H_2. \qquad (9.3)$$

We now have to imagine that this last reaction can be somehow reversed, although we do not actually have to carry out such a reverse process. Such a reverse process can always be imagined, although it may involve very bizarre and idealized steps such as extreme temperatures or pressures, frictionless pistons, semipermeable membranes of great selectivity, and so on. None of this matters; all that matters is that it is somehow possible. Then we have

$$yY + zZ = cC + dD + xX, \qquad -\Delta H_2. \qquad (9.4)$$

Notice the changed sign of ΔH_2 between Eqs. (9.3) and (9.4) (why is this?) We now have an alternate path for $aA + bB = cC + dD$, namely Eq. (9.2) followed by Eq. (9.4), which yields

$$aA + bB + xX = cC + dD + xX, \qquad \Delta H = \Delta H_1 - \Delta H_2. \quad (9.5)$$

It is usually true that the simple physical addition of X to $A + B$ or to $C + D$ (allowing no reaction to occur) has a negligible effect, so that we can rewrite Eq. (9.5) without error as

$$aA + bB = cC + dD, \qquad \Delta H = \Delta H_1 - \Delta H_2. \qquad (9.6)$$

Note how the fact that H is a state function has been used to good advantage. If we had been interested in the transformation at constant volume, we would have worked with ΔE instead of with ΔH.

The foregoing may seem a little abstract, so let us take a specific example. The heat of transition of diamond to graphite is of interest, but cannot be measured directly. So instead two measurements are made from which the desired quantity can be calculated. Pure oxygen is added and each is burned to carbon dioxide gas (ending up at the same temperature and pressure). The two heats involved here are relatively easy to measure because the oxidations proceed rapidly. The desired heat quantity is then obtained by subtraction, and the justification for the procedure comes from the fact that we are really dealing with state functions.

The most important thing to remember in dealing with thermo-chemical problems is to write out all changes of state in full. A difficulty sometimes occurs concerning the sign convention for a reaction like that given in Eq. (9.6). According to our previous sign convention for heat, Q is positive if heat flows from the surroundings to the system. So if a reaction evolves heat (i.e., heat flows from the system to the surroundings), Q is negative. Therefore $\Delta E = Q_V$ and $\Delta H = Q_p$ are *negative* numbers when the transition or reaction evolves heat. Unfortunately, there is a widespread tendency to refer to a reaction which evolves heat as having a "positive heat of reaction." So these "heats of transition" and "heats of reaction" have just the reverse sign from that conventionally used in thermodynamics. The safest way around this nuisance is always to work in terms of energy and enthalpy, and practically all modern thermochemical tables are so arranged. It is important to remember that the sign of ΔE or ΔH depends on how the change of state is written: note the difference between Eqs. (9.3) and (9.4).

As illustrated in the foregoing paragraphs, the values of ΔE and ΔH for any reaction can be calculated from the values of ΔE and ΔH for a number of simpler or more accessible reactions. This suggests that it may be worthwhile to prepare tables of ΔE and ΔH for a number of "elementary" reactions, and these can then be used as "building blocks" for constructing ΔE and ΔH for a vast number of complex reactions. In this way a tremendous quantity of thermodynamic information can be compressed into a few relatively small tables. The reactions usually chosen as "elementary" are those for the formation of compounds from their chemical elements in some conventional standard state. Of course such tabulated values do not necessarily represent direct measurements themselves—many will have been calculated from more complicated, but more easily measurable, reactions. The ΔH value for such an "elementary" reaction is usually called the *enthalpy of formation* of the compound, and can be found in published tables.

(b) *Isothermal Heats of Reaction*

A few remarks about the measurement of heats of transition and reaction are in order. For a transition between two phases which takes place at constant pressure and temperature (such as the melting of ice or the evaporation of water), the direct measurement is usually the easiest. A measured quantity of heat, usually produced electrically, is added to the system contained in a calorimeter (to approximate an adiabatic boundary), and the mass of solid melting or of liquid evaporating is measured. Simple division then gives the desired heat of transition per unit mass.

The direct measurement of a heat of reaction is much more difficult, however, especially if the reaction evolves heat. If the reaction absorbs heat, it is possible to add just enough heat electrically to keep the reacting system at constant temperature until the reaction is complete, and then this measured amount of heat is equal to the heat absorbed by the system during the reaction. But if the reaction evolves heat, there is usually no simple way of withdrawing heat to keep the system at constant temperature, and measuring this amount of heat accurately. Consequently the measurement is made in another way, and the desired isothermal heat of reaction is calculated. This calculation provides a nice example of the use of state functions and idealized processes in thermodynamics.

The actual measurement is made by allowing the reaction to take place adiabatically and measuring the resulting temperature change. (Many people would say the temperature rises in such an adiabatic process because heat is evolved. Note that the correct thermodynamic statement is just the opposite: the temperature rises because heat is *not* evolved!) Suppose we start with the reactants at temperature T_1, and that after these react adiabatically the products are found to be at temperature T_2. What is the heat that would have been evolved if we had allowed the reaction to occur at constant temperature?

Two idealized processes can be imagined for producing the same change in state. In the first we allow the reaction to occur at constant temperature T_1 and then heat the products up to T_2. In the second we heat the reactants from T_1 to T_2 and then let the reaction occur at constant temperature T_2. These three paths, one real and two imaginary, can be represented schematically for a constant pressure process as shown in Fig. 9.1. Since H is a state function, we can write

$$\Delta H_1 + \Delta H \text{ (products)} = \Delta H \text{ (adiabatic)} = 0, \qquad (9.7)$$

$$\Delta H \text{ (reactants)} + \Delta H_2 = \Delta H \text{ (adiabatic)} = 0. \qquad (9.8)$$

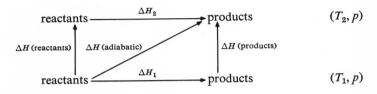

FIG. 9.1. Schematic diagram for the calculation of the iso-thermal heat of reaction from an adiabatic measurement.

Note that ΔH (adiabatic) must be equal to zero (why?). Now ΔH (products) and ΔH (reactants) can be expressed in terms of heat capacities. That is, by integrating $C_p = (\partial H / \partial T)_p$ we obtain

$$\Delta H \text{ (products)} = \int_{T_1}^{T_2} C_p \text{ (products) } dT, \qquad (9.9)$$

$$\Delta H \text{ (reactants)} = \int_{T_1}^{T_2} C_p \text{ (reactants) } dT. \qquad (9.10)$$

Substitution of Eq. (9.9) into Eq. (9.7), and of Eq. (9.10) into Eq. (9.8), yields

$$\Delta H_1 = -\int_{T_1}^{T_2} C_p \text{ (products) } dT, \qquad (9.11)$$

$$\Delta H_2 = -\int_{T_1}^{T_2} C_p \text{ (reactants) } dT. \qquad (9.12)$$

Thus T_1 and T_2 are measured, and ΔH_1 and ΔH_2 can then be calculated when the heat capacities are known. These heat capacities are often already available, but if not it is often not too difficult to measure them in the same calorimeter, if a heater is put into the calorimeter.

For reactions at constant volume instead of at constant pressure, the appropriate quantities are ΔE and C_V instead of ΔH and C_p.

(c) *Effect of Temperature on Heats of Reaction*

As a final example we shall consider how the heat of reaction at one temperature can be calculated from that at another temperature. We use exactly the same procedure as in the preceding example, and indeed the same schematic diagram of Fig. 9.1 can be used. Now, however, we know ΔH_1 at T_1 and wish to calculate ΔH_2 at some other temperature T_2 (not necessarily the temperature reached by carrying out the reaction adiabatically). Let us define

$$\Delta C_p \equiv C_p \text{ (products)} - C_p \text{ (reactants).} \tag{9.13}$$

Then by combining Eqs. (9.11) and (9.12) we easily obtain

$$\Delta H_2 = \Delta H_1 + \int_{T_1}^{T_2} \Delta C_p \, dT. \tag{9.14}$$

One word of caution is necessary in the use of Eqs. (9.11), (9.12), and (9.14). They are not perfectly general unless the reactants are in the same state of aggregation (gas, liquid, crystalline form) at T_2 as at T_1, and similarly for the products. The reason is that the expressions of Eqs. (9.9) and (9.10) do not allow for any phase transitions between T_1 and T_2, and an extra term must be added if such a transition occurs. The extra term is perfectly straightforward; for instance, Eq. (9.10) would become, for one transition of a reactant occurring at a temperature T',

$$\Delta H \text{ (reactants)} = \int_{T_1}^{T'} C_p \text{ (reactants) } dT + \Delta H \text{ (transition at } T')$$

$$+ \int_{T'}^{T_2} C_p' \text{ (reactants) } dT, \tag{9.15}$$

where the heat capacity is C_p at temperatures below T', and is C_p' at temperatures above T'. The rest of the argument then proceeds exactly as before.

(d) *Remarks on Thermochemistry*

We remarked at the beginning of this chapter that the second law was not involved in thermochemistry, and perusal of what has been done in the discussion so far shows that we have not used the second law at all. A careful perusal will further show that we have used very little of the first law. In fact, the only things we have used were the general properties of state functions and the definitions of heat capacities.

Because only general properties of state functions are involved, we can therefore extend the results so far obtained to include all the other state functions. In particular, tables can be set up to give values of ΔS, ΔA, and ΔG for a number of standard "elementary" reactions, just as they can be set up to give values of ΔE and ΔH. Such tables are particularly important for ΔA and ΔG, since these functions are the key ones used in calculations of physical and chemical equilibria, as we shall show in the next section.

The discussion of the effect of temperature on heats of reaction can also be applied to the other state functions with very little modification. For instance, if we know ΔS_1 at T_1 and the heat capacities of the reactants and products, we can calculate ΔS_2 at T_2, just as we did for ΔH. Exactly the same arguments apply, but we integrate $C_p = T(\partial S/\partial T)_p$ instead of $C_p = (\partial H/\partial T)_p$, and obtain

$$\Delta S_2 = \Delta S_1 + \int_{T_1}^{T_2} \Delta C_p \, d\ln T, \qquad (9.16)$$

which applies when no phase transitions occur between T_1 and T_2. The modification necessary when phase transitions occur should now be obvious.

CHEMICAL EQUILIBRIUM

The thermodynamic functions which describe the equilibrium of systems under the common practical conditions of constant temperature and volume, or of constant temperature and pressure, are A and G, respectively. They play very roughly the role for thermodynamic systems that the potential energy does for mechanical systems, and are sometimes called *free energy* or *thermodynamic potential*. The scientific literature is sometimes a little confused on this point, and it is not always obvious whether "free energy" refers to A or to G, especially since the letter F is often used for either one. (Physicists often call A the free energy and denote it by F; physical chemists often call G the free energy and denote it by F.)

Since systems are more frequently studied at constant pressure than at constant volume, we shall deal with G only, but the discussion goes over almost unchanged for constant volume systems if G is replaced by A. We shall first prove some general properties of G for equilibrium changes in state, and then specialize to ideal gases and ideal solutions to obtain more detailed results. This specialization is of wider use than might be anticipated, since it is often convenient to cast results for real systems into the same mathematical form as for ideal systems.

(a) *"Free Energy" Changes at Equilibrium*

To avoid awkward phrases and circumlocutions, for the remainder of this chapter we shall often call G the "free energy." Suppose that various amounts of a number of substances are placed together in a container at constant temperature and pressure, and that one or more chemical reactions are possible among these substances. The basic question to be investigated in this section is what are the relative amounts of these substances that exist together in equilibrium at a given temperature and pressure, and how can this information be related to other measurable properties such as heat capacities and heats of reaction. Since T and p are the independent variables, G is the obvious thermodynamic function with which to attempt a description of the system. For the whole system, the differential equation for G is, from Chapter 7,

$$dG = -SdT + Vdp.$$

Now suppose the reactions are made to proceed in one direction or the other, keeping T and p constant. This might be done by changing the volume. For example, if the system is a partially dissociated gas, then an increase or decrease in volume will cause more or less of the gas to be dissociated, T and p remaining constant. Since $dT = 0$ and $dp = 0$ for all such changes, we immediately obtain

$$\Delta G = 0 \qquad (p, T \text{ constant}). \tag{9.17}$$

A similar result holds for the Helmholtz function A if the process is carried out at constant T and V, but it is T and p that are usually the experimentally convenient independent variables.

In Eq. (9.17) we have the means of calculating the behavior of a chemically reacting mixture at equilibrium, provided we have some independent source of information on G. We have already seen how such information can be systematized and condensed into a table for any state function, provided we once agree on a choice of standard reactions and standard states. This is sufficiently important for calculations of chemical equilibrium to be worth a few additional remarks.

(b) Standard "Free Energy" Changes

The usual choice of a standard reaction is the formation of a compound from its chemical elements, with both products and reactants being in conventionally chosen standard states. Tables of such *standard free energies of formation* are available from a number of sources, such as the U.S. National Bureau of Standards and the American Petroleum Institute. For concreteness, let us consider a reaction between $A + B$ to produce $C + D$, as given in Eq. (9.1) of this chapter. If the standard state is denoted by a superscript symbol (°), then we can write

$$aA(p_A^\circ, T) + bB(p_B^\circ, T) = cC(p_C^\circ, T) + dD(p_D^\circ, T). \qquad (9.18)$$

This equation does *not* mean that A, B, C, and D are in equilibrium at temperature T and partial pressures p_A°, p_B°, p_C°, and p_D°. What it means is that we have taken a moles of substance A at p_A° and T and b moles of substance B at p_B° and T, and caused them (somehow) to react completely to form c moles of substance C at p_C° and T and d moles of substance D at p_D° and T. For this change in state we can write

$$\Delta G^\circ = c\tilde{G}_C^\circ + d\tilde{G}_D^\circ - a\tilde{G}_A^\circ - b\tilde{G}_B^\circ, \qquad (9.19)$$

where $\tilde{G}_A^\circ$, $\tilde{G}_B^\circ$, etc. are the standard free energies of formation per mole. If we adopt the convention that the stoichiometric coefficients a, b, c, d are to be taken as positive for products and negative for reactants, Eq. (9.19) can be written concisely and completely generally as

$$\Delta G^\circ = \sum_i \nu_i \tilde{G}_i^\circ, \qquad (9.20)$$

where ν_i is the stoichiometric coefficient for substance i.

Notice that since the p_i° have fixed numerical values by convention and the ν_i are fixed by the stoichiometry of the reaction, ΔG° *is a function of temperature alone*. This standard free energy change ΔG° will not in general be zero, unless the standard conditions happen to be the equilibrium conditions of the reaction. For the present we shall postpone the question of how tables of $\tilde{G}_i^\circ$ are obtained in practice, and merely assume that such tables are available.

(c) Equilibrium Constants for Ideal Gas and Ideal Solution Reactions

Consider the general gas reaction,

$$aA(p_A, T) + bB(p_B, T) = cC(p_C, T) + dD(p_D, T), \qquad (9.21)$$

where p_A, p_B, p_C, and p_D are arbitrary. Just as we wrote Eqs. (9.18)–(9.20), we can now write

$$\Delta G = \sum_i \nu_i \tilde{G}_i. \qquad (9.22)$$

But we can express $\tilde{G}_i$ in terms of $\tilde{G}_i^\circ$ and the equation of state:

$$\tilde{G}_i - \tilde{G}_i^\circ = \int_{p_i^\circ}^{p_1} \tilde{V}_i \, dp, \qquad \text{constant } T. \qquad (9.23)$$

So far the discussion has been general, but we now specialize to ideal gases in order to carry out the integration in Eq. (9.23), which becomes

$$\tilde{G}_i - \tilde{G}_i^\circ = RT \ln \frac{p_i}{p_i^\circ}. \qquad (9.24)$$

Substituting this into Eq. (9.22) we obtain

$$\Delta G = \sum_i \nu_i \tilde{G}_i^\circ + RT \sum_i \nu_i \ln \frac{p_i}{p_i^\circ},$$

which can be written as

$$\Delta G - \Delta G^\circ = RT \sum_i \nu_i \ln p_i - RT \sum_i \nu_i \ln p_i^\circ. \qquad (9.25)$$

This equation is our recipe for calculating ΔG for an arbitrary reaction at constant temperature. It is valid only for ideal gases. Since the choice of the p_i° is purely conventional, it is sensible to make a simplifying choice, and the usual one is to make all the p_i° equal to 1. That is, if pressure is to be measured in atmospheres, we choose the standard states all to be 1 atmosphere. This choice makes the last term in Eq. (9.25) go to zero.

The most interesting special case of Eq. (9.25) is that in which the p_i are the equilibrium pressures, $p_{\text{eq},i}$. By equilibrium pressure we mean the pressure of pure gas in equilibrium with the reaction mixture through a membrane permeable to that gas only. That is, we have in mind the same arrangement as used in discussing the Gibbs-Dalton law in Chapter 8, but now the gas mixture can undergo chemical reactions. But at equilibrium $\Delta G = 0$, so that we obtain the important relation

$$\Delta G^\circ = -RT \sum_i \ln (p_{\text{eq},i})^{\nu_i}. \qquad (9.26)$$

This is usually written in the form

$$\Delta G^\circ = -RT \ln K_p, \qquad (9.27)$$

where K_p is the *equilibrium constant*. The subscript p simply means that pressure units are being used. The definition of K_p is obviously

$$\ln K_p = \sum_i \ln (p_{\text{eq},i})^{\nu_i} \quad \text{or} \quad K_p = \prod_i (p_{\text{eq},i})^{\nu_i}. \qquad (9.28)$$

For the particular reaction $A + B = C + D$, this would be

$$K_p = \frac{(p_{\text{eq},C})^c (p_{\text{eq},D})^d}{(p_{\text{eq},A})^a (p_{\text{eq},B})^b}. \tag{9.29}$$

From Eq. (9.27) we see that K_p must be a function of temperature alone, since ΔG° is. However, ΔG° is a function of temperature alone in general, whereas K_p is a function of temperature alone only for ideal gases. What this means is that if we compress an equilibrium mixture at constant temperature, some reaction will take place and all the $p_{\text{eq},i}$ will change values to keep K_p constant (unless $c + d = a + b$, in which case no reaction occurs). Similarly, if an additional amount of one of the components is introduced into the mixture, reaction occurs so that K_p remains constant.

For real gases K_p depends on the total pressure and composition as well as on the temperature, but in many cases this dependence is weak and it is a good first approximation to consider K_p to be practically a constant at a fixed temperature. An enormous amount of chemical information is systematized in this way.

It is sometimes convenient to use other forms of the equilibrium constant which are equivalent to the one given above. If one or more of the reactants or products is a condensed phase (liquid or solid), its partial pressure is determined by the vapor pressure of the condensed phase, and hence is a constant at a given temperature. This constant vapor pressure is usually incorporated into K_p. For example, for the reaction

$$C(s) + H_2O(g) = H_2(g) + CO(g), \tag{9.30}$$

the equilibrium constant is written

$$K_p = \frac{p_{H_2} p_{CO}}{p_{H_2O}}. \tag{9.31}$$

From a practical point of view, this procedure eliminates the necessity of knowing a vapor pressure which will cancel out of any equilibrium calculations anyway.

There is no reason, other than possible convenience, to use pressure units for equilibrium constants. Mole fraction units are often used. Since $p_i = p x_i$, we can rewrite Eq. (9.29) as

$$K_p = \frac{x_C^c x_D^d}{x_A^a x_B^b} p^{c+d-a-b}, \tag{9.32}$$

or

$$K_p = K_x p^{\Delta n}, \tag{9.33}$$

where $\Delta n = c + d - a - b$ is the change in the number of moles on reaction. Equation (9.33) is a general relation for any reaction, with $\Delta n = \Sigma \nu_i$ and an obvious definition of K_x. Notice that K_x depends on pressure as well as on temperature, unless $\Delta n = 0$.

Equilibrium constants can also be written in terms of concentrations (moles/cm³). Since $c_i \equiv n_i/V$, we have $p_i = c_i RT$ for ideal gases, and the expression for K_p can be written

$$K_p = \frac{c_C^c c_D^d}{c_A^a c_B^b} (RT)^{\Delta n}, \tag{9.34}$$

or for a general reaction,

$$K_p = K_c(RT)^{\Delta n}, \tag{9.35}$$

with an obvious definition of K_c. Notice that K_c depends only on T.

Very similar results hold for ideal solutions of liquids, except that it is usually more convenient to use K_c or K_x than to use K_p. We can in fact take over all the results so far obtained for ideal gas mixtures and apply them to ideal solutions, by the simple trick of devising an alternative reversible process for carrying out the chemical reaction in solution. This alternate reversible process should involve the vapor, in order to bring in the results for gas mixtures. Consider the solution reaction

$$aA(x_A) + bB(x_B) = cC(x_C) + dD(x_D), \tag{9.36}$$

where x_A, x_B, x_C, and x_D are the mole fractions in solution. We now carry out this reaction by first vaporizing reversibly a moles of A and b moles of B from the solution at constant T and p. For this step $\Delta G = 0$ (why?). The reaction is then carried out in the gas phase, and the resulting c moles of C and d moles of D are reversibly condensed back into the solution. Since $\Delta G = 0$ for the condensation, we see that the total ΔG for the reaction is the same whether the reaction took place directly in the solution or indirectly through the gas phase. The whole process can be represented schematically as follows:

$$aA(p_A) + bB(p_B) \xrightarrow{\Delta G} cC(p_C) + dD(p_D) \qquad \text{vapor}$$

$$\Delta G = 0 \Big\uparrow \qquad\qquad\qquad \Big\downarrow \Delta G = 0$$

$$aA(x_A) + bB(x_B) \xrightarrow{\Delta G} cC(x_C) + dD(x_D) \qquad \text{liquid}$$

The previous expression for K_p therefore applies, which by Raoult's law can be written

$$K_p = \frac{(x_C)^c (x_D)^d}{(x_A)^a (x_B)^b} \frac{(p_C^\circ)^c (p_D^\circ)^d}{(p_A^\circ)^a (p_B^\circ)^b}, \tag{9.37}$$

where p_A°, p_B°, p_C°, and p_D° are the vapor pressures of the pure liquids A, B, C, and D, respectively. Since these depend only on temperature and total pressure (weakly through the Poynting relation), we have

$$K_x = \frac{(x_C)^c(x_D)^d}{(x_A)^a(x_B)^b}, \qquad (9.38)$$

which is primarily a function of temperature but is weakly dependent on the external pressure. A similar result holds for K_c. Notice that the x_i in Eq. (9.38) refer to the mole fractions in the liquid solution. Although a K_x could be written for the vapor phase which would look like Eq. (9.38), the mole fractions in that expression would refer to the vapor phase, and would not be equal to the mole fractions in the liquid.

In some practical applications dealing with both a gas and a liquid solution, it is convenient to use equilibrium constants in mixed units (e.g., both pressure and concentration units). Examples will be found in the section dealing with electrochemical cells in the next chapter.

(d) *Properties of Equilibrium Constants*

Equilibrium constants are so widely used in physico-chemical calculations that it is worth setting out some of their important properties here.

(1) *Combinatorial Behavior of Equilibrium Constants.* Since G is a state function, ΔG° for two reactions combines additively, just as do the heats of reaction discussed earlier in this chapter. But K_p is related to ΔG° logarithmically, and so K_p for two reactions combines multiplicatively. As an example, let us consider the same case used to illustrate the additivity of heats of reaction. Suppose we wish to know the equilibrium constant K (in any units) for the reaction

$$aA + bB = cC + dD, \qquad K = ?. \qquad (9.39)$$

For some reason we are unable to make a direct measurement, but we can measure the equilibrium constants for the following two reactions:

$$aA + bB + xX = yY + zZ, \qquad K_1, \qquad (9.40)$$

$$yY + zZ = cC + dD + xX, \qquad K_2. \qquad (9.41)$$

If we write out the expressions for K_1 and K_2 and multiply them together, we obtain

$$K_1K_2 = K. \qquad (9.42)$$

This is really just a concise mathematical statement about alternate paths always giving the same final result as far as state functions are concerned.

(2) *Effect of Temperature on Equilibrium Constants.* We first calculate the effect of temperature on G. From the fundamental equation, $dG = -S\,dT + V\,dp$, we find

$$\left(\frac{\partial G}{\partial T}\right)_p = -S. \tag{9.43}$$

Now we write this equation for both the products and reactants separately, and subtract these two equations to give

$$\left(\frac{\partial \Delta G}{\partial T}\right)_p = -\Delta S. \tag{9.44}$$

Here ΔG and ΔS refer to *any* change in state whatever. If we restrict ourselves to isothermal changes in state, that is, ones in which products and reactants are at the same temperature, then we can substitute for ΔS from the expression $\Delta G = \Delta H - T\Delta S$, obtaining

$$\left(\frac{\partial \Delta G}{\partial T}\right)_p = \frac{\Delta G - \Delta H}{T}. \tag{9.45}$$

This important relation is sometimes called the Gibbs-Helmholtz equation. It can be written more compactly as

$$\left[\frac{\partial(\Delta G/T)}{\partial T}\right]_p = -\frac{\Delta H}{T^2}. \tag{9.46}$$

If we apply this equation to the products and reactants in their standard states and use Eq. (9.27), which is $\Delta G° = -RT \ln K_p$, we obtain the desired final result

$$\left(\frac{\partial \ln K_p}{\partial T}\right)_p = \frac{\Delta H°}{RT^2}. \tag{9.47}$$

Notice that Eq. (9.46) is thermodynamically exact but Eq. (9.47) is only approximate, because the relation used for K_p is approximate.

Equation (9.47) shows that the variation of K_p with temperature is determined by $\Delta H°$, the standard heat of reaction. Thus if K_p is known at one temperature, and $\Delta H°$ is also known, then K_p can be predicted at any other temperature. Or, if K_p is known at two or more temperatures, the value of $\Delta H°$ can be calculated. This is actually a fairly

common method of determining heats of reaction (or transition) which
would be hard to measure directly. If we write Eq. (9.47) in the form

$$\left[\frac{\partial \ln K_p}{\partial(1/T)}\right]_p = -\frac{\Delta H^\circ}{R},\qquad(9.48)$$

we see that a plot of $\ln K_p$ vs. $1/T$ should be nearly a straight line whose
slope is $-\Delta H^\circ/R$.

Notice that Eqs. (9.47) and (9.48) apply to physical as well as
chemical equilibria. For instance, a common application is the determination of the heat of solution of a salt in water from measurements of
its solubility as a function of temperature. That this can be done with
the aid of Eq. (9.47) or (9.48) follows from the fact that a measurement
of solubility is a measurement of the equilibrium between solid salt and
solution. Notice also the similarity of Eq. (9.47) to the approximate
Clapeyron equation given back in Eq. (8.29), which was

$$\left(\frac{d \ln p}{dT}\right)_{\text{coex.}} = \frac{\Delta \tilde{H}}{RT^2}.$$

It is left as an entertainment for the reader to show that the similarity
is not accidental.

(3) *Equilibrium Constants from Thermal Data.* We now return to
the problem mentioned previously, but postponed; how can tables of
$\tilde{G}_i^\circ$ be obtained in practice? One of the best ways is from thermal data,
that is heat capacities and heats of transition, together with equation of
state data. At constant pressure we can determine the enthalpy and
entropy of a substance from heat capacity measurements, by integration
of the following equations:

$$H - H_0 = \int_{T_0}^{T} C_p \, dT + \sum_{\text{transitions}} \Delta H,\qquad(9.49)$$

$$S - S_0 = \int_{T_0}^{T} C_p \, d \ln T + \sum_{\text{transitions}} (\Delta H/T),\qquad(9.50)$$

where H_0 and S_0 are the enthalpy and the entropy at the reference
temperature T_0. They are, in effect, constants of integration. The value
of T_0 is often chosen to be $0^\circ K$. From these equations and the definition $G = H - TS$, we obtain

$$G - G_0 = (H - H_0) - T(S - S_0) - (T - T_0)S_0,\qquad(9.51)$$

where G_0 is the "free energy" at T_0. Since only the differences $(H - H_0)$
and $(S - S_0)$ are experimentally measurable, it would appear that the

last term in Eq. (9.51), which involves S_0 by itself, might cause some difficulty. Suppose we ignore this problem for the moment and just specialize to the standard state, so we can make up a table of $(G° - G_0°)$ for a large number of chemical substances. Then to calculate the equilibrium constant for any chemical reaction we just add up all the $(G° - G_0°)$ with the proper stoichiometric coefficients; that is we form

$$\Delta(G° - G_0°) = \sum_i \nu_i (\tilde{G}° - \tilde{G}_0°)_i. \tag{9.52}$$

But we are still left with an unknown quantity $\Delta G_0°$, since it is $\Delta G°$ that we need and we have calculated only

$$\Delta(G° - G_0°) = \Delta G° - \Delta G_0°. \tag{9.53}$$

The problem is how to find $\Delta G_0°$. This *cannot* be obtained from thermal data and the first and second laws alone; some direct equilibrium measurements must be made. Notice that $\Delta G_0°$ really involves two unknown constants, $\Delta H_0°$ and $\Delta S_0°$, as is obvious from the definition of G or from Eq. (9.51). In principle, any two extra measurements will do, because then we could solve for the two unknowns. Furthermore, $\Delta H_0°$ could be found from direct thermal measurements because it is just the heat of reaction at T_0.

This means that we cannot obtain standard free energies and hence equilibrium constants from thermal data alone, because we would require an equilibrium measurement to obtain $\Delta S_0°$. This is as far as the first and second laws can take us. Evaluation of $\Delta S_0°$ without having to measure it for every case of interest requires a new generalization of physical facts. It happens that such a generalization exists in the form of the Nernst Heat Postulate or Third Law of Thermodynamics which will be discussed in Chapter 14. In essence, it states that there are a large number of cases for which we can take $\Delta S_0° = 0$.

If we happen to be interested in the value of $(G - G_0)$ at some different pressure than the standard one, we can find it at any given temperature by integration of the equation of state, since $dG = V dp$ at constant temperature.

All of the foregoing systematics amounts to nothing more physical than the following: if ΔG is known at one temperature and pressure, we can calculate it at any other temperature and pressure by integration, given only the heat capacity and equation of state. The systematics just make it feasible to compile a set of numerical tables of manageable size, or in other words make possible a rather compact summary of a vast body of experimental data.

REMARKS

In this chapter we have tried to outline the basic procedures used in thermochemistry and to give a brief introduction to the systematic treatment of chemical equilibrium. It should be emphasized that we have introduced no new physical facts whatever, thermodynamic or otherwise; all we have done is to apply what had been set forth in earlier chapters. Furthermore, we have restricted the discussion to very simple systems, so that the equilibrium constants that have been derived are valid only for ideal gases and solutions, even though the general methods could have been applied to any systems. But the general treatment of chemical equilibrium is handled much more concisely and conveniently by the methods of Gibbs for open systems. After the Gibbsian approach to thermodynamics has been discussed in detail, we shall be able to give a general treatment of chemical equilibrium which will include the expressions of the present chapter as special cases.

PROBLEMS

In this chapter the energy unit used is often the calorie (cal) or the kilocalorie (kcal) rather than the joule, simply because most published tables are still given in such units. By definition, one thermochemical calorie is equal to exactly 4.1840 joule, and 1 kcal $= 10^3$ cal.

1. The enthalpies of formation of $H_2O(g)$ and $HCl(g)$ at 298.15°K and 1 atm pressure are -57.80 kcal/mole and -22.06 kcal/mole, respectively. Calculate the enthalpy change for the following reaction at 298.15°K and 1 atm pressure:

$$4HCl(g) + O_2(g) = 2Cl_2(g) + 2H_2O(g).$$

2. At 25°C the enthalpy change for the reaction

$$H_2SO_4 + 5H_2O = H_2SO_4 \cdot 5H_2O \qquad \text{(all liquids)}$$

is -13.87 kcal. Calculate the temperature change if 1 mole of H_2SO_4 is dropped into 5 moles of H_2O at 25°C. Assume no heat loss to the surroundings and that the specific heat of the solution is 1.00 cal/g-°C.

3. Given the following information:

$$1\ H_2SO_4 + \quad 1\ H_2O = 1\ H_2SO_4 \cdot \quad 1\ H_2O \qquad \Delta H = -\ 6.71 \text{ kcal at } 25°C,$$

$$1\ H_2SO_4 + 25\ H_2O = 1\ H_2SO_4 \cdot 25\ H_2O \qquad \Delta H = -17.28 \text{ kcal at } 25°C.$$

Calculate the enthalpy change at 25°C for the following dilution:

$$1 \ H_2SO_4 \cdot 1 \ H_2O + 24 \ H_2O = 1 \ H_2SO_4 \cdot 25 \ H_2O.$$

Calculate the temperature rise for this dilution if there is no heat loss to the surroundings. Assume the specific heat of the more dilute solution to be 1.00 cal/g-°C.

4. 10.000 moles of water and 0.100 mole of salt are kept separate in a calorimeter and the temperature adjusted to 20.00°C. Then the salt is dissolved in the water and the temperature change measured. The heat capacity of the calorimeter is found in a separate experiment to be 5.2 cal/°C.

(a) When NaCl is the salt, the temperature falls to 19.36°C, and the specific heat of the resulting solution is 0.97 cal/g-°C. Calculate ΔH of solution at 20.00°C.

(b) When KCl is the salt, the temperature falls to 17.71°C, and the specific heat of the resulting solution is 0.947 cal/g-°C. Calculate ΔH of solution at 20.00°C.

(c) The specific heat of solid NaCl is 0.21 cal/g-°C, of solid KCl is 0.163 cal/g-°C, and of water is 1.000 cal/g-°C. Calculate the enthalpies of solution of NaCl and KCl at 19.36°C and 17.71°C, respectively.

5. Copper sulfate occurs in anhydrous form, $CuSO_4$, and in a form involving water of crystallization in the lattice, $CuSO_4 \cdot 5 \ H_2O$. To find the heat of hydration of $CuSO_4$, the following experiments were performed. 40 moles of water and 0.100 moles of $CuSO_4$ were brought to 20.00°C and then mixed in a calorimeter. The temperature rose to 22.15°C. Then 39.5 moles of water and 0.100 mole of $CuSO_4 \cdot 5 \ H_2O$ were brought to 20.00°C and mixed in the calorimeter. The temperature fell to 19.63°C. Calculate ΔH for the reaction (20°C),

$$CuSO_4 + 5 \ H_2O = CuSO_4 \cdot 5 \ H_2O.$$

In a separate experiment, the heat capacity of the calorimeter was found to be 18.6 cal/°C and the specific heat of the $CuSO_4$ solution to be 0.975 cal/g-°C.

6. (a) Calculate how much the enthalpies of solution of NaCl and of KCl change for each 10°C increase or decrease of temperature. Use the data from problem 4, and assume all specific heats are independent of temperature. Pay careful attention to signs.

(b) Calculate how much ΔH for the reaction in problem 5 changes for each 10°C increase or decrease of temperature. The specific heat of $CuSO_4$ is 0.16, of $CuSO_4 \cdot 5 \ H_2O$ is 0.28, and of H_2O is 1.000 cal/g-°C.

7. Calculate the enthalpy change for the following reaction:

$$Hg(l) + I_2(g) = HgI_2(l), \qquad \Delta H = ?, \qquad 600°K, \ 1 \ atm,$$

given the enthalpy change for the reaction

$$Hg(l) + I_2(s) = HgI_2(\alpha), \quad \Delta H = -25.2 \text{ kcal, } 298°K, 1 \text{ atm,}$$

and the following thermal data:

$Hg(l)$: $\tilde{C}_p = 6.61$ cal/mole-°K
$I_2(s)$: $\tilde{C}_p = 9.59 + 11.90 \times 10^{-3}T$ cal/mole-°K
$\quad \Delta\tilde{H}$(fusion) $= 3.77$ kcal/mole at 386.8°K
$I_2(l)$: $\tilde{C}_p = 19.20$ cal/mole-°K
$\quad \Delta\tilde{H}$(vaporization) $= 9.97$ kcal/mole at 456°K
$I_2(g)$: $\tilde{C}_p = 8.89$ cal/mole-°K
$HgI_2(\alpha)$: $\tilde{C}_p = 18.50$ cal/mole-°K
$\quad \alpha\text{-}\beta$ transition, $\Delta\tilde{H} = 650$ cal/mole at 403°K
$HgI_2(\beta)$: $\tilde{C}_p = 20.20$ cal/mole-°K
$\quad \Delta\tilde{H}$(fusion) $= 4.50$ kcal/mole at 523°K
$HgI_2(l)$: $\tilde{C}_p = 25.00$ cal/mole-°K.

8. Calculate the entropy change for the following reaction:

$$Hg(l) + I_2(g) = HgI_2(l), \quad \Delta S = ?, \quad 600°K, 1 \text{ atm,}$$

given the entropy change for the reaction

$$Hg(l) + I_2(s) = HgI_2(\alpha) \quad \Delta S = -3.5 \text{ cal/°K, } 298°K, 1 \text{ atm,}$$

and the thermal data of problem 7.

9. Carbon dioxide dissolves in water to form the weak acid H_2CO_3, carbonic acid, which ionizes slightly according to the two-step process,

$$H_2CO_3 = H^+ + HCO_3^-, \quad K_c = 4.31 \times 10^{-7} \text{ mole/lit,}$$
$$HCO_3^- = H^+ + CO_3^{--}, \quad K_c = 5.6 \times 10^{-11} \text{ mole/lit.}$$

(a) Calculate the equilibrium constant for the double ionization reaction,

$$H_2CO_3 = 2 H^+ + CO_3^{--}, \quad K_c = ?.$$

Pay attention to the units of K_c.

(b) If 0.01 mole of carbon dioxide is dissolved in 1 liter of water, calculate the concentration of hydrogen ion (H^+), of bicarbonate ion (HCO_3^-), and of carbonate ion (CO_3^{--}) at equilibrium.

10. At 10,000°K, the equilibrium constants for the dissociation and ionization of oxygen are reported to be

$$O_2 = 2 O, \quad \ln K_p(\text{atm}) = 10.32,$$
$$O = O^+ + e^-, \quad \ln K_p(\text{atm}) = -7.81.$$

Calculate K_p for the following reaction:

$$O_2 = 2 O^+ + 2 e^-, \quad K_p = ?.$$

Pay attention to the units of K_p for this reaction.

11. The equilibrium constant for the reaction

$$N_2 + O_2 = 2\,NO$$

is 2.07×10^{-3} at 2500°K. What is the mole percent of NO (nitric oxide) present at equilibrium in air at 2500°K? How does this result depend on total pressure? Take air to be originally 20 mole percent O_2 and 80 mole percent N_2.

12. The equilibrium constant for the reaction

$$H_2 = 2\,H$$

is $K_p = 3.10 \times 10^{-6}$ atm at 2000°K. Taking 100 percent H_2 as the basis, calculate what fraction is dissociated at 2000°K if the pressure is 1 atm, and if the pressure is 0.01 atm. At what pressure is half the original H_2 dissociated?

13. At 25°C the solubility of I_2 in water is 1.32×10^{-3} mole/lit, while the solubility in 0.10 molar KI solution is 4.9×10^{-2} mole/lit. Calculate the equilibrium constant for the reaction in solution,

$$I_2 + I^- = I_3^-.$$

14. Estimate the equilibrium constant at 3000°K for the hydrogen dissociation reaction of problem 12. The standard enthalpy change for the reaction in this temperature range is approximately $\Delta H°/R = 58.10 \times 10^3$°K.

Chapter 10

SYSTEMS INVOLVING NEW VARIABLES; SURFACE EFFECTS, RADIATION, MAGNETISM, ELECTROCHEMICAL CELLS

All of the systems so far discussed have required only the mechanical variables pressure and volume in the description of their states. It is not necessary for the discussion to be limited to such systems, and in this chapter we shall discuss several systems which require different variables for their description. As in the preceding three chapters, no new thermodynamics is introduced in this chapter, only applications to new kinds of systems. Since these systems are new, we must begin by giving their macroscopic or phenomenological description; the principles of thermodynamics will then require that certain relationships must exist among the variables of the systems. Thus a substantial fraction of this chapter has nothing to do with thermodynamics as such, but consists of the macroscopic descriptions of systems, which we must have as a starting point for a thermodynamic discussion.

The change in the statement of the first and second laws needed to encompass new kinds of systems is very simple and straightforward. It consists only in including other kinds of terms besides pdV in the work term dW. In some cases the contributions from these other terms completely overshadow the contribution from the pdV term which has been our only concern so far.

The procedure in this chapter will therefore be, first to give the new work term and the nonthermodynamic description of the system, second to incorporate the new work term into the statement of the first and second laws, and third to deduce a few illustrative thermodynamic consequences by the usual analytical methods.

SURFACE EFFECTS

The surface of a liquid behaves in many respects as if it were an elastic membrane in a state of tension, so that the surface tends to contract to the smallest possible area.

(a) *Nonthermodynamic Description*

We begin by making the idealization that a system in which surface effects are important can be decomposed into a surface part and a bulk part. In other words, we treat the surface as if it really were a skin surrounding the system, and discuss the skin as a separate system. This is a very good approximation for many real systems of interest. The work required to increase the area of a surface film by an amount $d\mathscr{A}$ is

$$dW = -\sigma d\mathscr{A}, \tag{10.1}$$

where σ is the surface tension of the film (force per unit length). Notice the minus sign which was not present in $dW = pdV$; this occurs because the surface tension of a film acts in the opposite direction from the pressure of a gas. The sign is such that if the surface area is increased, work disappears from the surroundings. The process described by the above work term may or may not be reversible. It is reversible only if the deformation of the film occurs without hysteresis; that is, if the deformation is elastic and not plastic, so that σ and $\mathscr{A}$ are uniquely related at constant temperature.

To complete the description, we now need the analogue of an equation of state—a relation among σ, $\mathscr{A}$, and T. The first part of this description is that σ is a constant independent of $\mathscr{A}$ at a fixed temperature. The second part is an empirical relation giving σ as a function of T. One such relation which has been found to describe many liquid surfaces with reasonable accuracy is the Eötvös* equation,

$$\sigma \tilde{V}^{2/3} = k(T_c - T), \tag{10.2}$$

---

* Eötvös was a Hungarian baron, better known among physicists for his accurate experiments to test the equivalence of gravitational and inertial mass.

where $\tilde{V}$ is the molar volume of the liquid, T_c is the critical temperature, and k is an empirical constant which must be found experimentally. The molar volume depends somewhat on temperature and slightly on the pressure on the bulk liquid. The Eötvös equation predicts a decrease in surface tension with increasing temperature, until the surface tension (and the surface itself!) disappears at the critical temperature.

(b) Thermodynamic Consequences

Since we are neglecting the volume of the surface film in our description, we have only two of the usual four equations for the combined statement of the first and second laws:

$$dE = TdS + \sigma d\mathscr{A}, \tag{10.3}$$

$$dA = -SdT + \sigma d\mathscr{A}.* \tag{10.4}$$

From these we see that we can write

$$\sigma = \left(\frac{\partial E}{\partial \mathscr{A}}\right)_S = \left(\frac{\partial A}{\partial \mathscr{A}}\right)_T, \tag{10.5}$$

so that σ can also be thought of as the change in the Helmholtz function per unit change in surface area at constant temperature.

From Eqs. (10.3) and (10.4) we can write down relations analogous to the Maxwell relations:

$$\left(\frac{\partial T}{\partial \mathscr{A}}\right)_S = \left(\frac{\partial \sigma}{\partial S}\right)_{\mathscr{A}}, \tag{10.6}$$

$$\left(\frac{\partial S}{\partial \mathscr{A}}\right)_T = -\left(\frac{\partial \sigma}{\partial T}\right)_{\mathscr{A}}. \tag{10.7}$$

We can now carry out a number of calculations analogous to those performed in Chapters 7 and 8. We shall give only a few such calculations for purposes of illustration.

---

* It is possible to make the same kind of transformations previously used, thus

$$d(E - \mathscr{A}\sigma) = TdS - \mathscr{A}d\sigma,$$

$$d(A - \mathscr{A}\sigma) = -SdT - \mathscr{A}d\sigma.$$

Exactly such a transformation will be made in the discussion of magnetism in this chapter.

(1) *Calculation of Entropy Changes.* It is interesting to ask how the entropy of a film changes when its area is changed. This can be calculated from Eq. (10.7) if σ is known as a function of T. Applying Eq. (10.7) to the Eötvös equation and neglecting the small temperature dependence of $\tilde{V}$, we find

$$\left(\frac{\partial S}{\partial \mathscr{A}}\right)_T = -\left(\frac{\partial \sigma}{\partial T}\right)_{\mathscr{A}} \approx \frac{k}{\tilde{V}^{2/3}} = \frac{\sigma}{T_c - T}. \tag{10.8}$$

For an increase in surface area from $\mathscr{A}_1$ to $\mathscr{A}_2$, the entropy increase is

$$S_2 - S_1 = \frac{\sigma}{T_c - T}(\mathscr{A}_2 - \mathscr{A}_1). \tag{10.9}$$

(2) *Calculation of Temperature Changes.* Other calculations analogous to those carried out for fluids in Chapters 7 and 8 can be made for surfaces. For instance, we can ask what temperature change occurs when the area of a surface film is changed adiabatically and reversibly (i.e., at constant entropy). Clearly the independent variables are T and $\mathscr{A}$, so we write

$$dS = \left(\frac{\partial S}{\partial T}\right)_{\mathscr{A}} dT + \left(\frac{\partial S}{\partial \mathscr{A}}\right)_T d\mathscr{A} = 0, \tag{10.10}$$

from which we obtain

$$\left(\frac{\partial T}{\partial \mathscr{A}}\right)_S = -\frac{\left(\frac{\partial S}{\partial \mathscr{A}}\right)_T}{\left(\frac{\partial S}{\partial T}\right)_{\mathscr{A}}}. \tag{10.11}$$

The heat capacity of the film is

$$C_{\mathscr{A}} = T\left(\frac{\partial S}{\partial T}\right)_{\mathscr{A}}, \tag{10.12}$$

which together with the Maxwell-like relation of Eq. (10.7) gives the desired answer:

$$\left(\frac{\partial T}{\partial \mathscr{A}}\right)_S = \frac{T}{C_{\mathscr{A}}}\left(\frac{\partial \sigma}{\partial T}\right)_{\mathscr{A}}. \tag{10.13}$$

This result is exact. Since $C_{\mathscr{A}}$ is positive and $(\partial\sigma/\partial T)_{\mathscr{A}}$ is negative, an adiabatic increase in surface area results in a decrease in the film temperature. If we obtain $(\partial\sigma/\partial T)_{\mathscr{A}}$ from an approximate empirical relation like Eq. (10.8) obtained by differentiating the Eötvös equation, we get an explicit (but approximate) expression for the temperature change:

$$\left(\frac{\partial T}{\partial \mathscr{A}}\right)_S \approx -\frac{\sigma T}{C_{\mathscr{A}}(T_c - T)}. \tag{10.14}$$

(3) *Surface Energy.* The energy E of a surface can be quite easily calculated by using the Helmholtz function A, since Eq. (10.5) showed that the surface tension is essentially the Helmholtz function per unit area. In fact, if we assume that σ is strictly independent of surface area, we can integrate Eq. (10.5) at constant T to obtain

$$A - A_0 = \sigma \mathscr{A}, \tag{10.15}$$

where A_0 is the constant of integration (actually a function of temperature). Since $S = -(\partial A / \partial T)_{\mathscr{A}}$ and $E = A + TS$, we find the entropy and energy of the surface to be

$$S - S_0 = -\left(\frac{\partial \sigma}{\partial T}\right)_{\mathscr{A}} \mathscr{A}, \tag{10.16}$$

$$E - E_0 = \left[\sigma - T\left(\frac{\partial \sigma}{\partial T}\right)_{\mathscr{A}}\right] \mathscr{A}, \tag{10.17}$$

where S_0 and E_0 are functions of T. We recognize Eq. (10.16) to be merely an integrated form of the second Maxwell-like relation given in Eq. (10.7), as it should be. Using the Eötvös equation and neglecting the small temperature dependence of $\tilde{V}$, we find the surface energy per unit area to be approximately

$$\frac{E - E_0}{\mathscr{A}} \approx \frac{kT_c}{\tilde{V}^{2/3}}, \tag{10.18}$$

which is almost independent of temperature.

(4) *Vapor Pressure of Small Droplets.* As a final example we shall consider the effect of surface tension on the vapor pressure of a liquid droplet. It turns out that the vapor pressure is appreciably increased if the droplet diameter is made small enough, so the result is of considerable interest in cloud physics and meteorology. The physical basis for the calculation is that the surface acts like a tight skin permeable to vapor but not to liquid, so that the liquid inside the droplet is at a slightly higher pressure than the surrounding vapor with which it is in equilibrium. We first calculate the excess pressure on the liquid and then use the Poynting relation obtained in Chapter 8 to find the effect on the vapor pressure.

The calculation of the excess pressure on the liquid, Δp, involves only mechanical reasoning and has no thermodynamic content. Using the principle of virtual work, we ask how much work is done in increasing the volume of a spherical drop by dV. We equate this to

$\sigma d\mathscr{A}$, where $d\mathscr{A}$ is the area increase accompanying the volume increase dV. The work done is equal to dV times the pressure difference, so

$$(\Delta p)dV = \sigma d\mathscr{A}. \qquad (10.19)$$

For a droplet of radius r, we have $V = \tfrac{4}{3}\pi r^3$ and $\mathscr{A} = 4\pi r^2$, so that $dV = 4\pi r^2\, dr$ and $d\mathscr{A} = 8\pi r\, dr$. Inserting these geometric relations into Eq. (10.19), we find

$$\Delta p = 2\sigma/r. \qquad (10.20)$$

(For a bubble we would have $\Delta p = 4\sigma/r$, since there are two surfaces!)

For thermodynamic equilibrium between the liquid and the surrounding vapor we must have (see the derivation of the Poynting relation in Chapter 8)

$$\tilde{V}_1 dp_1 = \tilde{V}_2 dp_2, \qquad (10.21)$$

where the subscript 1 refers to the liquid and the subscript 2 to the vapor. We now integrate Eq. (10.21) between two limiting cases: the liquid is in one big lump ($r = \infty$) and the vapor pressure is p_0; the liquid is hydrostatically compressed to $p_0 + \Delta p$, and the vapor pressure becomes p. Carrying out the integration and using Eq. (10.20) for Δp, we obtain

$$\int_{p_0}^{p_0+(2\sigma/r)} \tilde{V}_1 dp_1 = \int_{p_0}^{p} \tilde{V}_2 dp_2. \qquad (10.22)$$

We cannot go further unless we know the equation of state of the liquid and the vapor, so as to carry out the integrations explicitly. If we make the simplifying assumptions of incompressible liquid and ideal vapor, we can integrate Eq. (10.22) to obtain

$$\tilde{V}_1(2\sigma/r) = RT \ln (p/p_0), \qquad (10.23)$$

where $\tilde{V}_1$ is the molar volume of the liquid. From this result we see that the vapor pressure increases as the drop size decreases. An assembly of different sized droplets could not be in equilibrium with the same vapor phase; the larger droplets would increase in size at the expense of the smaller ones.

RADIATION

Radiation will be described by the usual mechanical variables of p and V, just like a fluid. The only reason for including it in this chapter on special systems is that it has a rather peculiar equation of state, and does not obey a conservation law as does ordinary matter (i.e., radiation can be created and destroyed). A thermodynamic discussion of radiation obviously requires that the radiation be in equilibrium. This means that the radiation must be enclosed in some sort of opaque container, and that it must be in equilibrium with the container walls, which are at some constant temperature. Such radiation is called *cavity radiation* or *black-body radiation*, and is the only kind we shall discuss. The radiation can be sampled by a small hole in the container wall; the hole must be large enough to permit a true sample to be withdrawn, but small enough not to perturb the radiation equilibrium appreciably.

The radiation coming from the small sampling hole has an energy flux (joules/cm²-sec) which depends only on the temperature of the cavity, and not at all on its volume, shape, or material of construction. This can be proved by an argument based directly on the second law. Suppose two cavities A and B are placed in communication by connecting their two sampling holes with a tube having perfectly reflecting inner walls. If A and B are at the same temperature, the amount of energy flowing from A to B must be exactly the same as that flowing from B to A. If this were not so, we could change the temperature of one cavity by an amount dT and have energy flowing from a lower to a higher temperature without any changes occurring in the surroundings. This is contrary to the second law, and so the energy flows must be exactly equal.

This equality must hold individually for every frequency as well as for the overall radiation at all frequencies. If filters which pass only one frequency were placed between the two cavities, the argument would be valid as before. Thus the frequency distribution of cavity radiation (that is, the relative energy per unit interval of frequency) must depend only on the temperature, and is independent of the volume, shape, or materials of construction of the cavity walls.

(a) *Nonthermodynamic Description*

To carry the discussion any further with thermodynamic arguments, we must now have some raw material in the form of extra-thermodynamic facts about cavity radiation. The choice of which facts to select as a starting-point is somewhat a matter of taste; we shall choose a relation between radiation pressure and radiation energy density, which is the energy per unit volume. It was long suspected that light exerts a pressure when it impinges on an object, but it was not until the development of the electromagnetic theory of light by Maxwell that a satisfactory theoretical basis was given. Maxwell showed that the pressure exerted by a *parallel* beam of light is equal to the energy density (energy per unit volume) of the light. For isotropic radiation the pressure exerted on the walls of the cavity containing the radiation is only 1/3 the pressure exerted by a parallel beam. We can thus summarize the necessary facts about radiation as follows:

$$e(T) = \frac{E}{V},\qquad(10.24)$$

$$p = \tfrac{1}{3}e,\qquad(10.25)$$

where the radiation density $e(T)$ depends only on the temperature of the cavity.

(b) Thermodynamic Consequences

The results given by Eqs. (10.24) and (10.25) are all we need to start a thermodynamic discussion. From this we shall derive the dependence of p and e on temperature (Stefan-Boltzmann law), and the behavior of cavity radiation on isothermal and adiabatic expansion.

(1) *Stefan-Boltzmann Law.* There are a number of ways of carrying out the derivation, all of which are of course equivalent. We shall start with the usual statement of the first and second laws,

$$dE = TdS - pdV,$$

substitute for E and p from Eqs. (10.24) and (10.25), solve for dS, and use cross-differentiation. From Eq. (10.24) we have

$$dE = edV + Vde,\qquad(10.26)$$

which, when substituted back together with $p = \tfrac{1}{3}e$, yields

$$dS = \frac{4}{3}\frac{e}{T}dV + \frac{V}{T}de.\qquad(10.27)$$

Since dS is an exact differential, cross-differentiation yields

$$\frac{4}{3}\left[\frac{\partial(e/T)}{\partial e}\right]_V = \left[\frac{\partial(V/T)}{\partial V}\right]_e.\qquad(10.28)$$

Since constant e is the same as constant T, we can carry out the differentiations and obtain

$$\frac{4}{3}\left(\frac{1}{T}\right) - \frac{4e}{3T^2}\left(\frac{dT}{de}\right) = \frac{1}{T}$$

or

$$\frac{de}{e} = 4\left(\frac{dT}{T}\right), \tag{10.29}$$

which integrates to

$$e = aT^4, \tag{10.30}$$

where a is a constant of integration. Since $p = \frac{1}{3}e$, the radiation pressure depends on the fourth power of the temperature. This is a rather significant result to have obtained with radiation pressure as a starting-point, which illustrates the power of thermodynamics. The limitations of thermodynamics are also illustrated by this result, for the constant a is completely undetermined, and cannot be determined by any further thermodynamic contortions, no matter how elaborate.

(2) *Isothermal Expansion.* It is interesting to inquire as to how much heat is required to maintain a constant temperature in the cavity if the volume of the cavity with its equilibrium radiation is reversibly increased. Noting that $dQ = TdS$, we go back to Eq. (10.27) and substitute $e = aT^4$ into it, obtaining

$$dQ = TdS = \left(\frac{4}{3}\right)aT^4dV + 4VaT^3dT. \tag{10.31}$$

For an isothermal process the last term vanishes and we can easily integrate to obtain

$$Q = \left(\frac{4}{3}\right)aT^4\,\Delta V, \qquad \text{constant } T. \tag{10.32}$$

Radiation behaves like an ideal photon gas; we might therefore be tempted to apply the known results for the isothermal expansion of an ordinary ideal gas, writing

$$dQ = TdS = dE + pdV = pdV,$$

from which we obtain $Q = \frac{1}{3}aT^4\Delta V$, on substituting in the radiation pressure and the Stefan-Boltzmann law. Why is there a discrepancy of a factor of 4? Simply because photons are not conserved; the number of photons increases proportionally to the volume on isothermal expansion of cavity radiation.

A closer analogy with real fluids is furnished by a vaporizing liquid. If we consider the system to be only the vapor phase and put the liquid outside the boundary, then when the volume is increased, more vapor is created from the liquid and passes into the system. When the volume of cavity radiation is increased, new radiation "evaporates" from the walls of the cavity. The heat required to maintain the walls at constant temperature is given by Eq. (10.32). We might thus expect that Eq. (10.32) has a certain analogy to the Clapeyron equation derived in Chapter 8. Looking back at the derivation, we find that the Clapeyron equation applies to any system whose equation of state is of the form $p = f(T)$; the analogy of cavity radiation with a vapor-liquid equilibrium is therefore fundamental and not dependent on any model. We could in fact have derived Eq. (10.32) more quickly by noting that the Clapeyron equation applies to cavity radiation and writing

$$Q_p = \Delta H = (T \, \Delta V) \left(\frac{dp}{dT}\right). \tag{10.33}$$

Taking $p = \frac{1}{3}aT^4$ and differentiating, we immediately obtain Eq. (10.32).

(3) *Adiabatic Expansion.* To carry out an adiabatic expansion of cavity radiation we imagine that the walls of the cavity are very thin so that they have essentially zero heat capacity. We then proceed as usual to write an expression for the entropy change dS on changing the volume and temperature, equate dS to zero, and solve the resulting differential equation. Equation (10.31) is already such an expression, so we set $dS = 0$ and obtain

$$\frac{dV}{V} = -\frac{3dT}{T}. \tag{10.34}$$

This integrates to

$$VT^3 = \text{constant}, \tag{10.35}$$

which should be compared with the corresponding result for an ideal gas, Eq. (7.93). Equation (10.35) means, for example, that an eightfold increase in the volume of the cavity decreases the equilibrium temperature by a factor of two.

Thermodynamic discussion of the expansion of cavity radiation is sometimes useful in problems of stellar dynamics and thermonuclear explosions.

MAGNETISM

The important variables in a thermodynamic discussion of magnetic materials are the temperature, the external magnetic field $\mathcal{H}$, and the magnetization of the material, or the magnetic moment of the whole system, $\mathcal{M}$. We shall discuss only solid magnetic materials, which can be considered incompressible for all the applications treated. Pressure and volume therefore do not need to be considered as variables. If we wished to discuss a phenomenon such as magnetostriction, or a magnetic gas such as O_2, NO, or NO_2, then such an approximation should not be made, and pressure and volume should be included.

(a) Nonthermodynamic Description

The work required to increase the magnetization of a magnetic material by an amount $d\mathcal{M}$ in the presence of a uniform external magnetic field $\mathcal{H}$ is

$$dW = -\mathcal{H}\,d\mathcal{M}. \tag{10.36}$$

The sign is such that if the magnetization is increased, work disappears from the surroundings. Except for the sign, $\mathcal{H}$ is clearly analogous to p, and $\mathcal{M}$ analogous to V in a simple fluid. Equation (10.36) is true in general only for isotropic materials; anisotropic materials introduce nothing new in principle, but do complicate the algebra considerably.

To complete the description, we now need a magnetic equation of state—a relation among $\mathcal{H}$, $\mathcal{M}$, and T. This, as always, comes from outside thermodynamics. Magnetic materials are usually classified into three groups, according to their behavior in a magnetic field:

(1) Diamagnetic—$\mathcal{M}$ is in the opposite direction from $\mathcal{H}$.
(2) Paramagnetic—$\mathcal{M}$ is in the same direction as $\mathcal{H}$, but is only moderately large. Salts of the rare earth metals are paramagnetic, as are the gases O_2 and NO.
(3) Ferromagnetic—a kind of exaggerated paramagnetism in which $\mathcal{M}$ is very large. Ferromagnetic materials also exhibit the phenomenon of permanent magnetism, whereby they remain magnetized in the absence of a magnetic field. Iron and nickel are ferromagnetic.

We shall consider only paramagnetic and ferromagnetic materials, and shall consider only one simple equation of state for each.

For paramagnetic substances, Paul Langevin developed a statistical-mechanical theory which yields the following equation of state:

$$\frac{\mathcal{M}}{\mathcal{M}_0} = L(y), \tag{10.37}$$

$$y = \frac{\mu \mathcal{H}}{kT}, \tag{10.38}$$

where μ is the magnetic moment per atom (of the order of 10^{-20} cgs
units), k is Boltzmann's constant (1.3805×10^{-16} erg/°K), and $L(y)$
is a special function called the Langevin function. In macroscopic
units, Eq. (10.38) would be written as

$$y = \frac{\mathcal{M}_0 \mathcal{H}}{nRT}, \tag{10.39}$$

where R is the gas constant and n is the number of moles of magnetic
atoms present in the material. The Langevin function is defined as

$$L(y) = \coth y - \frac{1}{y},$$

$$= \frac{e^y + e^{-y}}{e^y - e^{-y}} - \frac{1}{y}. \tag{10.40}$$

This function approaches unity for large y, and for small y is practically
a straight line, being well approximated by the expression

$$L(y) = \frac{y}{3} - \frac{y^3}{45} + \cdots. \tag{10.41}$$

A sketch of $L(y)$ is shown in Fig. 10.1. This can be seen by Eq. (10.37)
to be equivalent, except for numerical scale factors, to a plot of $\mathcal{M}$
vs. $\mathcal{H}$ or of $\mathcal{M}$ vs. $1/T$. This also shows that the physical interpretation
of the constant $\mathcal{M}_0$ is that it is the saturation magnetic moment of the
material; i.e., the limiting magnetic moment at very high fields or very
low temperatures.

If we insert typical numerical values of μ or $\mathcal{M}_0$, we find that
below room temperature very high magnetic fields are needed to get
off the initial linear portion of the Langevin curve. In this linear region
$\mathcal{M}$ is proportional to $\mathcal{H}$. The ratio $\mathcal{M}/\mathcal{H}$ is known as the magnetic
susceptibility; at low temperatures the susceptibility is thus given by
the limiting expression coming from the first term of Eq. (10.41),

$$\chi \equiv \frac{\mathcal{M}}{\mathcal{H}} = \frac{\mathcal{M}_0^2}{3nRT}. \tag{10.42}$$

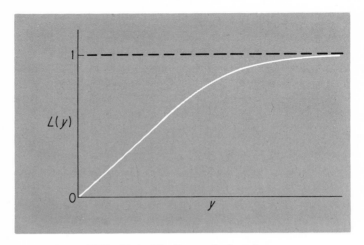

FIG. 10.1. The Langevin function.

The fact that χ is inversely proportional to T for paramagnetic substances was originally discovered experimentally by Pierre Curie, and is known as Curie's law. It is the basis of many temperature measurements at very low temperatures, where gas thermometry is impossible.

For ferromagnetic materials, Pierre Weiss proposed a modification of the Langevin theory which stated that Eq. (10.37) could still be used for $\mathscr{M}$, provided that an effective field $\mathscr{H}_{\text{eff}}$ replaced the external field $\mathscr{H}$. The effective field consists of the external field plus an internal field which is directly proportional to the magnetization of the material. Thus an initial magnetization of the material tends to magnetize it further; this is a simple model of a so-called cooperative effect. The Weiss magnetic equation of state can be written as

$$\frac{\mathscr{M}}{\mathscr{M}_0} = L\left(\frac{\mathscr{M}_0 \mathscr{H}_{\text{eff}}}{nRT}\right), \qquad (10.43a)$$

$$\mathscr{H}_{\text{eff}} = \mathscr{H} + v\mathscr{M}, \qquad (10.43b)$$

where v is a constant (different for different materials) which measures the tendency of the magnetization to magnetize the material further. We would have an explicit equation of state relating $\mathscr{M}$, $\mathscr{H}$, and T if we could eliminate $\mathscr{H}_{\text{eff}}$ between these two equations. Unfortunately, this is difficult to do analytically because of the complicated behavior of the Langevin function, but a graphical solution is easy to carry out. To condense the notation, we define

$$y \equiv \frac{\mathcal{M}_0 \mathcal{H}_{\text{eff}}}{nRT} ,$$ (10.44)

$$\Theta \equiv \frac{\nu \mathcal{M}_0^2}{3nR} ,$$ (10.45)

and rearrange Eqs. (10.43) as follows:

$$\frac{\mathcal{M}}{\mathcal{M}_0} = L(y),$$ (10.46a)

$$\frac{\mathcal{M}}{\mathcal{M}_0} = -\frac{\mathcal{H}}{\nu \mathcal{M}_0} + \frac{T}{3\Theta} y .$$ (10.46b)

We now plot these two equations for $\mathcal{M}/\mathcal{M}_0$ as a function of y; the solution is given by the point of intersection of the two curves. The intersection point will be different for each different initial choice of $\mathcal{H}$ and T, so that $\mathcal{M}/\mathcal{M}_0$ can be found as a function of $\mathcal{H}$ and T by choosing a series of initial values of $\mathcal{H}$ and T and solving Eqs. (10.46) graphically for $\mathcal{M}/\mathcal{M}_0$.

The graphical solution is illustrated in Fig. 10.2. Equation (10.46a) is the Langevin function shown in Fig. 10.1, and Eq. (10.46b) is just a

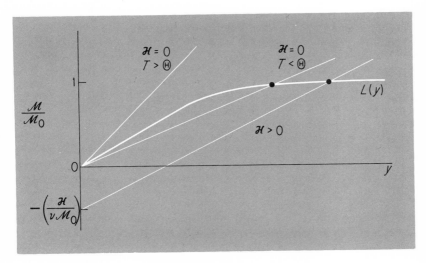

FIG. 10.2. Graphical determination of the Weiss magnetic equation of state.

straight line of slope $(T/3\Theta)$ and intercept $-(\mathscr{H}/\nu\mathscr{M}_0)$. From the figure it can be seen that the two curves always intersect if $\mathscr{H} > 0$, but if $\mathscr{H} = 0$ so that the straight line goes through the origin, then the two curves may or may not intersect depending on the slope of the straight line. There is a critical temperature below which they intersect, so that magnetization occurs even if $\mathscr{H} = 0$; there is thus spontaneous magnetization. This critical temperature is such that the slope of the straight line is the same as the initial slope of $L(y)$; referring back to Eq. (10.41) or Eq. (10.42) to find this initial slope, we find the critical temperature to be $T = \Theta$. This temperature is called the Curie temperature. Below the Curie temperature the two curves intersect at large values of $\mathscr{M}/\mathscr{M}_0$ even in zero external field; the material is almost completely magnetized. Above the Curie temperature the intersection occurs at small values of $\mathscr{M}/\mathscr{M}_0$ even for large $\mathscr{H}$; only slight magnetization can be achieved without the application of extremely high fields.

The foregoing graphical considerations show how we can obtain explicit expressions for the magnetic equation of state in certain interesting limiting cases. In the first place, the magnetization is small for $T > \Theta$, so we can use the expansion of $L(y)$ given by Eq. (10.41), and Eq. (10.46a) then becomes

$$\frac{\mathscr{M}}{\mathscr{M}_0} = \frac{y}{3} + \cdots.$$

This can be combined with Eq. (10.46b) to obtain an explicit relation between $\mathscr{M}$, $\mathscr{H}$, and T, by eliminating y. The result is

$$\chi \equiv \frac{\mathscr{M}}{\mathscr{H}} = \frac{C}{T - \Theta}, \qquad \text{for } T > \Theta, \qquad (10.47a)$$

where

$$C = \frac{\Theta}{\nu} = \frac{\mathscr{M}_0^2}{3nR}. \qquad (10.47b)$$

This relation is known as the Curie-Weiss law; it looks just like Curie's law for paramagnetic substances with T replaced by $(T - \Theta)$. This result also shows that Θ and ν can be determined experimentally by measuring χ as a function of T above the Curie temperature. A plot of $1/\chi$ vs. T should give a straight line whose slope and intercept (extrapolated, of course) give Θ and ν.

In the second limiting case, we see that for $T < \Theta$ the material is almost completely magnetized even for very weak magnetic fields. Even for $\mathscr{H} = 0$ the material is spontaneously magnetized. A plot of the spontaneous magnetization $\mathscr{M}_{sp}$ (i.e., $\mathscr{M}$ at $\mathscr{H} = 0$) is shown schematically in Fig. 10.3. A mathematical expression for the whole curve is complicated, but the important feature is that the curve comes in to the abscissa with a vertical tangent, and we can obtain an expression for this part of the curve without difficulty. It is determined by

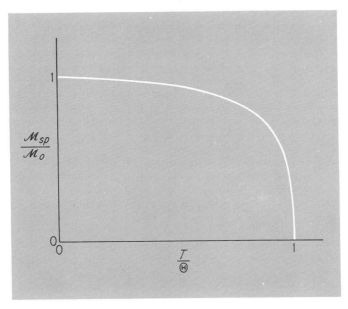

FIG. 10.3. Schematic diagram of the temperature dependence of the spontaneous magnetization of a ferromagnetic material.

the initial bending over of $L(y)$ away from its linear portion, so we need the first two terms of Eq. (10.41) for $L(y)$. Thus Eqs. (10.46a) and (10.46b) become

$$\frac{\mathscr{M}_{sp}}{\mathscr{M}_0} = \frac{y}{3} - \frac{y^3}{45} + \cdots, \tag{10.48a}$$

$$\frac{\mathscr{M}_{sp}}{\mathscr{M}_0} = \frac{T}{3\Theta} y. \tag{10.48b}$$

Eliminating y by substitution from the second equation into the first, we obtain

$$\frac{\mathscr{M}_{sp}}{\mathscr{M}_0} = \left(\frac{\Theta}{T}\right)\left(\frac{\mathscr{M}_{sp}}{\mathscr{M}_0}\right) - \frac{3}{5}\left(\frac{\Theta}{T}\right)^3\left(\frac{\mathscr{M}_{sp}}{\mathscr{M}_0}\right)^3 + \cdots,$$

or

$$\left(\frac{\mathcal{M}_{\mathrm{sp}}}{\mathcal{M}_0}\right)^2 = \frac{5}{3}\left(\frac{T}{\Theta}\right)^3\left(\frac{\Theta}{T} - 1\right) = \frac{5}{3}\left(\frac{T}{\Theta}\right)^2\left(1 - \frac{T}{\Theta}\right). \qquad (10.49)$$

This equation can only be true for T near Θ, since we have kept only the first two terms of $L(y)$. We therefore make no important error by setting $(T/\Theta)^2 \approx 1$ to obtain

$$\frac{\mathcal{M}_{\mathrm{sp}}}{\mathcal{M}_0} = \left[\frac{5}{3}\left(1 - \frac{T}{\Theta}\right)\right]^{\frac{1}{2}}, \qquad T \lesssim \Theta. \qquad (10.50)$$

This is the equation of the curve of Fig. 10.3 around its vertical portion. It is easily verified that the tangent for Eq. (10.50) is vertical at $T = \Theta$.

Weiss' theory of ferromagnetic materials is apparently marred by the experimental fact that most such materials do not always show spontaneous magnetization below the Curie temperature. To account for this, Weiss proposed the idea of magnetic domains. In each domain the material is spontaneously magnetized in one direction, but the different domains are oriented in different directions so that the bulk specimen has almost no net magnetization. The domain structure of ferromagnetic materials was subsequently directly observed by clever techniques of microscopic surface examination of specimens. The spontaneous magnetization at a given temperature can be brought into evidence by applying a strong magnetic field to align the different domains in one direction.

This completes the rather lengthy disussion of the magnetic equation of state. In theoretical pedigree and agreement with experiment, the Langevin equation is roughly analogous to the ideal gas equation, and the Weiss equation analogous to the van der Waals equation for real gases. As usual, none of this matters so far as any thermodynamic discussion is concerned, and we now proceed to such a discussion.

(b) Thermodynamic Consequences

Since we are neglecting any volume change of the magnetic material, we have only two of the usual four equations for the combined statement of the first and second laws:

$$dE = TdS + \mathcal{H}d\mathcal{M}, \qquad (10.51)$$

$$dA = -SdT + \mathcal{H}d\mathcal{M}. \qquad (10.52)$$

From these we can immediately write down the usual Maxwell-like relations:

$$\left(\frac{\partial T}{\partial \mathcal{M}}\right)_S = \left(\frac{\partial \mathcal{H}}{\partial S}\right)_{\mathcal{M}},$$ (10.53)

$$\left(\frac{\partial S}{\partial \mathcal{M}}\right)_T = -\left(\frac{\partial \mathcal{H}}{\partial T}\right)_{\mathcal{M}}.$$ (10.54)

Notice that $\mathcal{M}$ is an independent variable in both Eqs. (10.51) and (10.52). Experimentally it is usually easier to measure the external field than the magnetization, and so there is some advantage to converting to $\mathcal{H}$ as an independent variable. To do this we merely define new state functions according to the Legendre transformation, as was discussed in Chapter 7 and as was mentioned earlier in this Chapter. These functions are readily found to be $(E - \mathcal{H}\mathcal{M})$ and $(A - \mathcal{H}\mathcal{M})$; in terms of these the statement of the first and second laws becomes

$$d(E - \mathcal{H}\mathcal{M}) = TdS - \mathcal{M}d\mathcal{H},$$ (10.55)

$$d(A - \mathcal{H}\mathcal{M}) = -SdT - \mathcal{M}d\mathcal{H},$$ (10.56)

from which we obtain two more Maxwell-like relations,

$$\left(\frac{\partial T}{\partial \mathcal{H}}\right)_S = -\left(\frac{\partial \mathcal{M}}{\partial S}\right)_{\mathcal{H}},$$ (10.57)

$$\left(\frac{\partial S}{\partial \mathcal{H}}\right)_T = \left(\frac{\partial \mathcal{M}}{\partial T}\right)_{\mathcal{H}}.$$ (10.58)

This is essentially all the thermodynamic apparatus we shall need for the treatment of magnetic materials. We shall give only three examples: the dependence of internal energy on magnetization, the magnetic specific heat, and adiabatic demagnetization. The first and third examples are very closely analogous to calculations we have already done for other types of systems; the second example involves novel features, even though the calculation methods are the same as always.

(1) *Dependence of Internal Energy on Magnetization.* This calculation is analogous to the calculation of the dependence of E on V for a simple fluid, given the equation of state. For instance, given $pV = nRT$, what is $(\partial E/\partial V)_T$? We did not previously do this calculation directly, but used the argument in reverse to show that the ideal gas temperature was the same as the thermodynamic temperature. Here we

proceed from the equation of state and ask for $(\partial E/\partial \mathcal{M})_T$. From Eq. (10.51) we obtain

$$\left(\frac{\partial E}{\partial \mathcal{M}}\right)_T = T\left(\frac{\partial S}{\partial \mathcal{M}}\right)_T + \mathcal{H},\tag{10.59}$$

and with the aid of the Maxwell-like relation of Eq. (10.54) we obtain the desired result:

$$\left(\frac{\partial E}{\partial \mathcal{M}}\right)_T = \mathcal{H} - T\left(\frac{\partial \mathcal{H}}{\partial T}\right)_{\mathcal{M}}.\tag{10.60}$$

This finishes the thermodynamic part of the argument. We now need an explicit equation of state to calculate $(\partial \mathcal{H}/\partial T)_{\mathcal{M}}$ and hence $(\partial E/\partial \mathcal{M})_T$.

For paramagnetic substances we note that Langevin's equation involves $\mathcal{H}$ and T always in the ratio $\mathcal{H}/T$. This means that $(\partial \mathcal{H}/\partial T)_{\mathcal{M}} = \mathcal{H}/T$, and Eq. (10.60) thus states that E is independent of $\mathcal{M}$ at constant T. To demonstrate this result more formally, we define Λ to be the inverse function of L; that is, if $z = L(y)$, then $\Lambda(z) = y$. Applying this to the magnetic equation of state, we find

$$\Lambda\left(\frac{\mathcal{M}}{\mathcal{M}_0}\right) = \frac{\mathcal{M}_0\mathcal{H}}{nRT},\tag{10.61}$$

or

$$\mathcal{H} = \left(\frac{nRT}{\mathcal{M}_0}\right)\Lambda\left(\frac{\mathcal{M}}{\mathcal{M}_0}\right).\tag{10.62}$$

Differentiating, we find that

$$\left(\frac{\partial \mathcal{H}}{\partial T}\right)_{\mathcal{M}} = \frac{\mathcal{H}}{T},\tag{10.63}$$

which substituted back into Eq. (10.60) shows that

$$\left(\frac{\partial E}{\partial \mathcal{M}}\right)_T = 0.\tag{10.64}$$

Thus the internal energy of a paramagnetic substance is independent of magnetization, a result analogous to $(\partial E/\partial V)_T = 0$ for an ideal gas.

For ferromagnetic substances we apply the inverse function Λ to the Weiss equation of state and obtain

$$\Lambda\left(\frac{\mathcal{M}}{\mathcal{M}_0}\right) = \frac{\mathcal{M}_0(\mathcal{H} + \nu\mathcal{M})}{nRT}.\tag{10.65}$$

By differentiation we find that

$$\left(\frac{\partial \mathcal{H}}{\partial T}\right)_{\mathcal{M}} = \frac{nR}{\mathcal{M}_0}\Lambda\left(\frac{\mathcal{M}}{\mathcal{M}_0}\right) = \frac{\mathcal{H} + \nu\mathcal{M}}{T},\tag{10.66}$$

from which it follows that

$$\left(\frac{\partial E}{\partial \mathscr{M}}\right)_T = -v\mathscr{M}. \tag{10.67}$$

The energy of a ferromagnetic material thus depends on the magnetization, just as the energy of a van der Waals gas depends on the volume.

(2) *Magnetic Specific Heat.* The specific heat of a paramagnetic substance is quite normal at $\mathscr{H} = 0$ compared to that of other solids, but the specific heat of a ferromagnetic substance exhibits a peculiarity even in the absence of an external field. As the temperature is raised from below the Curie point, the specific heat exhibits a rise as T approaches Θ, and then a rather abrupt drop at $T = \Theta$ to a value like that of a normal solid. We wish to show by purely thermodynamic arguments that this behavior follows from the magnetic equation of state. The physical reason for the peculiar behavior of ferromagnetic materials is that the spontaneous magnetization changes rapidly with temperature near the Curie temperature (see Fig. 10.3), vanishing abruptly at $T = \Theta$.

We thus expect that the heat capacity of a magnetic material will depend on the magnetization of the material, so that T and $\mathscr{M}$ are likely choices of independent variables. Since TdS is the heat transferred, we start with the entropy. Accordingly, we write

$$dS = \left(\frac{\partial S}{\partial T}\right)_{\mathscr{M}} dT + \left(\frac{\partial S}{\partial \mathscr{M}}\right)_T d\mathscr{M}. \tag{10.68}$$

Dividing by dT and multiplying by T we obtain

$$T\frac{dS}{dT} = T\left(\frac{\partial S}{\partial T}\right)_{\mathscr{M}} + T\left(\frac{\partial S}{\partial \mathscr{M}}\right)_T \frac{d\mathscr{M}}{dT}.$$

With some obvious definitions of heat capacities and the use of the Maxwell-like relation of Eq. (10.54), this can be written as

$$C_{\text{total}} = C_{\mathscr{M}} - T\left(\frac{\partial \mathscr{H}}{\partial T}\right)_{\mathscr{M}} \frac{d\mathscr{M}}{dT}. \tag{10.69}$$

This is a completely general thermodynamic relation, valid for any magnetic material. If we specialize to $\mathscr{H} = 0$, then for paramagnetic substances $\mathscr{M} = 0$ at all T and for ferromagnetic substances $\mathscr{M} = 0$ at $T > \Theta$, so that $C_{\text{total}} = C_{\mathscr{M}}$ for these circumstances. For a ferromagnetic material at $T < \Theta$, we have to evaluate $(\partial \mathscr{H}/\partial T)_{\mathscr{M}}$. This was already done in Eq. (10.66), so for the case of a ferromagnetic material at $\mathscr{H} = 0$ we have

$$C_{\text{total}} = C_{\mathscr{M}} - v\mathscr{M}\frac{d\mathscr{M}}{dT}, \tag{10.70}$$

where of course $\mathscr{M}$ must be the spontaneous magnetization since we are considering the special case of $\mathscr{H} = 0$. We have an expression for $\mathscr{M}_{\text{sp}}$ as a function of T only near $T < \Theta$, so we can evaluate $d\mathscr{M}/dT$ explicitly only in this temperature range, but this is sufficient to show the specific heat anomaly. By differentiating Eq. (10.49) we find

$$2\mathscr{M}\frac{d\mathscr{M}}{dT} = -\frac{5}{3}\left(\frac{\mathscr{M}_0^2}{\Theta}\right)\left(\frac{T}{\Theta}\right)^2\left[1 - 2\left(\frac{\Theta}{T}\right)\left(1 - \frac{T}{\Theta}\right)\right]. \tag{10.71}$$

Putting this back into Eq. (10.70) and substituting for Θ its definition given in Eq. (10.45), we obtain the final result

$$C_{\text{total}} = C_{\mathscr{M}} + \frac{5}{2}nR\left(\frac{T}{\Theta}\right)^2\left[1 - 2\left(\frac{\Theta}{T} - 1\right)\right], \qquad T \leqslant \Theta. \tag{10.72}$$

Since $C_{\mathscr{M}}$ is nearly constant, we see that C_{total} rises as T approaches Θ, until at $T = \Theta$ it is greater than $C_{\mathscr{M}}$ by $\frac{5}{2}nR$. It then abruptly drops to $C_{\mathscr{M}}$ just above $T = \Theta$, since the magnetization vanishes there. In other words, there is a discontinuity in C_{total} of $\frac{5}{2}nR$ right at $T = \Theta$, and the discontinuity is a direct consequence of the vertical tangent of the spontaneous magnetization curve shown in Fig. 10.3. The value of the numerical coefficient is correct for a Weiss ferromagnetic material, but not for a real material.

The specific heat anomaly depends on the existence of spontaneous magnetization below the Curie temperature. The fact that real ferromagnetic materials exhibit the anomaly even when they exhibit no apparent overall magnetization is thus circumstantial evidence for something like a domain structure.

Other useful results can also be derived from Eq. (10.69). Since the heat capacity depends on the magnetization, we can expect that it will depend on the external magnetic field for paramagnetic substances and for ferromagnetic substances at $T > \Theta$, since the external magnetic field changes the magnetization. The working out of this relation from Eq. (10.69) and the magnetic equation of state is left as an exercise for the reader.

(3) *Magneto-Caloric Effect (Adiabatic Demagnetization)*. This is simply a calculation of the temperature change undergone by a material when it is adiabatically demagnetized, and is thus essentially like the calculations of temperature changes discussed in Chapter 7. It is only for historical reasons that the result for magnetic materials has a special name. Demagnetization is carried out experimentally by placing a magnetic material in a strong magnetic field (of the order of 10^4 gauss), adiabatically isolating it, and then turning off the field or removing the material from the field. Clearly the natural independent variables are then T and $\mathscr{H}$, and we wish to calculate $(\partial T/\partial \mathscr{H})_S$, the entropy being constant because the process is carried out adiabatically (and presumably reversibly). Proceeding as in Chapter 7, we write

$$dS = \left(\frac{\partial S}{\partial T}\right)_{\mathscr{H}} dT + \left(\frac{\partial S}{\partial \mathscr{H}}\right)_T d\mathscr{H} = 0. \tag{10.73}$$

We now solve for $(\partial T/\partial \mathscr{H})_S$, define a heat capacity at constant field as $C_{\mathscr{H}} = T(\partial S/\partial T)_{\mathscr{H}}$, and use the Maxwell-like relation of Eq. (10.58) to express $(\partial S/\partial \mathscr{H})_T$ in terms of quantities derivable from a magnetic equation of state:

$$\left(\frac{\partial T}{\partial \mathscr{H}}\right)_S = -\frac{\left(\frac{\partial S}{\partial \mathscr{H}}\right)_T}{\left(\frac{\partial S}{\partial T}\right)_{\mathscr{H}}} = -\frac{T}{C_{\mathscr{H}}}\left(\frac{\partial \mathscr{M}}{\partial T}\right)_{\mathscr{H}}, \tag{10.74}$$

or

$$(dT)_S = -\frac{T}{C_{\mathscr{H}}}\left(\frac{\partial \mathscr{M}}{\partial T}\right)_{\mathscr{H}} d\mathscr{H}. \tag{10.75}$$

Notice that this result was obtained in exactly the same manner as the analogous result for the reversible adiabatic expansion of a gas; in fact Eq. (10.74) could have been written down by inspection from Eq. (7.64) by writing $-\mathscr{H}$ for p and $\mathscr{M}$ for V.

Since magnetization at constant external field decreases with increasing temperature, we have $(\partial \mathscr{M}/\partial T)_{\mathscr{H}} < 0$, and $d\mathscr{H} < 0$ because we demagnetize the system; therefore Eq. (10.74) requires that $dT < 0$; the temperature drops. To calculate the exact temperature drop we need to know $C_{\mathscr{H}}$ and the magnetic equation of state, which information is extra-thermodynamic. We shall illustrate the explicit calculation for a Weiss ferromagnetic material above the Curie point, and for a Langevin paramagnetic material. The results will be only approximate because the equations of state are only approximate; Eq. (10.74), however, is exact. A ferromagnetic material below the Curie point shows little effect because it is always almost completely magnetized, so that $(\partial \mathscr{M}/\partial T)_{\mathscr{H}}$ is very small.

An external field of the order of 10^4 gauss is sufficiently weak that we can use the limiting forms of the equations of state given by the Curie-Weiss law and the Curie law. For a ferromagnetic substance this limiting form was

$$\frac{\mathscr{M}}{\mathscr{H}} = \frac{(\Theta/\nu)}{T - \Theta},$$

from which we find by differentiation the result

$$\left(\frac{\partial \mathscr{M}}{\partial T}\right)_{\mathscr{H}} = -\frac{(\Theta/\nu)\,\mathscr{H}}{(T - \Theta)^2}. \tag{10.76}$$

The temperature change on adiabatic demagnetization is thus

$$(dT)_S = \frac{1}{\nu C_{\mathscr{H}}} \frac{(T/\Theta)}{[(T/\Theta) - 1]^2}\, \mathscr{H}\, d\mathscr{H}. \tag{10.77}$$

As $T \to \Theta$, the temperature drop becomes appreciable. This provides an experimental method for determining ν and Θ without having to measure $\mathscr{M}$.

For a paramagnetic substance we use Curie's law,

$$\frac{\mathscr{M}}{\mathscr{H}} = \frac{\mathscr{M}_0^2}{3nRT},$$

from which we obtain

$$\left(\frac{\partial \mathscr{M}}{\partial T}\right)_{\mathscr{H}} = -\frac{\mathscr{M}_0^2\,\mathscr{H}}{3nRT^2}. \tag{10.78}$$

The temperature drop is therefore

$$(dT)_S = \frac{\mathscr{M}_0^2}{3nRC_{\mathscr{H}}T}\, \mathscr{H}\, d\mathscr{H}. \tag{10.79}$$

To integrate this equation, we need to know $C_{\mathscr{H}}$ as a function of T and $\mathscr{H}$, and we shall not carry the analysis further here. Adiabatic demagnetization of paramagnetic materials provides a very powerful experimental technique for achieving temperatures below $1°K$. Ferromagnetic materials of course are not used for magnetic cooling because their Curie points are so high (for iron Θ is $780°K$). Temperatures below $10^{-2}\,°K$ can be achieved by adiabatic demagnetization, starting with a paramagnetic salt at about $2°K$ and using a magnetic field of about 20,000 oersted. For his work on the attainment of low temperatures by this technique, and for his other pioneering work on low-temperature phenomena, W. F. Giaque was awarded the Nobel prize in 1949.

ELECTROCHEMICAL CELLS

In this section we discuss some effects of an electric field on thermodynamic systems. There is of course an analogy with the magnetic field and magnetic materials of the preceding section; the analogy in fact is so close as to make the subject of electric fields and dielectric materials uninteresting from the present point of view, amounting to no more than a trivial change of notation. It is more interesting to consider some phenomena involving electric fields and electric charges which have no magnetic analogue, namely the case of electrochemical cells, which produce electrical work from chemical and physical changes that take place in the state of the system (and *vice versa*).

(a) *Nonthermodynamic Description*

Suppose we have a thermodynamic system with two electrical leads (electrodes) coming out of it. The amount of work which must disappear from the surroundings when an amount of electric charge dq is reversibly transferred from one lead to the other (by discharging an ideal capacitor or operating an ideal generator) is

$$dW_{el} = +\mathscr{E}dq, \qquad (10.80)$$

where $\mathscr{E}$ is the electromotive force (emf) of the system, which is called an electrochemical cell because the transfer of charge is accompanied by chemical and physical changes in the state of the system. Note that dq by convention refers to positive charge, and the fact that there is a $+$ sign in Eq. (10.80) is simply the convention which tells when $\mathscr{E}$ is to be considered positive or negative. For the first time in this chapter an identifying subscript appears on the new work term, since it is often necessary to include the ordinary pdV work term as well.

Equation (10.80) can be only part of the story, for we are interested in the chemical changes which occur in the cell, and Eq. (10.80) says nothing about these. The new information which fulfills this function is contained in Faraday's law of electrolysis: *the number of chemical equivalents involved in the reaction in the cell is proportional to the electrical charge transferred.* This can be written mathematically in the form

$$dq = \mathscr{F}\,dn_{eq},\qquad(10.81)$$

where dn_{eq} is the number of chemical equivalents involved in the reaction connected with the passage of dq coulombs of electricity, and $\mathscr{F}$ is a constant of proportionality called the Faraday constant or simply the *faraday*. It must be determined experimentally, and the best present value is

$$\mathscr{F} = 96{,}487.0 \text{ coulomb/equivalent.}\qquad(10.82)$$

According to atomic theory, $\mathscr{F}$ is the product of the electronic charge times the Avogadro number, or $\mathscr{F}$ is the charge of one mole of electrons, but as always thermodynamics is indifferent to the source of its initial data and Eqs. (10.81) and (10.82) could just as well be laws of continuum matter rather than of atomistic matter.

We still need a rigorous definition of a chemical equivalent. The most fundamental physical definition would be as a submultiple of a mole, which is defined in terms of the mass of the carbon-12 isotope. The numerical factor of the submultiple is usually clear from chemical knowledge (if not, a little more chemical investigation is in order for that particular case). The practical electrochemical definition (secondary standard would be a more accurate phrase) is that one equivalent is the mass of substance which appears or disappears when that amount of electricity is passed which will cause 107.870 g of silver to appear or disappear.

The foregoing exhausts the fundamental physics and chemistry needed for a nonthermodynamic description of electrochemical cells, but unfortunately does not exhaust the subject. Two additional matters must be mentioned which can be troublesome: the question of the reversibility of the cell, and the question of notation and sign conventions. Reversibility is clearly a thermodynamic matter, and we can give only a severely limited discussion of an electrochemical cell unless it is thermodynamically reversible. Henceforth we assume our cells to be reversible, with a warning that this is always a matter for careful experimental test. The notations and sign conventions used in electrochemistry are basically arbitrary, but the subject is sufficiently old and rich in observations that chaos would result without some general agreement on symbols and signs.

The conventions are most easily explained by an example. Electrodes which are gaseous can be constructed by continuously passing the gas over an inert metal which serves as the lead wire, and whose surface has often been treated to increase its effective area. We can make an electrochemical cell by dipping a hydrogen electrode and a chlorine electrode into a solution of hydrochloric acid. Such a cell would be represented as follows (using platinum leads):

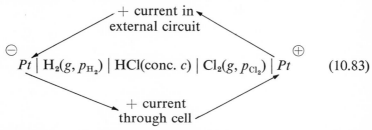

$$Pt \mid H_2(g, p_{H_2}) \mid HCl(\text{conc. } c) \mid Cl_2(g, p_{Cl_2}) \mid Pt \qquad (10.83)$$

The convention is that the sign of $\mathscr{E}$ is positive if the cell *as written* tends to produce a current of positive electricity from left to right *through the cell* (from right to left in the external circuit). This is shown by the arrows and the positive and negative signs, which of course are not written down in the conventional representation. It must be remembered that the concept of positive current is itself a convention, and the electrons or other negative charges are flowing in the opposite direction. The change in state for the passage of one faraday through the cell in the direction shown is

$$\tfrac{1}{2}H_2(g, p_{H_2}) + \tfrac{1}{2}Cl_2(g, p_{Cl_2}) = HCl(\text{conc. } c). \qquad (10.84)$$

There is no necessity for the pressures of H_2 and Cl_2 gas to be equal. The pdV work term must then be written in two parts, as $(p_{H_2}dV_{H_2} + p_{Cl_2}dV_{Cl_2})$.

If the cell of Eq. (10.83) had been written backwards, then the sign of $\mathscr{E}$ would have to be reversed, and the cell reaction of Eq. (10.84) would also have to be reversed for current moving from left to right through the cell.

(b) Thermodynamic Consequences

The usual four equivalent equations giving the combined statement of the first and second laws now become

$$dE = TdS - pdV - \mathscr{E}\mathscr{F}dn_{eq}, \qquad (10.85)$$

$$dH = TdS + Vdp - \mathscr{E}\mathscr{F}dn_{eq}, \qquad (10.86)$$

$$dA = -SdT - pdV - \mathscr{E}\mathscr{F}dn_{eq}, \qquad (10.87)$$

$$dG = -SdT + Vdp - \mathscr{E}\mathscr{F}dn_{eq}. \qquad (10.88)$$

Most electrochemical cells are operated under conditions of constant temperature and pressure, so that the Gibbs function is most convenient. Most of the use of electrochemical cells is to make chemical reactions occur reversibly (i.e. at equilibrium), so that their measured emf is an accurate indication of the thermodynamic properties of the equilibrium chemical system. This is a great experimental advantage, for the emf can be measured potentiometrically with great accuracy, and with practically no current flowing through the cell because the emf of the potentiometer opposes that of the cell. The remainder of this section will be devoted to a brief discussion of how such experimental information is used in thermodynamic calculations.

(1) *Thermodynamic Functions From EMF Measurements.* For an electrochemical cell operated at constant T and p, we see from Eq. (10.88) that

$$dG = -\mathscr{E}\mathscr{F}\,dn_{eq}. \tag{10.89}$$

If a finite change in state is carried out by allowing a finite amount of electricity to pass reversibly through the cell, then Eq. (10.89) can be integrated to yield

$$\Delta G = -\mathscr{E}\mathscr{F} n_{eq}, \tag{10.90}$$

where n_{eq} is the number of equivalents involved in the change in state. We therefore see that we can obtain ΔG for a chemical reaction at constant T and p by simply measuring the emf of a suitable reversible electrochemical cell. This is a very powerful technique for the determination of the "standard free energies" used in the calculation of equilibrium constants, as discussed in Chapter 9.

Furthermore, if the cell emf is measured at several different temperatures, so that $(\partial\mathscr{E}/\partial T)_p$ can be determined, we can also find the entropy and enthalpy changes in the reaction. From Eq. (10.88) we see that $S = -(\partial G/\partial T)_{p,n}$, so that by subtraction we find

$$\Delta S = -\left(\frac{\partial\Delta G}{\partial T}\right)_{p,n} = n_{eq}\mathscr{F}\left(\frac{\partial\mathscr{E}}{\partial T}\right)_{p,n}. \tag{10.91}$$

Since $\Delta H = \Delta G + T\,\Delta S$ we further find that

$$\Delta H = -T^2\left[\frac{\partial(\Delta G/T)}{\partial T}\right]_{p,n} = -n_{eq}\mathscr{F}\left[\frac{\partial(\mathscr{E}/T)}{\partial(1/T)}\right]_{p,n}, \tag{10.92}$$

the first part of the expression being simply the Gibbs-Helmholtz equation already given in Eq. (9.46). Thus the heat of the reaction ΔH can be found directly from the slope of a graph of $\mathscr{E}/T$ vs. $1/T$.

Conversely, if ΔG and ΔH are known for a reaction, then the emf and its temperature dependence can be calculated for the reversible cell in which the reaction occurs.

(2) *Systematics—Standard Half-Cell Potentials.* In Chapter 9 it was shown that the thermodynamic functions for a large number of complicated reactions could be built up from a table of thermodynamic functions for a much smaller number of "elementary" reactions. The possibility of building up tables in this way depends essentially only on the properties of state functions. Since the emf of a reversible electro-chemical cell is proportional to the Gibbs function, it follows that emf's can be summarized in compact tables in the same way as any other thermodynamic state function. In particular, the overall cell reaction can be considered to be the sum of two reactions, one occurring at each electrode, and the cell emf can be considered to be the difference of two electrical potentials, one for each electrode or half-cell. Of course, the absolute value of a half-cell potential is without thermodynamic meaning; only the sum of two half-cell potentials has meaning as a cell emf. This simply means that for tabulation purposes we must arbitrarily choose a numerical value for one standard half-cell potential, and then this fixes the numerical values for all other half-cell potentials. We must also agree on a choice of standard states in order to prepare a tabulation, just as in the case of direct chemical and physical transformations discussed in Chapter 9.

As an example, consider the cell shown in Eq. (10.83) with its cell reaction given by Eq. (10.84). The half-reaction at the left-hand electrode would be

$$\tfrac{1}{2}H_2(g, p_{H_2}) = H^+(\text{conc. } c) + e^-, \qquad (10.93a)$$

and the half-reaction at the right-hand electrode would be

$$Cl^-(\text{conc. } c) = \tfrac{1}{2}Cl_2(g, p_{Cl_2}) + e^-, \qquad (10.93b)$$

where the symbol e^- stands for 96,487.0 coulombs (i.e., one mole of electronic charge). Note that these reactions are written so that electrons enter the external circuit on the left and are removed on the right. This is consistent with the convention of positive current flowing from left to right through the cell.

The half-cell potentials depend not only on the electrode reaction but also on the physical states of the substances involved; i.e., on the pressures of gases and the concentrations of solutions. A choice of standard states must thus be made. For ideal gases the conventional choice is a pressure of 1 atmosphere, and for ideal solutions the conventional choice is a concentration of 1 molal; the standard temperature is 25°C. (It should be recalled from Chapter 8 that a 1 molal solution contains 1 mole of solute per 1000g of solvent.) The corresponding potential is called a standard half-cell potential, and is denoted by a superscript symbol (°). The numerical scale is conventionally fixed by assigning $\mathscr{E}° = 0$ for a standard hydrogen electrode. Tables of standard

TABLE 10.1—SOME STANDARD HALF-CELL POTENTIALS AT 25°C.

Electrode (half-cell)	Electrode Reaction	$\mathscr{E}°$, volts
Na; Na$^+$	Na $=$ Na$^+$ + e$^-$	+2.714
Zn; Zn^{++}	Zn $=$ Zn^{++} + 2e$^-$	0.763
Fe; Fe^{++}	Fe $=$ Fe^{++} + 2e$^-$	0.440
Pb; Pb^{++}	Pb $=$ Pb^{++} + 2e$^-$	0.126
Fe; Fe^{+++}	Fe $=$ Fe^{+++} + 3e$^-$	0.036
D$_2$; D$^+$	D$_2$ $=$ 2D$^+$ + 2e$^-$	0.0034
H$_2$; H$^+$	H$_2$ $=$ 2H$^+$ + 2e$^-$	0
Cu; Cu^{++}	Cu $=$ Cu^{++} + 2e$^-$	−0.337
Ag; Ag$^+$	Ag $=$ Ag$^+$ + e$^-$	−0.7991
Br$_2$(l); Br$^-$	2Br$^-$ $=$ Br$_2$(l) + 2e$^-$	−1.0652
Cl$_2$(g); Cl$^-$	2Cl$^-$ $=$ Cl$_2$(g) + 2e$^-$	−1.3595
Pb, PbO$_2$; Pb^{++}	Pb^{++} + 2H$_2$O $=$ PbO$_2$ + 4H$^+$ + 2e$^-$	−1.455

half-cell potentials are given in various reference books; an abbreviated table is given above, all for aqueous solutions. The last reaction in the table is one which occurs in automobile storage batteries. When using such tables to calculate $\mathscr{E}°$ for a cell with a given overall reaction, we must remember that it is $\Delta G°$ which is directly additive, not $\mathscr{E}°$, and the value of n_{eq} must thus not be overlooked.

From Table 10.1 we could calculate the standard emf, $\mathscr{E}°$, for any cell formed from a pair of electrodes listed in the table, but this would refer only to 1 atm pressure and 1 molal concentration. The dependence of the emf on the pressure and concentration can be easily calculated from the results of Chapter 9, however, where it was shown how the dependence of ΔG on pressure and concentration could be calculated. If the overall cell reaction involves only gases, we can use Eq. (9.25) directly, which was

$$\Delta G - \Delta G° = RT \sum_i \nu_i \ln \frac{p_i}{p_i°}.$$ (10.94)

Since $\Delta G = -n_{eq}\mathscr{F}\mathscr{E}$, we can write this as

$$\mathscr{E} = \mathscr{E}^\circ - \frac{RT}{n_{eq}\mathscr{F}} \sum_i v_i \ln \frac{p_i}{p_i^\circ} \tag{10.95}$$

If some of the substances involved in the reaction are in solution, we can go through the same argument as in Chapter 9, finding an alternate reversible process involving only gases and then using Raoult's law for ideal solutions. With this procedure, Eq. (10.95) can be generalized to

$$\mathscr{E} = \mathscr{E}^\circ - \frac{RT}{n_{eq}\mathscr{F}} \sum_i v_i \ln \frac{p_i}{p_i^\circ} - \frac{RT}{n_{eq}\mathscr{F}} \sum_j v_j \ln \frac{m_j}{m_j^\circ}, \tag{10.96}$$

where the summation over the index i includes all the gases, and the summation over the index j includes all the solutions, whose molality is m_j. The choice of the p_i° and m_j° is quite arbitrary and the conventional choice is $p_i^\circ = 1$ atm and $m_j^\circ = 1$ molal, as already mentioned.

At equilibrium $\Delta G = 0$ and hence $\mathscr{E} = 0$ also, so that Eq. (10.96) becomes

$$\mathscr{E}^\circ = \frac{RT}{n_{eq}\mathscr{F}} \ln K, \tag{10.97}$$

where K is a general equilibrium constant, which can be in mixed pressure and concentration units. This equation shows how standard half-cell potentials can be used to determine equilibrium constants for chemical reactions.

It is evident from Eq. (10.96) that the corresponding expression for a half-cell potential can be considered to have a similar form. For example, the half-cell potential of the chlorine electrode depends on pressure and concentration in the following way:

$$\mathscr{E}_{Cl_2} = \mathscr{E}^\circ_{Cl_2} - \frac{RT}{n_{eq}\mathscr{F}} \ln \left[\frac{p_{Cl_2}}{(m_{Cl^-})^2} \right]. \tag{10.98}$$

This result also indicates how Table 10.1 could be set up to refer to standard states consisting of ideal gases at 1 atm and ideal solutions at 1 molal concentration, when in fact practically none of the actual systems listed behaves ideally at such pressures and concentrations. The procedure is to make measurements at pressures and concentrations sufficiently low that the system does behave ideally (ideal gases and solutions represent the limiting behavior of real gases and solutions), and then use an ideal gas/ideal solution equation like Eq. (10.98) to calculate the hypothetical value of $\mathscr{E}^\circ$ that the cell would have if it did behave ideally at 1 atm and 1 m.

One of the most important uses of the table of standard half-cell potentials is the prediction of chemical equilibria. For instance, the table is so ordered that any substance will displace the one below it from solution. For exampl⌐, iron dipped into a solution of copper salt will displace the copper, which comes out as a metal while the iron goes into solution. A nail can be copper-plated in this way. Similarly, zinc will liberate hydrogen gas from acid solutions (which contain H^+ ions), but copper will not. It must be remembered, however, that most of the results for chemical equilibria in Chapter 9, and for electrochemical cells in this chapter, are restricted to ideal gases and solutions. The generalization to include nonideal systems is considered in Chapter 13.

We have now come to the end of the applications of the first and second laws to rather simple systems. Extensions to moɪe complicated systems are straightforward, but generally become quite cumbersome. Gibbs formulated a much neater and more elegant approach. This involves some change in viewpoint, but not much new physics, the first and second laws still forming the basis of the approach. The next three chapters are devoted to the development of this approach.

PROBLEMS

1. A spherical drop of water 1 cm in diameter is reversibly and isothermally spread out into the form of a circular sheet 100 cm in diameter, at 25°C. The surface tension of water at 25°C is 72.0 dyne/cm, independent of surface area. Calculate the work involved in the process. Neglect edge effects and remember that a sheet has two surfaces.

2. (a) Assume that the surface tension of a liquid depends only on temperature. Then a Clapeyron-like equation should be valid. Show that

$$\frac{d\sigma}{dT} = -\frac{\Delta S}{\Delta \mathscr{A}} = -\frac{Q_\sigma}{T},$$

where Q_σ is the heat absorbed when the surface area is increased by unit amount at constant temperature.

(b) The surface tension of water is given as follows:

t, °C	0	10	20	30	40	50	60	70	80	100
σ, dyne/cm	75.6	74.22	72.75	71.18	69.56	67.91	66.18	64.4	62.6	58.9

Make a plot of σ against $\log T$ and estimate Q_σ from the slope. Approximately how much does Q_σ vary over this temperature range?

(c) Is heat evolved or absorbed from the surroundings when the surface area of water is increased at constant temperature? From the results of part (b), calculate how much heat is evolved or absorbed at 25°C for an area increase of 1 cm².

(d) At 25°C the surface area of a drop of water is increased by 1 cm². Calculate W, Q, ΔS, and ΔE for this change in state. Refer to problem 1.

3. Evaluate the difference in the two heat capacities of a liquid film, $C_\sigma - C_\mathscr{A}$, in terms of quantities derivable from a surface equation of state.

4. Calculate the size of water droplet which has a vapor pressure greater by 0.1% (1 part in 1000) than bulk water at 25°C. At 25°C the surface tension of water is 72.0 dyne/cm and the molar volume is 18.0 cm³/mole.

5. A one-dimensional system is characterized by the variables F, l, T (tension, length, and temperature).

(a) Starting with $dW = -Fdl$, prove that

$$\left(\frac{\partial T}{\partial l}\right)_S = -\frac{T}{C_l}\left(\frac{\partial F}{\partial l}\right)_T\left(\frac{\partial l}{\partial T}\right)_F,$$

where C_l is the heat capacity at constant length.

(b) A rubber band is approximately a one-dimensional system. When a stretched rubber band is released adiabatically, its temperature falls. From this empirical fact and the result of part (a) above, prove that a rubber band held at constant tension will become *shorter* if its temperature is raised.

6. The Ferguson equation for the temperature dependence of surface tension is

$$\sigma = \sigma_0\left(1 - \frac{T}{T_c}\right)^n,$$

where σ_0 and n are constants.

(a) Find the surface entropy and surface energy per unit area for a liquid surface obeying the Ferguson equation.

(b) Evaluate $(\partial T/\partial \mathscr{A})_S$, the temperature change for reversible adiabatic stretching, for such a surface.

7. Prove that the entropy density of cavity radiation is

$$s = \frac{4}{3}aT^3 = \frac{4}{3}\frac{e}{T},$$

given that the energy density is $e = aT^4$ and the pressure is $p = \frac{1}{3}e$.

8. A quantity of cavity radiation at a temperature of 10,000°K is expanded adiabatically and reversibly. How much must its volume increase in order for its temperature to fall to 1,000°K? How much will its pressure decrease in the process?

9. Derive an expression for $(\partial C_{\mathscr{H}}/\partial\mathscr{H})_T$ for a magnetic solid in terms of quantities which can be evaluated from a magnetic equation of state. Evaluate $(\partial C_{\mathscr{H}}/\partial\mathscr{H})_T$ for substances obeying the Curie law and the Curie-Weiss law.

10. For an isentropic process involving a paramagnetic substance obeying Curie's law, show that

$$\mathscr{H}\mathscr{M}^{-\gamma} = \text{constant},$$

where

$$\gamma = C_{\mathscr{H}}/C_{\mathscr{M}}.$$

11. For certain processes a paramagnetic gas, such as O_2 or NO, can be regarded as consisting of two separate subsystems in thermal equilibrium with one another. One subsystem behaves like an ordinary gas which can perform only pressure-volume work, and the other subsystem behaves like a simple paramagnetic material which can perform work only against an external magnetic field.

(a) Consider such a gas undergoing an isentropic expansion in a magnetic field. Derive the necessary relationship between $d\mathscr{H}$ and dV to keep $T =$ constant, in terms of quantities which can be evaluated from equations of state.

(b) Evaluate the expression obtained in part (a) for an ideal gas obeying Curie's law.

12. The adiabatic demagnetization of a paramagnetic substance is studied as a function of initial temperature T_1 and initial magnetic field $\mathscr{H}_1$. It is found that a plot of $(T_1/T_2)^2$ against $\mathscr{H}_1^2$ is a straight line, where T_2 is the final temperature and where the final magnetic field is zero. If the substance obeys Curie's law, prove that this experimental result requires that

$$C_{\mathscr{H}} = \frac{A}{T^2}(1 + B\mathscr{H}^2),$$

where A and B are constants such that $AB = \mathscr{M}_0^2/3nR$.

13. (a) Find the entropy change when one mole of gadolinium sulfate is placed in a magnetic field of 10,000 oersted, the temperature being held constant at $1.5°K$.

(b) Find the change in temperature if the gadolinium sulfate is then adiabatically demagnetized.

Take the Curie constant to be $\mathscr{M}_0^2/(3nR) = 7.85$ cm^3-$°$K/mole, and the heat capacity to be represented by

$$\tilde{C}_{\mathscr{H}} = (1/T^2)(2.66 + 7.85 \times 10^{-7}\mathscr{H}^2)\text{ joule/mole-}°\text{K}.$$

14. (a) Find the entropy change when one mole of nickel is placed in a magnetic field of 10,000 oersted, the temperature being held constant at $427°C$.

(b) Find the change in temperature if the nickel is then adiabatically demagnetized.

Take the Curie temperature to be 358°C, the Curie-Weiss constant to be $C = \Theta/v = 0.400 \text{ cm}^3\text{-°K/mole}$, and the molar heat capacity to be 32 joule/mole-°K.

15. Calculate the total work performed in the electrolysis of acidified water to produce 1 mole of H_2 and $\frac{1}{2}$ mole of O_2 at 1 atm and 25°C. The emf used was 1.23 volt. Take the gases to be ideal and the density of the solution to be 1.00 g/cm³.

16. Use the data in Table 10.1 to calculate the emf of the following cells. Write the cell reaction and calculate the equilibrium constant for the reaction as written.

(a) Cu | $CuBr_2$(1 molal) | $Br_2(l)$ | Pt
(b) D_2(1 atm) | DCl(1 molal) || $ZnCl_2$(1 molal) | Zn
(c) Pb, PbO_2 | Pb^{++}(1 molal) | Pb

17. Write the electrode reaction for the half-cell Pt | Fe^{++}; Fe^{+++}. Use the data of Table 10.1 to calculate $\mathscr{E}°$ for this half-cell.

18. The standard enthalpy of formation of HCl(1 molal) is -40.023 kcal/mole. From this information and the data in Table 10.1, calculate the emf at 0°C and at 50°C of the following cell:

$$\text{Pt} \mid H_2(1 \text{ atm}) \mid \text{HCl}(1 \text{ molal}) \mid Cl_2(1 \text{ atm}) \mid \text{Pt}$$

Assume the standard enthalpy to be independent of temperature.

19. The emf of a gaseous electrode can be used to measure gas pressure. The standard emf of the cell

$$\text{Pt} \mid H_2(p \text{ atm}) \mid \text{HCl}(1 \text{ molal}) \mid \text{AgCl}(s) \mid \text{Ag}$$

is $\mathscr{E}° = 0.2225$ volt at 25°C and $p = 1$ atm. What is the hydrogen pressure when the cell gives an emf of 0.2146 volt?

20. A solution 0.10 molal in $PbAc_2$ and 0.01 molal in $FeAc_3$ is reversibly electrolyzed between Pt electrodes at 25°C. Use the data in Table 10.1 to decide which metal first deposits on the cathode. What is the concentration of the first metal remaining in solution when the second metal begins to deposit? Assume ideal solutions.

Chapter 11

CRITERIA FOR EQUILIBRIUM

In the preceding chapters we have stated the two laws of thermodynamics and developed from these a number of theorems and techniques which are useful in solving problems. In all of these developments the concept of equilibrium played a fundamental role from the very beginning, either implicitly or explicitly. Indeed, the state functions which play the main role in applications—energy, enthalpy, entropy, Helmholtz and Gibbs functions—are only defined for systems in equilibrium. We now propose to reverse the line of argument and use some of our derived results to establish criteria for deciding whether a system is or is not in equilibrium. In other words, our original definition that "a system is in equilibrium if and only if it is in a state from which no change is possible without net changes in the surroundings," is really not very easy to use. We propose to replace it by criteria involving state functions, so that we can apply standard calculational techniques more easily.

We have in fact already established one criterion for equilibrium in the discussion of entropy in Chapter 6. We may state this criterion as follows:

An isolated system is in equilibrium if and only if $\Delta S < 0$ for all possible variations for which E remains unchanged.

This statement can be symbolized as

$$(\Delta S)_E < 0, \tag{11.1}$$

174

and furnishes both a necessary and sufficient condition for equilibrium. This follows from the second law through the inequality of Clausius ($dS \geqslant dQ/T$). Thus $Q = 0$ for an isolated system by definition, and since $\Delta E = Q - W$, constant E must mean that $W = 0$, which assures that no net changes will occur in the surroundings in accordance with our original definition of equilibrium. But the inequality of Clausius requires that $\Delta S \geqslant 0$ for an isolated system for all changes. Thus if we find that $\Delta S < 0$ for all "possible variations," these variations are not really possible and no change in the system can in fact take place. The system is therefore in equilibrium. No real loss of generality results from the restriction to isolated systems, since we can always imagine the system to be isolated by redrawing the boundaries far enough away that no heat or matter flows across them.

The meaning of the phrase "possible variations" requires some clarification. By this we mean to imply the following calculation procedure. A new state of the system is chosen which differs from the state under test in its value of one or more of the macroscopic variables describing the state of the system, but which has the same energy, and then ΔS for the transition to the new state is calculated. This procedure is repeated with respect to all the different macroscopic variables for which the investigator wishes to test for equilibrium (i.e., for all those he considers "possible"). If $\Delta S < 0$ for all such new states, then the original state was the true equilibrium state. This procedure raises two questions. The first is whether some variations are to be considered as not possible, such as a gas leaking slowly through the solid walls of a container, or a mixture of hydrogen and oxygen at room temperature slowly reacting to produce water? Such variations are indeed to be considered as "not possible." Whether certain variations are to be considered as possible or not is in the last analysis dependent on the purpose of the investigator and on the time scale of his measurements. This need cause us no additional concern, since the whole abstract concept of equilibrium depends on these conditions anyway, as was discussed in Chapter 2.

The second question is more subtle. How are we to calculate $(\Delta S)_E$ for two states unless they are *both* equilibrium states, since otherwise ΔS is not defined? The answer is that we must imagine that we can impose sufficient constraints on the system, such as by inserting or removing impervious partitions or special semi-permeable membranes, so that each of the new states is an equilibrium state subject to the special extra constraints we apply in our imagination. Then the quantity $(\Delta S)_E$ is well defined and can be calculated. The true equilibrium state, however, is the one with the maximum entropy, i.e., for which all possible $(\Delta S)_E < 0$, and is the state sought by the system when all the extra (imaginary) constraints are removed. An example may make this procedure more obvious. Suppose we put a fixed number of grams of a volatile liquid in a closed container, and ask how much of the substance is in the vapor phase and how much in the liquid phase in the final equilibrium state. Clearly we should calculate $(\Delta S)_E$ for the variations of the fraction of the original liquid which is in the vapor phase. Actually only one such fraction represents the true equilibrium state, but we can vary this fraction at will for calculational purposes by inserting an imaginary impermeable surface between the liquid and vapor phases. This extra constraint allows us to deal only with equilibrium states, although only one of these states is the true equilibrium state which would exist in the absence of the extra constraint.

Another example of an extra imaginary constraint arises in chemical applications of thermodynamics, when we may wish, for example, to calculate the degree of chemical dissociation of a substance at equilibrium. To be able to vary the degree of dissociation at will and still deal with equilibrium states, we may imagine introducing an "anticatalyst" which slows down the chemical reaction so much that we may assume its rate to be infinitely slow. In all these cases there is never any difficulty in making the calculation because of the extra constraints required. In fact the procedure is simple enough that such calculations are usually performed without even bothering with an explicit statement of the extra constraints used. Our only reason for discussing the question at all is to demonstrate that the use of the equilibrium criterion involves no logical inconsistency.

ENERGY CRITERION

The entropy criterion given by Eq. (11.1) is often inconvenient to use, although it is easy to derive from the second law. A more useful criterion is

An isolated system is in equilibrium if and only if $\Delta E > 0$ for all possible variations for which S remains unchanged.

This statement can be symbolized as

$$(\Delta E)_S > 0. \tag{11.2}$$

We can easily prove the equivalence of these two criteria. First let us suppose a system is in a state for which $(\Delta S)_E < 0$ for *all* possible variations, but for which $(\Delta E)_S < 0$ for *some* variation. We can prove the impossibility of this situation by carrying out a possible variation in two steps which produces a contradiction. For the first step we carry out the variation for which $(\Delta E)_S < 0$; that is, $\Delta E_1 < 0$ and $\Delta S_1 = 0$. For the second step we add heat reversibly to the system without doing any work until the total energy change for the two steps together is zero. In this second step we must have $\Delta S_2 > 0$ by the definition of entropy. So for the two steps together we have as a possible variation $\Delta E = 0$, $\Delta S > 0$. But this is impossible because $(\Delta S)_E < 0$ for *all* possible variations by hypothesis.

This is only half the proof, the other half consisting of the converse proof that if $(\Delta E)_S > 0$ for *all* possible variations then there can be *no* variation for which $(\Delta S)_E > 0$. For suppose that there is *some* variation for which $(\Delta S)_E > 0$; then we can carry out a contradictory variation in two steps. For the first step we carry out the variation for which $\Delta S_1 > 0$ and $\Delta E_1 = 0$. Now we remove heat reversibly without doing work until the total entropy change for the two steps together is zero. In this second step we must have $\Delta E_2 < 0$ by the first law ($\Delta E = Q - W$ and $Q < 0$, $W = 0$). So the possible variation consisting of the two steps together has $\Delta S = 0$ and $\Delta E < 0$, which is impossible by hypothesis. This completes the proof of the equivalence of the entropy and the energy criteria.

In the next two chapters we will take the energy criterion as a starting point and derive a number of very useful relations that must hold if a system is to exist in equilibrium. These relations are sufficiently powerful for solving problems that they are very widely used in practice, instead of using the equilibrium criteria directly. The phase rule is perhaps the best known of these. Before we go on to do this, however, it is interesting to develop criteria involving other state functions. These are not quite as general as the entropy and energy criteria, but can be very useful if we wish to solve a problem by the direct use of an equilibrium criterion.

HELMHOLTZ FUNCTION CRITERION

It is not difficult to establish that when a system has a uniform temperature, a necessary and sufficient condition for equilibrium is

$$(\Delta A)_T > 0, \tag{11.3}$$

for all possible variations, where $A = E - TS$. The proof is as follows. Suppose that $(\Delta E)_S > 0$ for *all* possible variations, but that $(\Delta A)_T < 0$ for *some* variation. We can show that such a situation is impossible by a two-step process. For the first step, carry out the variation $\Delta A_1 < 0$, $\Delta T_1 = 0$. Then, from the definition of A we have

$$\Delta E - T\Delta S = \Delta A + S\Delta T,$$

so that for this first step

$$\Delta E_1 - T\Delta S_1 < 0,$$

or

$$\Delta E_1 < T\Delta S_1. \tag{11.4}$$

Now for the second step add or subtract an amount of heat reversibly without doing any work such that $\Delta S_2 = -\Delta S_1$. For such a step we have

$$\Delta E_2 = T\Delta S_2. \tag{11.5}$$

Adding Eqs. (11.4) and (11.5), we obtain for the overall variation

$$\Delta E_1 + \Delta E_2 < T(\Delta S_1 + \Delta S_2) = 0,$$

or $\Delta E < 0$ and $\Delta S = 0$ for this overall variation. But this is impossible by hypothesis. We leave it as an exercise for the reader to prove that if $(\Delta A)_T > 0$ for *all* variations, then there can be *no* variation for which $(\Delta E)_S < 0$.

The criterion involving the Helmholtz function is more restricted than the criterion involving the energy, in the sense that we assume from the beginning that the temperature is uniform at equilibrium. This assumption happens to be correct, but we should be able to *prove* it, and this is done in the next chapter with the aid of the energy criterion.

OTHER CRITERIA

It should now be easy for the reader to prove to his satisfaction that the following conditions on the enthalpy and the Gibbs function are valid criteria for equilibrium:

$$(\Delta H)_{S,p} > 0, \tag{11.6}$$

$$(\Delta G)_{T,p} > 0, \tag{11.7}$$

for all possible variations. These criteria are useful for systems of uniform pressure.

CRITERIA FOR STABILITY

In the discussion thus far we have been tacitly assuming that the variation represented by the symbol Δ is infinitesimal, but that it includes all orders of infinitesimals, and not just the first order. In this case a system fulfilling these criteria is in a state of *stable equilibrium*. In the next chapter we want to apply these criteria in much the same way that the principle of virtual work in mechanics is applied, and it is convenient mathematically to do so in terms of only first-order infinitesimals, for which the possible variation is denoted by the symbol δ. To do so we need only add the sign of equality to our previous conditions, and obtain

$$(\delta S)_E \leqslant 0, \tag{11.8}$$

$$(\delta E)_S \geqslant 0, \tag{11.9}$$

$$(\delta A)_T \geqslant 0, \tag{11.10}$$

etc.

These are less stringent conditions than before; for example a system may be in *unstable equilibrium* for some possible variations, in which case we would have $(\delta E)_S = 0$ but $(\Delta E)_S < 0$. A mechanical analogy would be a system consisting of a ball balanced on top of an inverted hemispherical bowl: for infinitesimal displacements sideways we have $\delta E = 0$ because the top of the bowl has zero slope, but $\Delta E < 0$ because of the negative curvature. An example of a thermodynamic system in unstable equilibrium would be a small drop of liquid in contact with its vapor at constant temperature and pressure. It should be recalled from Chapter 10 that the vapor pressure of a drop depends on its radius, and from this it is possible to show that the Gibbs function for the system has a maximum rather than a minimum, so that $(\delta G)_{T,p} = 0$ but $(\Delta G)_{T,p} < 0$ for evaporation or condensation. If the drop should evaporate a little, it will continue to evaporate until gone; if a little vapor should condense on the drop, it will continue to grow.

PROBLEMS

1. Prove that if $(\Delta A)_T > 0$ for *all* possible variations, then there can be *no* variation for which $(\Delta E)_S < 0$.

2. Starting from the entropy or energy criterion for equilibrium, prove that another equilibrium criterion is that $(\Delta H)_{S,p} > 0$ for all possible variations.

3. Starting from the entropy or energy criterion for equilibrium, prove that another equilibrium criterion is that $(\Delta G)_{T,p} > 0$ for all possible variations.

4. (a) Two blocks of metal at different temperatures T_1 and T_2 are put in contact through a diathermal wall, and the whole surrounded by an adiabatic envelope. Use the entropy criterion to prove that this system is not in equilibrium.

(b) Suppose that an adiabatic wall rather than a diathermal wall had been placed between the metal blocks. Would the system then have been in equilibrium? Why?

5. Two soap bubbles of the same size are connected together by a fine tube as shown in Fig. P11.5. The temperature is kept constant.

FIG. P11.5

(a) Show that the condition $(\delta A)_T \geqslant 0$ requires that the total surface area must be a minimum or a maximum, but that the condition $(\Delta A)_T > 0$ requires that the area must be a minimum.

(b) Prove that the configuration drawn above is unstable; i.e., that $(\delta A)_T = 0$ but $(\Delta A)_T < 0$. What is the configuration for stable equilibrium?

Neglect the compressibility of the air inside the bubbles, so that the total volume remains constant.

6. Ten grams of liquid water are placed in a previously evacuated container of 1000 cm³ volume and held at 100°C. At equilibrium we will find that m grams of the water have evaporated to form vapor, and $(10 - m)$ grams remain liquid.

(a) From the equilibrium condition $(\delta A)_T \geqslant 0$ for the whole system, prove that the pressures of the two phases must be equal. Remember that the total volume is constant.

(b) From the results of part (a), find the value of m. The equilibrium vapor pressure of liquid water at 100°C is 1 atm. Assume the density of the liquid water to be constant at 1.0 g/cm³, and that water vapor is an ideal gas.

7. Consider an isolated supercooled liquid, and consider the possible variation consisting of an amount δm freezing and raising the temperature by an amount δT.

(a) Devise a reversible path for bringing about this possible variation, and compute the entropy change involved. Assume constant specific heats for all phases.

(b) Use the entropy criterion and the results of part (a) to show that a supercooled liquid is absolutely unstable; that is, that $(\delta S)_E > 0$.

8. Show from data given in standard thermodynamic tables that a mixture of $H_2 + O_2$ at 25°C and 1 atm is unstable with respect to the formation of H_2O at constant temperature and pressure. Hint: show that $(\delta G)_{T,p} < 0$ for this possible variation.

Chapter 12

OPEN SYSTEMS AND PHASE EQUILIBRIUM

In the preceding chapter we derived a number of criteria for equilibrium. We are now going to apply them to heterogeneous systems and derive some very general and useful relations. It is well to make clear at this point that this program is going to involve some change in our method of attack and in our viewpoint. Previously we have regarded a system as a sort of "black box" on which we operated by devices in the surroundings. From the changes in the surroundings we drew conclusions about the system, but we seldom inquired as to the structure of the system itself. For simple homogeneous systems this is a very useful and general point of view, but for heterogeneous systems it becomes cumbersome at best. Indeed if we carry the "black box" approach to an extreme, there is no point in even using the words "homogeneous" and "heterogeneous," since we never look at the structure of the system and such distinctions then have no observational meaning. It is therefore worthwhile to look into the structure of a system to a limited extent, so that we can at least recognize the existence of phases. We will regard each phase as a homogeneous subsystem, and inquire as to the relation of its properties to the properties of the other phases. This will of necessity involve the introduction of a little extra-thermodynamic material in the form of some assumptions about the behavior of matter, such as the assumption that the volume of the system is equal to the sum of the volumes of its phases. These assumptions are so general and so well fulfilled for most real systems, however, that there is little objection to this procedure. Furthermore, when an assumption obviously breaks down, it is usually easy to see how to modify it to fit the situation. This point of view was adopted by

J. Willard Gibbs in his treatment of heterogeneous equilibrium, and he derived many results which were so far ahead of their time that some were later rediscovered experimentally for special cases, the investigators not realizing that they had been anticipated by Gibbs.*

First and Second Laws for Open Systems

If we are going to regard each phase as a subsystem, then an extension of the first and second laws is necessary, since matter can pass from one phase to another and we have as yet formulated the laws only for closed systems. The formulation of the first and second laws for open systems must be our first order of business. This is a worthwhile task in any case, since many real systems of great interest are open systems, especially in chemical and biological investigations.

We give first a somewhat casual argument which, while not rigorous, at least makes plausible the form of the first and second laws for open systems. The state of a closed system was determined by the specification of a few macroscopic variables such as pressure, volume, temperature, etc. For an open system it is obvious that it will be necessary in addition to specify the amounts of the different substances composing the system in order to determine its state. That is, for a closed system we could think of the internal energy, say, as some function of S and V,

$$E = E(S, V), \tag{12.1}$$

but for an open system we must think of it as a function also of the amounts $n_1, n_2, \cdots, n_N$ of the N different substances which compose it,

$$E = E(S, V, n_1, \cdots, n_N). \tag{12.2}$$

Since E is a state function we can write the differential equation,

$$dE = \left(\frac{\partial E}{\partial S}\right)_{V,n} dS + \left(\frac{\partial E}{\partial V}\right)_{S,n} dV + \left(\frac{\partial E}{\partial n_1}\right)_{S,V,n} dn_1 + \cdots + \left(\frac{\partial E}{\partial n_N}\right)_{S,V,n} dn_N, \tag{12.3}$$

* Gibbs was Professor of Mathematical Physics at Yale University in 1871–1903. He is regarded by many as the greatest scientist ever produced in America. Besides his thermodynamic work, he made important contributions to statistical mechanics, electromagnetic theory, and vector analysis. His work in thermodynamics has an air of permanence about it which is most unusual for a physical theory. Except for the minor matter of notation, his major thermodynamical papers are just as valid and useful today as when they were written in the 1870's.

where the subscript n on the partial derivatives means that all the amounts of substances, except the one in the derivative, are being held constant during the differentiation. As far as the derivatives with respect to entropy and volume are concerned, the system behaves as a closed system if all the n's are held constant during the differentiation. We can therefore go to the first and second laws for a closed system, $dE = TdS - pdV$, and find that

$$\left(\frac{\partial E}{\partial S}\right)_{V,n} = T, \tag{12.4}$$

$$\left(\frac{\partial E}{\partial V}\right)_{S,n} = -p. \tag{12.5}$$

Let us now *symbolize* all the other derivatives as

$$\left(\frac{\partial E}{\partial n_i}\right)_{S,V,n} \equiv \mu_i, \tag{12.6}$$

and then Eq. (12.3) can be written as

$$dE = TdS - pdV + \mu_1 dn_1 + \cdots + \mu_N dn_N. \tag{12.7}$$

This is the desired result. It is sometimes condensed slightly by using summation notation:

$$dE = TdS - pdV + \sum_{i=1}^{N} \mu_i dn_i. \tag{12.8}$$

The quantity μ_i is called the *chemical potential* of the substance i. From Eq. (12.8) and the definitions $H = E + pV$, $A = E - TS$, $G = H - TS$, we can easily derive the following:

$$dH = TdS + Vdp + \sum_{i=1}^{N} \mu_i dn_i, \tag{12.9}$$

$$dA = -SdT - pdV + \sum_{i=1}^{N} \mu_i dn_i, \tag{12.10}$$

$$dG = -SdT + Vdp + \sum_{i=1}^{N} \mu_i dn_i. \tag{12.11}$$

Several objections can be raised against the foregoing derivation. First of all it is by no means clear how the internal energy of an open system is to be defined. We clearly cannot use our previous definition of $dE = dW$ (adiabatic), since a system enclosed in an adiabatic envelope will of necessity be a closed system. Secondly, it is not clear what is meant by an increase in internal energy dE when a quantity of matter dn_i is added to the system. How is this increase dE to be measured, at least in principle if not in practice? Thirdly it seems odd that we should derive results for open systems from results for closed systems without introducing additional new assumptions, since closed systems are only special cases of open systems rather than *vice versa*. It would be well to bring these assumptions into the open where they can be scrutinized. Despite these objections Eq. (12.8)–(12.11) are correct, and we could in fact meet the objections by *postulating* the existence of the internal energy function for open systems and then proceeding as we did above. Now it is certain that we are going to have to introduce *some* new postulates in order to treat open systems, because we will surely never be able to carry a system between two states solely by the performance of adiabatic work if these two states differ in that the system in one state has a different mass than in the other state. No amount of adiabatic work is going to create or destroy mass (relativistic effects are neglected).

We can thus make the foregoing derivation rigorous by direct postulate. There is nothing illogical about such a procedure, but it is not very instructive from a physical point of view. Let us now try to give a more detailed derivation and see if we can put whatever new postulates may be necessary on a more physical basis. Let us first ask ourselves about the behavior of the internal energy function E if we have two separate systems which we combine into one composite system by the purely formal process of redrawing the boundaries to include both systems. There is no problem about defining internal energy functions for the separate systems, which we may call E_1 and E_2, by doing adiabatic work. We must remember, however, that only energy differences ΔE_1 and ΔE_2 are really defined, and E_1 and E_2 each has an arbitrary zero of energy. Similarly there is no problem about defining an internal energy function for the composite system, which we may call E_{1+2}, by doing adiabatic work. Of course E_{1+2} also has an arbitrary zero of energy, but there seems to be no objection to writing

$$E_{1+2} = E_1 + E_2, \tag{12.12}$$

in which now the zero of energy for E_{1+2} is no longer arbitrary but depends directly on our previous choice of arbitrary zeroes for E_1 and E_2.

(a) First Law

We can now use this additivity property to calculate the energy change on reversibly and adiabatically adding an infinitesimal amount dn_i of some substance i to a system, keeping the volume constant.

Suppose the system has an energy E and a volume V. Now set up a second system consisting of an infinitesimal amount dn_i of substance i, whose temperature, pressure, and any other thermodynamic variables are such that the second system *would be* in equilibrium with the first system *if* it were placed in contact with it through a membrane permeable only to heat and to the substance i. See Fig. 12.1 for a schematic

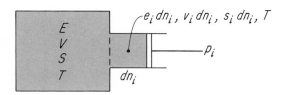

FIG. 12.1. Schematic representation of an open system.

representation. Since energy, volume, and entropy are extensive quantities,* we can write them for the infinitesimal system as $e_i\,dn_i$, $v_i\,dn_i$, and $s_i\,dn_i$, respectively, where e_i, v_i, and s_i are the energy, volume, and entropy per unit mass of the infinitesimal system.

Let us now incorporate the infinitesimal system into the large system in two steps, both of which are adiabatic: (1) extend the boundary of the large system to include the infinitesimal system; (2) push the piston in reversibly until the original volume is restored. By the additivity assumption the first step gives for the energy change

$$dE_1 = e_i\,dn_i, \tag{12.13}$$

since dQ and dW are both zero. In the second step we now have a closed system with $dQ = 0$, so

$$dE_2 = dW = p_i\,dV = p_i v_i\,dn_i, \tag{12.14}$$

since $dV = v_i\,dn_i$. Adding (12.13) and (12.14) we obtain

$$dE = dE_1 + dE_2 = (e_i + p_i v_i)\,dn_i. \tag{12.15}$$

The same argument can be repeated for any number N of substances, so that in general

---

* An extensive quantity is one which is directly proportional to the mass of the system. An intensive quantity is independent of the mass of the system.

$$dE = \sum_{i=1}^{N} (e_i + p_i v_i)\, dn_i. \tag{12.16}$$

If we now allow heat and work to flow across the boundary, we find $dE = dQ - dW$ as for a closed system, so that for a general change in state we can write

$$dE = dQ - dW + \sum_{i=1}^{N} (e_i + p_i v_i)\, dn_i. \tag{12.17}$$

This is the *first law for open systems.*

(b) *Second Law*

We can go through the same additivity argument for the entropy that we used for the energy. In the preceding two-step process the entropy changes would therefore be

$$dS_1 = s_i\, dn_i \quad \text{(extension of the boundary)} \tag{12.18}$$

$$dS_2 = 0 \quad \text{(reversible adiabatic process),} \tag{12.19}$$

or in general for any number N of substances,

$$dS = \sum_{i=1}^{N} s_i\, dn_i. \tag{12.20}$$

If heat also flows across the boundary of the system reversibly, we expect to be able to write

$$dS = \sum_{i=1}^{N} s_i\, dn_i + \frac{dQ_R}{T}. \tag{12.21}$$

This is the *second law for open systems.*

(c) *Combined First and Second Laws*

For a reversible process the first law, Eq. (12.17), gives

$$dE = dQ_R - dW_R + \sum_{i=1}^{N} (e_i + p_i v_i)\, dn_i. \tag{12.22}$$

Substituting from Eq. (12.21) the value of dQ_R,

$$dQ_R = T\, dS - \sum_{i=1}^{N} T s_i\, dn_i, \tag{12.23}$$

we obtain

$$dE = T\, dS - dW_R + \sum_{i=1}^{N} (e_i + p_i v_i - T s_i)\, dn_i. \tag{12.24}$$

For simple compression processes, $dW_R = pdV$, as before. Let us now give the group in parentheses in the summation a special symbol:

$$\mu_i \equiv e_i + p_i v_i - T s_i, \qquad (12.25)$$

so that Eq. (12.24) can be written

$$dE = TdS - pdV + \sum_{i=1}^{N} \mu_i dn_i. \qquad (12.26)$$

This is exactly the result we obtained previously, but we at least now see that its validity involves an additivity property for energy and entropy. This additivity seems eminently plausible, but it does not follow as a consequence of our formulation of the first and second laws for closed systems, and so must be regarded as an additional postulate involving the properties of matter.

The *chemical potential* μ which appears in the thermodynamic equations for open systems occupies a central role in our treatments of phase equilibrium and reaction equilibrium in this and the following chapter. It is a quantity for which it is worthwhile to acquire a physical "feel," which usually comes from noting some of its properties and how it might be measured experimentally (just as in the case of entropy). Hopefully this will be acquired gradually in this and the next chapter. We can note one useful property of the chemical potential already, from the definition $\mu_i = e_i + p_i v_i - T s_i$. Recall that the quantities e_i, p_i, v_i, and s_i referred to unit mass of the *pure* substance i, before it was pushed into the composite system. Since $G = E + pV - TS$, we see that μ_i is simply the Gibbs function per unit mass (usually moles or grams) of pure substance i. If the substance is not pure, then we must for the moment be content with the derived result, namely, $\mu_i = (\partial E/\partial n_i)_{S,V,n}$.

For reference, we put the following equations in one place:

$$dE = TdS - pdV + \sum_{i=1}^{N} \mu_i dn_i \qquad (12.27a)$$

$$dH = TdS + Vdp + \sum_{i=1}^{N} \mu_i dn_i \qquad (12.27b)$$

$$dA = -SdT - pdV + \sum_{i=1}^{N} \mu_i dn_i \qquad (12.27c)$$

$$dG = -SdT + Vdp + \sum_{i=1}^{N} \mu_i dn_i \qquad (12.27d)$$

The above are valid provided only compression work is involved, but the extension to include other kinds of work should be obvious. These equations are worth committing to memory; practically everything of interest can be derived from them by simple mathematical operations like differentiation and integration.

PHASE EQUILIBRIUM

Let us now apply the criteria for equilibrium to a heterogeneous system consisting of p phases and N components. We shall assume for simplicity that none of the components can be transformed into any other (i.e., no chemical reactions occur), so that the amount of each component can be varied without changing the amounts of the other components. In the next chapter we shall drop this restriction and succeed in deriving the so-called law of mass action for chemical equilibrium. For simplicity let us also assume that there are no electric, magnetic, or gravitational fields, and that so-called surface effects are absent. All these restrictions can be dropped, but it is helpful to work out the simplest sort of case first. Because of the absence of surface effects we can assign to each phase in the system its own private energy and entropy, independent of the behavior of any other phase. The application of the criterion $(\delta E)_S \geqslant 0$ for all possible variations can therefore be written as a sum of terms, one for each phase. If we denote the phase by superscript primes, this is

$$\delta E = \delta E' + \delta E'' + \delta E''' + \cdots + \delta E^p \geqslant 0. \qquad (12.28)$$

If surface effects were present, we could allow for them by adding additional terms in this expression. Equation (12.28) is only part of the criterion; the remaining part is $S = $ constant, or what is the same thing, $\delta S = 0$. Writing out δS in terms of each of the phases, we obtain

$$\delta S = \delta S' + \delta S'' + \delta S''' + \cdots + \delta S^p = 0. \qquad (12.29)$$

We have previously pointed out that the volume of the system can be taken constant with no real loss of generality, so that we can also write

$$\delta V = \delta V' + \delta V'' + \delta V''' + \cdots + \delta V^p = 0. \qquad (12.30)$$

Furthermore, the total amount of each component in all the phases together must be constant, since we are neither creating, destroying, nor transforming any of the substances. This can be written mathematically as

$$\begin{aligned}
\delta n_1 &= \delta n_1' + \delta n_1'' + \delta n_1''' + \cdots + \delta n_1^p = 0, \\
\delta n_2 &= \delta n_2' + \delta n_2'' + \delta n_2''' + \cdots + \delta n_2^p = 0, \\
& \vdots \\
\delta n_N &= \delta n_N' + \delta n_N'' + \delta n_N''' + \cdots + \delta n_N^p = 0,
\end{aligned} \right\} \qquad (12.31)$$

a total of N equations.

Now let us consider each phase as an open system and write our expression for the first and second laws for each phase. Thus for the first phase we would have

$$\delta E' = T' \delta S' - p' \delta V' + \sum_{i=1}^{N} \mu_i' \delta n_i'. \qquad (12.32)$$

Putting all the expressions into Eq. (12.28) we can write one big equation,

$$\begin{aligned}
\delta E &= T' \delta S' - p' \delta V' + \mu_1' \delta n_1' + \cdots + \mu_N' \delta n_N' \\
&\quad + T'' \delta S'' - p'' \delta V'' + \mu_1'' \delta n_1'' + \cdots + \mu_N'' \delta n_N'' \\
& \qquad \vdots \qquad \vdots \qquad \vdots \qquad \qquad \vdots \\
&\quad + T^p \delta S^p - p^p \delta V^p + \mu_1^p \delta n_1^p + \cdots + \mu_N^p \delta n_N^p \geq 0. \qquad (12.33)
\end{aligned}$$

Notice that we have not required the temperatures and pressures of the different phases to be equal. It may seem odd that any useful information could be extracted from such a cumbersome looking expression, but it can be done rather easily. We may regard this expression as an algebraic equation involving the variables $\delta S'$, $\delta V'$, dn_i', $\cdots$, δS^p, δV^p, δn_i^p, a total of $(N + 2)p$ variables. The quantities T', p', μ_i', $\cdots$, T^p, p^p, μ_i^p are the coefficients. If each of the variables $\delta S'$, etc., were at our free disposal and could be varied independently of the others, then the coefficients of the equation would *all* have to be zero for Eq. (12.33) to hold. There would be no other way for Eq. (12.33) to be satisfied. Unfortunately the actual situation is a little more complicated because the variables are not independently variable. For instance, if we wanted to increase the volume of the first phase we would simultaneously have to decrease the volume of at least one other phase in order to keep the total volume constant. Another way of saying this is that besides Eq. (12.33) there are $N + 2$ other equations that have to be satisfied, namely Eqs. (12.29), (12.30) and (12.31), which state that the total entropy, volume, and mass of each component are constant. In other words, there are $N + 3$ simultaneous equations, so that only

$$(N + 2)p - (N + 2)$$

of the variables are independent.

The straightforward algebraic procedure for handling these simultaneous equations is to use the $N + 2$ extra equations to eliminate $N + 2$ of the variables in Eq. (12.33). Then all the remaining

$$(N + 2)p - (N + 2)$$

variables will be independent, and their coefficients must all be zero. So let us solve Eqs. (12.29), (12.30) and (12.31) for $\delta S'$, $\delta V'$, and $\delta n', \cdots \delta n'_N$, substitute these expressions into Eq. (12.33), and collect terms:

$$\delta E = (T'' - T')\delta S'' - (p'' - p')\delta V'' + (\mu''_1 - \mu'_1)\delta n''_1 + \cdots + (\mu''_N - \mu'_N)\delta n''_N +$$

$$+ (T^p - T')\delta S^p - (p^p - p')\delta V^p + (\mu^p_1 - \mu'_1)\delta n^p_1 + \cdots + (\mu^p_N - \mu'_N)\delta n^p_N \geqslant 0.$$

$$(12.34)$$

Notice that we have algebraically eliminated all the $N + 2$ primed variables appearing in the first line of Eq. (12.33). There are only $(N + 2)(p - 1)$ variables left, and they are all independent because we have no other conditions left to impose upon them. Now the only way for Eq. (12.34) to be satisfied for all possible variations is for all the coefficients to be exactly zero. Otherwise it would be easy to produce violations of Eq. (12.34); for instance we could hold all the entropies, volumes, and masses of components appearing in Eq. (12.34) constant except one, say n''_1. Then all the differential variables $\delta S''$, $\delta V''$, $\cdots$, δn^p_N are zero except $\delta n''_1$. If we consider removing a little of component 1 from the double-primed phase, then $\delta n''_1 < 0$, all the other terms are zero, and therefore $\delta E < 0$, which violates Eq. (12.34). The only way out would be for the coefficient of $\delta n''_1$ to be zero, i.e., for $\mu''_1 = \mu'_1$. This same argument can be applied to each of the variables in turn, and it thereby follows that every coefficient in Eq. (12.34) must be zero. This is a very important result; let us write it out explicitly:

$$
\begin{aligned}
T'' &= T'; & p'' &= p'; & \mu_1'' &= \mu_1'; & \cdots \mu_N'' &= \mu_N'; \\
T''' &= T'; & p''' &= p'; & \mu_1''' &= \mu_1'; & \cdots \mu_N''' &= \mu_N'; \\
\cdot\;\;\;\; & & \cdot\;\;\; & & \cdot\;\;\; & & \cdot\;\;\; & \\
\cdot\;\;\;\; & & \cdot\;\;\; & & \cdot\;\;\; & & \cdot\;\;\; & \\
\cdot\;\;\;\; & & \cdot\;\;\; & & \cdot\;\;\; & & \cdot\;\;\; & \\
T^p &= T'; & p^p &= p'; & \mu_1^p &= \mu_1'; & \cdots \mu_N^p &= \mu_N'.
\end{aligned}
\tag{12.35}
$$

In words: *a heterogeneous system is in equilibrium if and only if the temperature, pressure, and chemical potential of each component is the same in every phase.*

GIBBS' PHASE RULE

Let us do a little counting of equations and variables in Eq. (12.35). If we have three variables and two simultaneous linear equations, it is apparent from simple algebra that one of the variables can be chosen independently, that is given any value we please within the range of applicability of the equations, and then the two equations fix the values of the other two variables. The excess of variables over equations we may call the number of degrees of freedom of the system of equations. Now let us look at the set of equations given by Eq. (12.35) above. There are $(N + 2)$ columns of equations and $(p - 1)$ equations in each column, a total of $(N + 2)(p - 1)$ equations. In each column there are p variables (e.g., in the first column the variables are T', T'', T''', $\cdots$, T^p), so that there are $p(N + 2)$ variables altogether. So the excess of variables over equations is simply

$$
(N + 2)p - (N + 2)(p - 1) = N + 2. \tag{12.36}
$$

Thus in our system of N components and p phases we can arbitrarily pick any $N + 2$ of the variables describing the system. All the rest of the variables describing the system are then fixed by the conditions of equilibrium. In other words, we can choose $N + 2$ variables of the system as we please, but then nature fixes the rest of them for us. Any attempt on our part to choose more than $N + 2$ variables independently will result in a condition of non-equilibrium, which usually will change spontaneously to an equilibrium state and in so doing destroy our original system by destroying one or more of the p phases.

An example may make the above discussion clearer. Suppose we have a system consisting of liquid water in equilibrium with its vapor (one component, two phases). Each phase can be described by three variables: two extensive variables (energy and volume, say) and the mass of the phase. This is a total of six variables, of which three can be chosen arbitrarily. Actually this is more freedom of choice than we usually care to bother about; in particular we seldom care about the mass of each phase. We really are usually interested only in knowing that *some* vapor and *some* liquid are present, not in how much of each. In other words, we are more interested in the *intensive* variables than in the *extensive* variables. So for a system of p phases, there are p variables that are seldom of interest, namely the mass of each of the phases. Let us remove these p uninteresting variables from our excess of variables over equations, and call this reduced number the number of degrees of freedom, denoted by the symbol F. *The number of degrees of freedom of an equilibrium system is therefore defined to be the number of intensive variables describing the system which can be chosen arbitrarily without destroying the system (i.e., destroying one or more phases.)* Subtracting p from Eq. (12.36), we obtain the usual form of the *phase rule:*

$$F = N + 2 - p. \tag{12.37}$$

Let us return to our water vapor-liquid example. According to Eq. (12.37) we have $F = 1 + 2 - 2 = 1$ degree of freedom. Only one intensive variable can therefore be chosen or varied arbitrarily; if we pick the temperature, then the pressure is fixed by the requirement that both phases be present. If we pick the pressure, then there is only one temperature for which two phases will be in equilibrium.

We have obtained Eq. (12.37) by the rather pedestrian bookkeeping procedure of counting up variables and equations, something any competent scientist would probably do as a matter of course. We should not be led on this account to regard Eq. (12.37) as trivial, for it is not. It can correlate an enormous quantity of information about very complex systems, and indeed whole books have been written on the subject of the phase rule. We must here be content with only the few simple following examples.

We see from Eq. (12.37) that a one-component system can exist in at most three phases, in which case there are *no* degrees of freedom.

Water at its triple point is an example. All the variables of the system are fixed as long as all three phases are present; in particular, the temperature cannot vary, which makes it clear why triple points are so useful as fixed points in thermometry. They can also be used as fixed pressure points for calibration of pressure gauges.

A two-component system can exist in at most four phases. An example would be an aqueous solution of sodium sulfate (Na_2SO_4) in equilibrium with vapor and two crystalline solid forms. The solid forms are crystallographically distinct; one is anhydrous Na_2SO_4 and the other contains "water of crystallization" bound rather firmly into the crystal lattice, so that the formula is written $Na_2SO_4 \cdot 10H_2O$. The four phases would be vapor, solution, Na_2SO_4, and $Na_2SO_4 \cdot 10H_2O$. By Eq. (12.37) we have $F = 2 + 2 - 4 = 0$, so if all four phases are present the temperature and pressure are fixed and cannot vary. This particular system happens to furnish a very convenient fixed temperature point at 32.383°C.

For further examples, the reader must be referred to more specialized books, particularly those dealing with chemical and metallurgical applications.

CHEMICAL POTENTIAL FOR SIMPLE SYSTEMS

We now wish to apply the methods of this chapter to some of the simple systems considered in Chapter 8. The central problem comes down to finding experimentally (or by some microscopic theory of matter) the chemical potential in terms of easily measureable properties of the system, such as pressure, temperature, or composition. This is not information which is forthcoming from thermodynamics. As a matter of fact we have by now reduced the actual thermodynamics involved in solving problems to a few very simple mathematical operations, such as algebraic solution of one of the equations in Eq. (12.35), or cross-differentiation and integration of one of the equations in Eq. (12.27). Except for the fact that for simplicity we have so far excluded chemical reactions, surface effects, and electric, magnetic, and gravitational fields from consideration, we have pretty well carried the purely thermodynamic developments to their limit, and derived results of sufficient generality and power to handle most problems routinely. We therefore turn for illustrations to particular systems, most of which are chosen to be rather simple to serve as clear demonstrations of methods.

(a) *Pure Fluids*

We have already pointed out that the chemical potential for a pure substance is simply its Gibbs function per unit mass. Since for a pure substance

$$dG = -SdT + Vdp,$$

we can divide by the mass (on a molar basis) and obtain

$$d\mu = -\tilde{S}dT + \tilde{V}dp. \tag{12.38}$$

If we now hold T constant and integrate, we obtain

$$\mu = \int \tilde{V}dp + \mu°(T), \tag{12.39}$$

where $\mu°(T)$ is the constant of integration, which is really a function of temperature (held constant in the integration). If we know the equation of state of the fluid, the integral in Eq. (12.39) can be evaluated. For example, for an *ideal gas* $\tilde{V} = RT/p$, and therefore

$$\mu = RT \ln p + \mu°(T). \tag{12.40}$$

The numerical magnitude of $\mu°(T)$ in Eq. (12.40) clearly depends both on our choice of a reference state and on our choice of units for p (atmospheres, dynes/cm², etc.), but it is nevertheless a function of temperature alone.

The form of Eq. (12.40) is sufficiently useful that it is often retained for *real gases*. A quantity called the *fugacity* is defined by the equation

$$\mu = RT \ln f + \mu°(T). \tag{12.41}$$

The units of fugacity are the same as those of pressure, and the constant $\mu°(T)$ is chosen so that as the pressure approaches zero (where real gases approach ideal behavior), the fugacity approaches the pressure. That is,

$$\lim_{p \to 0} \frac{f}{p} = 1. \tag{12.41a}$$

We could have written Eq. (12.40) in terms of volume rather than pressure by substituting $dp = -(RT/\tilde{V}^2)d\tilde{V}$ into Eq. (12.39) and integrating to obtain

$$\mu = -RT \ln \tilde{V} + (\mu°)', \tag{12.42}$$

where a prime has been added to the integration constant to distinguish it from the constant of Eq. (12.40).

For an *incompressible liquid* the integration of Eq. (12.39) is also easy, and yields

$$\mu = \tilde{V}p + \mu^{\circ}(T). \tag{12.43}$$

(b) *Ideal Gas Mixtures*

We can use the foregoing results to obtain an expression for the chemical potential of an ideal gas A in a mixture. Consider the mixture placed in contact with pure gas A through a membrane permeable only to A, and the pressure of A adjusted so that it is in equilibrium with the mixture (see Fig. 8.6). At equilibrium the chemical potential of A must be the same on both sides of the membrane, and therefore

$$\mu_A = RT \ln p_A + \mu_A^{\circ}(T), \tag{12.44}$$

where μ_A is the chemical potential of A in the mixture, and p_A is the pressure of A in the pure gas in equilibrium with the mixture. If the Gibbs-Dalton law holds, then $p_A = x_A p$, where p is the total pressure of the mixture and x_A the mole fraction of A in the mixture. Substituting this result into Eq. (12.44) we find

$$\mu_A = RT \ln x_A + RT \ln p + \mu_A^{\circ}(T). \tag{12.45}$$

If we do not happen to be concerned with variations in the total pressure of gas mixture, then the term $RT \ln p$ can also be considered a constant of integration. Equation (12.44) can be extended to real gases by defining the fugacity of component A such that $\mu_A = RT \ln f_A + \mu_A^{\circ}(T)$.

(c) *Ideal Solutions*

Ideal solutions obey Raoult's law, according to which the partial pressure p_A of component A in the solution is related to the vapor pressure p_A° of pure component A (at the same temperature) by $p_A = x_A p_A^{\circ}$. At equilibrium the chemical potential of A in the vapor phase must equal the chemical potential of A in the liquid phase. If the vapor is ideal, then

$$(\mu_A)_{\text{liq}} = RT \ln p_A + (\mu_A^{\circ})_{\text{vap}}. \tag{12.46}$$

Substituting Raoult's law and remembering that p_A° depends on temperature alone (why?), we can write for the *liquid*,

$$\mu_A = RT \ln x_A + \mu_A^{\circ\prime}(T), \tag{12.47}$$

where we have incorporated the term involving p_A° into the integration constant. Equation (12.47) is sometimes taken as the definition of an ideal solution; notice that it involves the ideality of the vapor in addition to Raoult's law. Note also that $\mu_A^{\circ\prime}$ here has a simple physical interpretation: it is the chemical potential of the pure solvent, since $RT \ln x_A$ is zero when $x_A = 1$.

Just as in the case of gases, we often find it convenient to keep the form of Eq. (12.47) even for non-ideal solutions. This is done by defining the *activity* a_A such as to preserve the form

$$\mu_A = RT \ln a_A + \mu_A^{\circ\prime} = RT \ln \gamma_A x_A + \mu_A^{\circ\prime}, \qquad (12.48)$$

where a_A is the activity and γ_A is the activity coefficient. The integration constant $\mu_A^{\circ\prime}$ is often chosen so that the activity becomes the same as the mole fraction in the limit of infinite dilution, for which the solution approaches ideality. That is, $\lim \gamma_A = 1$. Sometimes the integration constant is chosen so that the activity and molality become equal at infinite dilution. Such choices are basically arbitrary, and are made for convenience only.

APPLICATIONS TO SIMPLE SYSTEMS

We can now apply our present methods for open systems to obtain some of the results obtained in Chapter 8 by application of the first and second laws for closed systems.

(a) *Clapeyron Equation*

For a pure substance the chemical potential in phase 1 must be equal to that in phase 2, at equilibrium. Thus

$$\mu_1 = \mu_2,$$

or

$$d\mu_1 = d\mu_2,$$

but this is the same as $d\tilde{G}_1 = d\tilde{G}_2$, which was the starting point for one of our previous derivations of the Clapeyron equation. Without repeating the remainder of the derivation, we can therefore see that we shall obtain the same results as before.

(b) *Poynting Relation*

Again the chemical potential of the substance in the two phases (liquid at pressure p_1 in equilibrium with its vapor at pressure p_2) must be equal. As for the Clapeyron equation, this condition leads to $d\tilde{G}_1 = d\tilde{G}_2$, which was our starting point for the derivation of the Poynting relation, and we must obtain the same result as before.

(c) *Boiling Point Elevation of a Solution*

In this application we again equate the chemical potential of the liquid (the solvent) to that of the vapor, but a little care is necessary with the temperature-dependent constants of integration. We shall also need some information on these constants, since a temperature change is involved. As compensation for this extra trouble, we can obtain exact results in place of the idealized approximate results of Chapter 8. As in Chapter 8, let us denote the solvent by the subscript A. Let us also denote the solution by the subscript l and the vapor by the subscript g. Then at equilibrium at a pressure p and a temperature T,

$$\mu_{Al}(T, p) = \mu_{Ag}(T, p). \tag{12.49}$$

We would like to incorporate the properties of the pure solvent into our final relation, so we note that at the *same* pressure p, but a different (lower) temperature T_0, pure solvent is in equilibrium with vapor. Denoting the pure solvent by the superscript zero, we write

$$\mu_{Al}^0(T_0, p) = \mu_{Ag}(T_0, p). \tag{12.50}$$

We would like to convert Eq. (12.50) to a relation referring to T rather than T_0, and then we could subtract it from Eq. (12.49) and obtain the desired final relation. Note that Eq. (12.50) refers to pure liquid and pure vapor, and for a pure substance

$$\frac{\mu}{T} = \frac{\tilde{H}}{T} - \tilde{S},$$

which by differentiation at constant pressure gives

$$
\begin{aligned}
d\left(\frac{\mu}{T}\right) &= \tilde{H}\, d\left(\frac{1}{T}\right) + \frac{1}{T}\, d\tilde{H} - d\tilde{S} \\
&= \tilde{H}\, d\left(\frac{1}{T}\right) \text{ at const. } p,
\end{aligned}
$$

since $d\tilde{H} = T\, d\tilde{S}$ at constant p. Now we integrate from T_0 to T and obtain

$$\frac{\mu(T, p)}{T} - \frac{\mu(T_0, p)}{T_0} = \int_{(1/T_0)}^{(1/T)} \tilde{H}\, d\left(\frac{1}{T}\right). \tag{12.51}$$

We have two such equations, one for the pure liquid and one for the pure vapor. If we subtract them, the terms in $\mu(T_0, p)$ cancel by Eq. (12.50) and we obtain

$$\mu_{Ag}(T, p) - \mu_{Al}^0(T, p) = T \int_{(1/T_0)}^{(1/T)} (\tilde{H}_g - \tilde{H}_l)\, d\left(\frac{1}{T}\right). \tag{12.52}$$

Let us now combine this with Eq. (12.49), our original equilibrium equation, whereby $\mu_{Ag}(T, p)$ cancels and we obtain the final result

$$\mu_{Al}(T, p) - \mu_{Al}^0(T, p) = T \int_{(1/T_0)}^{(1/T)} (\tilde{H}_g - \tilde{H}_l) \, d\left(\frac{1}{T}\right). \qquad (12.53)$$

This result is thermodynamically exact. Note that $(\tilde{H}_g - \tilde{H}_l)$ is just the heat of vaporization per mole of pure liquid at pressure p, and that this latent heat may be a function of temperature but is nevertheless an experimentally accessible quantity. To proceed further we must know $\mu_{Al}(T, p)$ as a function of composition and $(\tilde{H}_g - \tilde{H}_l) = \Delta \tilde{H}_v$ as a function of temperature.

Suppose the solution is ideal and the heat of vaporization is a constant; then we can easily integrate and write

$$RT \ln x_A = T \Delta \tilde{H}_v \left(\frac{1}{T} - \frac{1}{T_0}\right). \qquad (12.54)$$

But this expression is exactly the same as we obtained previously, Eq. (8.45). The use of the chemical potential has allowed us to give a more elegant derivation, and moreover a derivation in which we clearly see the approximations and thus also how to improve them if necessary.

(d) *Freezing Point Depression of a Solution*

This derivation goes very similarly to that for the boiling point elevation, with the pure solid A taking the place of the pure vapor A. We will not repeat the details, but the final exact thermodynamic result is

$$\mu_{Al}(T, p) - \mu_{Al}^0(T, p) = -T \int_{(1/T_0)}^{(1/T)} (\tilde{H}_l - \tilde{H}_s) \, d\left(\frac{1}{T}\right), \qquad (12.55)$$

where $(\tilde{H}_l - \tilde{H}_s)$ is the heat of fusion per mole of the pure solid at a pressure p. If we assume the solution to be ideal and $(\tilde{H}_l - \tilde{H}_s) = \Delta \tilde{H}_f$ to be constant, we integrate and obtain

$$RT \ln x_A = -T \Delta \tilde{H}_f \left(\frac{1}{T} - \frac{1}{T_0}\right), \qquad (12.56)$$

which is the same as Eq. (8.53).

(e) *Osmotic Pressure of a Solution*

Here again the derivation is similar. At equilibrium the chemical potential of solvent A in the solution at temperature T and pressure p is equal to the chemical potential of pure A at the same temperature but at a reduced hydrostatic pressure equal to $(p_0 - \pi)$, where p_0 is the normal vapor pressure of pure A and π is the osmotic pressure (by definition). That is,

$$\mu_A(T, p) = \mu_A^0(T, p_0 - \pi). \tag{12.57}$$

But by Eq. (12.38), for a pure fluid at constant T

$$d\mu_A^0 = \tilde{V}_0 \, dp, \tag{12.58}$$

where $\tilde{V}_0$ is the molar volume of pure A. Integration of Eq. (12.58) from a pressure $(p_0 - \pi)$ up to p_0 gives

$$\mu_A^0(T, p_0) - \mu_A^0(T, p_0 - \pi) = \int_{p_0-\pi}^{p_0} \tilde{V}_0 \, dp. \tag{12.59}$$

Subtraction of this from Eq. (12.57) gives

$$\mu_A(T, p) - \mu_A^0(T, p_0) = -\int_{p_0-\pi}^{p_0} \tilde{V}_0 \, dp, \tag{12.60}$$

which is thermodynamically exact.* If we now make the approximations (or idealizations) that the left-hand side is equal to $RT \ln x_A$ and that $\tilde{V}_0$ is independent of pressure, we can integrate and obtain

$$RT \ln x_A = -\tilde{V}_0 \pi, \tag{12.61}$$

which is the same as Eq. (8.58).

From these examples we can see how problems of phase equilibrium can be solved if the chemical potential is known.

PROBLEMS

1. Prove the following relations:

(a) $\mu_i = \left(\dfrac{\partial H}{\partial n_i}\right)_{S,p,n} = \left(\dfrac{\partial A}{\partial n_i}\right)_{T,V,n} = \left(\dfrac{\partial G}{\partial n_i}\right)_{T,p,n}.$

(b) $\left(\dfrac{\partial T}{\partial n_i}\right)_{S,V,n} = \left(\dfrac{\partial \mu_i}{\partial S}\right)_{V,n}, \qquad \left(\dfrac{\partial p}{\partial n_i}\right)_{S,V,n} = -\left(\dfrac{\partial \mu_i}{\partial V}\right)_{S,n}.$

(c) $\left(\dfrac{\partial T}{\partial n_i}\right)_{S,p,n} = \left(\dfrac{\partial \mu_i}{\partial S}\right)_{p,n}, \qquad \left(\dfrac{\partial V}{\partial n_i}\right)_{S,p,n} = \left(\dfrac{\partial \mu_i}{\partial p}\right)_{S,n}.$

(d) $\left(\dfrac{\partial S}{\partial n_i}\right)_{T,V,n} = -\left(\dfrac{\partial \mu_i}{\partial T}\right)_{V,n}, \qquad \left(\dfrac{\partial p}{\partial n_i}\right)_{T,V,n} = -\left(\dfrac{\partial \mu_i}{\partial V}\right)_{T,n}.$

(e) $\left(\dfrac{\partial S}{\partial n_i}\right)_{T,p,n} = -\left(\dfrac{\partial \mu_i}{\partial T}\right)_{p,n}, \qquad \left(\dfrac{\partial V}{\partial n_i}\right)_{T,p,n} = \left(\dfrac{\partial \mu_i}{\partial p}\right)_{T,n}.$

* If the alternate definition of osmotic pressure mentioned in Chapter 8 is used, the lower limit of the integral is $p - \pi'$ instead of $p_0 - \pi$.

2. Any extensive property $X(n_1, n_2, \cdots, n_N)$ of a phase can be written as

$$X = \sum_{i=1}^{N} n_i \left(\frac{\partial X}{\partial n_i}\right)_{p,T,n}.$$

(a) Show that the Gibbs function of a phase is given by

$$G = \sum_{i=1}^{N} n_i \mu_i.$$

(b) Show that the volume of a phase is given by

$$V = \sum_{i=1}^{N} n_i \left(\frac{\partial \mu_i}{\partial p}\right)_{T,n}.$$

3. Suppose one of the N components is absent from one of the p phases of a heterogeneous system, say n_1''. Then $\delta n_1''$ can only be positive, never negative, and its coefficient in Eq. (12.34) does not have to be zero, but only has to be positive. Prove that the phase rule still holds for this heterogeneous system.

4. (a) Start with the relation $G = \sum n_i \mu_i$ and derive the Gibbs equation

$$-V dp + S dT + \sum n_i d\mu_i = 0,$$

or

$$-\tilde{V} dp + \tilde{S} dT + \sum x_i d\mu_i = 0.$$

(b) From this derive the Gibbs-Duhem equation

$$\sum x_i d\mu_i = 0 \qquad (T, p \text{ constant}),$$

or

$$\sum_{i=1}^{N} x_i \left(\frac{\partial \mu_i}{\partial x_j}\right)_{T,p} = 0.$$

(c) Show that for a two-component system the Gibbs-Duhem equation becomes

$$\left(\frac{\partial \mu_1}{\partial \ln x_1}\right)_{T,p} = \left(\frac{\partial \mu_2}{\partial \ln x_2}\right)_{T,p}.$$

(d) Show that for a two-component liquid phase whose vapor can be treated as an ideal gas mixture,

$$\left(\frac{\partial \ln p_1}{\partial \ln x_1}\right)_{T,p} = \left(\frac{\partial \ln p_2}{\partial \ln x_2}\right)_{T,p},$$

where p_1 and p_2 are the partial pressures of the components in the vapor, and x_1 and x_2 are the mole fractions in the liquid. This is often referred to as the Duhem-Margules equation.

5. A liquid solution having mole fractions x_i is in equilibrium with its vapor having mole fractions y_i. If the liquid follows Raoult's law and the

vapor behaves as an ideal gas mixture, show that for any two components,

$$\frac{y_2}{y_1} = \frac{p_2^0 \, x_2}{p_1^0 \, x_1},$$

where the p_1^0 are the vapor pressures of the pure components.

6. Henry's "law" states that the solubility of a gas in a liquid is directly proportional to its partial pressure in the gas phase; that is, $x_B = Kp_B$. This "law" is usually a good approximation for dilute solutions. Use the Gibbs-Duhem equation derived in Problem 4(b) to prove that if a solvent obeys Raoult's law, then the solute *must* obey Henry's law if the vapors form an ideal gas mixture. If the solvent obeys Raoult's law at all compositions, what can you say about the quantity K in Henry's law? If the solvent obeys Raoult's law only for dilute solutions, what can you say about K?

7. Use the results of Problem 4 to show that the activity coefficients of a two-component mixture must obey the relation,

$$x_1 \, d \ln \gamma_1 = -x_2 \, d \ln \gamma_2.$$

8. Consider a two-component liquid solution in equilibrium with its vapor, which behaves as an ideal gas mixture.

(a) Show that if $p_1 = p_1^0 x_1^\nu$ for one component at all compositions, where ν is a constant, then the second component must obey the relation $p_2 = p_2^0 x_2^\nu$, where p_1^0 and p_2^0 are the vapor pressures of the pure components.

(b) Show that the total vapor pressure of the solution in part (a) can exhibit a maximum or minimum as a function of composition, if the values of p_1^0, p_2^0, and ν are appropriate.

(c) Show that at such a maximum or minimum vapor pressure the liquid and vapor phases must have the same compositions.

9. Derive an expression for the chemical potential of a gas that obeys the virial equation of state.

10. Derive an expression for the chemical potential of a gas that obeys the van der Waals equation of state. Hint: use V as the independent variable.

11. Show how the integration constant $\mu^0(T)$ in Eq. (12.40) can be evaluated if $\tilde{C}_p$ is known as a function of temperature.

12. Derive Eq. (12.55) for the freezing point depression.

13. Use Eqs. (12.55) and (12.56) to derive an expression for the activity of a salt solution which shows a freezing point depression equal to α times that of an ideal solution of the same concentration. Assume $\Delta \tilde{H}_f$ to be constant.

14. Equation (12.60) can be used to obtain a relationship between the vapor pressure and the osmotic pressure of a solution of a non-volatile

solute. The chemical potential of the solvent must equal the chemical potential of the vapor; this condition determines the left-hand side of the equation.

(a) Prove that the general relation between vapor pressure and osmotic pressure must be

$$\int_p^{p_0} \tilde{V}_g \, dp = \int_{p_0-\pi}^{p_0} \tilde{V}_l \, dp,$$

where $\tilde{V}_g$ and $\tilde{V}_l$ are the molar volumes of pure solvent vapor and liquid, respectively.

(b) Suppose the vapor obeys the virial equation of state and the liquid obeys the equation of state

$$\tilde{V}_l = \tilde{V}_0(1 - \beta p),$$

where $\tilde{V}_0$ is the molar volume at zero pressure, and β is a constant. Derive the relation between the vapor pressure p and the osmotic pressure π, neglecting third and higher virial coefficients.

15. Three widely used methods for the experimental determination of the chemical potential (or activity) of a non-volatile solute in a solution are by measurement of: (1) the vapor pressure, (2) the freezing point depression, and (3) the osmotic pressure of the solution. Discuss each of these, noting specifically what quantities must be measured and what equations must be used.

16. The effect of a gravitational field on a heterogeneous system can be treated by the addition of the proper work term to the first law equations. This term is $dW_g = -\phi_g \, dm$, where ϕ_g is the gravitational potential and m is the mass of the system. It is customary to write $\phi_g = gh$, where g is the acceleration due to gravity and h is the height measured from some reference height (such as sea level), and to write dm in terms of molar quantities as

$$dm = \sum_{i=1}^{N} M_i \, dn_i,$$

where M_i is the molecular weight of the ith component.

(a) Write the expression for δE for each phase, and then use the criterion $(\delta E)_{S,V} \geqslant 0$ to prove that a heterogeneous system is in equilibrium if and only if T, p, and each $(\mu_i + M_i gh)$ is the same in every phase.

(b) Use the fact that $(\mu_i + M_i gh)$ is a constant to show that the pressure of an ideal gas in a gravitational field is given by

$$\ln (p''/p') = -(Mg/RT)(h'' - h'),$$

where p' is the pressure at the height h'.

(c) Show that for a real gas,

$$\ln (p''/p') = -(Mg/RT)(h'' - h') - (1/RT)\int_{p'}^{p''} [\tilde{V} - (RT/p)] \, dp.$$

17. Ice exists in many forms. Six forms are found below 40,000 bar, and the following data have been obtained on the different observed triple points.

(a) Check whether these data are thermodynamically consistent by carrying out a cycle around each triple point and seeing if V and H are indeed state functions.

(b) Use these data to draw an approximate phase diagram (pressure vs. temperature) for water. In what portions of this diagram does the Clapeyron equation apply?

(c) What phases are present at 20°C and 10,000 bar; at −20°C and 5,000 bar? How many degrees of freedom does the system have under these conditions?

Triple Point	Phase Change	$\Delta \bar{V}$ (cm³/g)	$\Delta \bar{H}$ (joule/g)
vapor-liquid-ice I	liquid-vapor	206,290	2500
0.01°C, 6.08 × 10⁻³ bar	ice I-vapor	206,290	2833
	liquid-ice I	0.090	−333.4
liquid-ice I-ice III	liquid-ice I	0.1352	−234
−22.0°C, 2074 bar	ice III-ice I	0.1818	− 21.6
	ice III-liquid	0.0466	212
ice I-ice II-ice III	ice III-ice I	0.1963	− 8.8
−34.7°C, 2128 bar	ice II-ice I	0.2178	42.2
	ice II-ice III	0.0215	51.0
liquid-ice III-ice V	ice III-liquid	0.0241	257
−17.0°C, 3462 bar	ice V-liquid	0.0788	261
	ice V-ice III	0.0547	3.9
ice II-ice III-ice V	ice II-ice III	0.0145	70.5
−24.3°C, 3442 bar	ice V-ice III	0.0546	3.9
	ice V-ice II	0.0401	− 66.6
liquid-ice V-ice VI	ice V-liquid	0.0527	293
0.16°C, 6257 bar	ice VI-liquid	0.0916	294
	ice VI-ice V	0.0389	1
liquid-ice VI-ice VII	ice VI-liquid	0.0330	354
81.6°C, 21,970 bar	ice VII-liquid	0.0910	354
	ice VII-ice VI	0.0580	0

18. The equilibrium between liquid and vapor of a two-component mixture can be represented as curves of boiling temperature as a function of composition at constant total pressure. Two typical boiling point curves are shown in Fig. P12.18. The system is all liquid below the "liq" curve and all vapor above the "vap" curve; it is part liquid and part vapor between the two curves. Both phases must have the same temperature at equilibrium.

(a) Describe the system at the points whose temperatures and *overall* compositions are given by A, B, C, D. How many degrees of freedom does the system have in each case? Note that one degree of freedom is lost because pressure is constant.

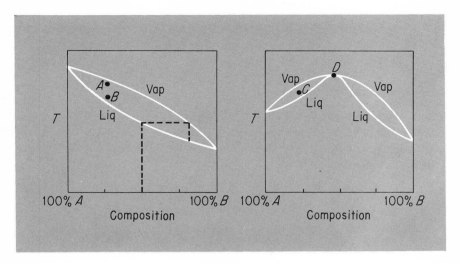

FIG. P12.18

(b) Fractional distillation can be thought of as a series of repeated single distillations, in which a little vapor is taken off from the liquid, condensed, then a little vapor taken from this condensed liquid, and so on for many repetitions. One such sequence is shown as the dashed lines starting at an original overall composition of 50% *A*-50% *B*. Describe what happens according to the above phase diagrams when mixtures of original overall composition 25% *A*-75% *B* and 75% *A*-25% *B* are fractionally distilled.

Chapter 13

OPEN SYSTEMS AND CHEMICAL EQUILIBRIUM

The results for phase equilibrium in the preceding chapter involved a number of restrictions, namely that none of the components could be transformed into any other, that there were no electric, magnetic, or gravitational fields, and that there were no surface effects. In this chapter we shall drop the first restriction and derive the *general* laws of chemical equilibrium, which we had obtained in Chapter 9 only for ideal gases and solutions. The other restrictions can also be dropped, but we shall not work out any of the details. One of the best sources for most of these very general results is still the original work of J. W. Gibbs (reprinted in 1961 by Dover Publications, Inc., New York).

From a mathematical point of view, the problem is simply that some of the equations of condition have to be changed; these were the extra $N + 2$ equations imposing conditions on the criterion $\delta E \geqslant 0$. In particular, the N equations stating that the total amount of each component in all the phases together is constant must now be modified because some substances can appear or disappear because of the chemical reactions. Another way of looking at the problem mathematically is to say that the variables $\delta n_1, \cdots, \delta n_N$ are no longer independent because there are relations among them due to the existence of chemical reactions. In fact, if there are r chemical reactions possible, we might expect that only $(N - r)$ variables are independent in the mathematical sense, and that therefore the phase rule will still hold with $(N - r)$ replacing N in Eq. (12.37). This indeed turns out to be the case, but we shall have to go through the mathematical argument in detail to establish the result rigorously.

The fact that the amounts of all N substances are not independently variable is usually recognized by a form of nomenclature. Any of the N substances is called a *species*; any of the $(N - r)$ substances chosen as independent is called a *component*. Which of the species are chosen to be components is arbitrary, and at most a matter of convenience.

STOICHIOMETRY OF CHEMICAL REACTIONS

We now see what is involved in dropping the restriction of no chemical reactions, but we must still formulate it in mathematical language. What is needed is a variable that will describe how far a chemical reaction can be said to proceed in either direction. This is easily obtained from the stoichiometry of the chemical reaction, which is really just a statement of the conservation of total mass. Consider a simple reaction like

$$\nu_1 s_1 + \nu_2 s_2 = \nu_3 s_3, \tag{13.1}$$

where the s_i stand for chemical substances and the ν_i are the usual stoichiometric coefficients. All that Eq. (13.1) says is that if ν_1 moles of s_1 disappear, then ν_2 moles of s_2 also disappear and ν_3 moles of s_3 appear. To put it another way, if ds_1 moles of s_1 and ds_2 moles of s_2 disappear, then these amounts must be in the ratio of the stoichiometric coefficients:

$$\frac{ds_1}{ds_2} = \frac{\nu_1}{\nu_2}. \tag{13.2}$$

A similar result holds for ds_3, which has the opposite sign from ds_1 because s_3 is a product and s_1 a reactant. This sign can be absorbed into ν_3 by the usual convention that the ν_i are taken as positive for products and negative for reactants, so that we can write

$$\frac{ds_1}{ds_3} = \frac{\nu_1}{\nu_3}. \tag{13.3}$$

Equations (13.2) amd (13.3) can be combined and a new quantity defined by writing

$$\frac{ds_1}{\nu_1} = \frac{ds_2}{\nu_2} = \frac{ds_3}{\nu_3} \equiv d\alpha, \tag{13.4}$$

where α is the *degree of advancement* of the reaction, defined so that $d\alpha$ is positive for the reaction going to the right and negative going to the left. This is the desired quantity. Remember that its definition depends on a sign convention adopted for the ν_i, by which Eq. (13.1) would now be written as

$$\nu_1 s_1 + \nu_2 s_2 + \nu_3 s_3 = 0,$$

with ν_3 positive and ν_1 and ν_2 negative.

Having defined α, we can now see how to formulate the condition of conservation of mass. If there is one reaction, then the condition on substance number 1 can be written as

$$\delta n_1 = \delta n_1' + \delta n_1'' + \cdots + \delta n_1^p + \nu_1 \delta \alpha. \tag{13.5}$$

The first p terms give the variations due to the physical transfer of various amounts of substance 1 among the p phases, and the last term gives the variation due to the chemical transformation. In other words, the amount which disappears due to the chemical reaction has to be made up by the disappearance of various amounts from all the phases, or else n_1 changes.

The result is easily generalized to r independent reactions. Using a superscript on ν and α to label the reaction, we find the condition on the ith substance to be

$$\delta n_i = \delta n_i' + \delta n_i'' + \cdots + \delta n_i^p + \nu_i^{(1)} \delta \alpha^{(1)} \cdots + \nu_i^{(r)} \delta \alpha^{(r)}. \tag{13.6}$$

This completes the bookkeeping chore for the conservation of mass, and we can now proceed with the thermodynamic part of the argument.

CONDITIONS FOR EQUILIBRIUM

At equilibrium we have, as before, the condition $(\delta E)_{S,V} \geqslant 0$. We also must have the condition that the total amount of each species must remain constant at equilibrium. If this were not so, the amounts of the different substances in the system would be changing and the system would obviously not be in a steady state. These conditions can be written out as

$$\begin{aligned} \delta E &\geqslant 0, \\ \delta S &= 0, \\ \delta V &= 0, \\ \delta n_1 &= 0, \\ \delta n_2 &= 0, \\ &\vdots \\ \delta n_N &= 0. \end{aligned} \tag{13.7}$$

The first equation is the one containing the thermodynamics; the remaining $(N + 2)$ equations are equations of condition or equations of restraint. We now put in the thermodynamic content by considering each phase as an open system, writing the expression for the first and second laws for each phase, and putting these all together in the first equation above, obtaining

$$\delta E = T'\delta S' - p'\delta V' + \mu_1'\delta n_1' + \cdots + \mu_N'\delta n_N' +$$

$$\cdots$$

$$+ T^p\delta S^p - p^p\delta V^p + \mu_1^p\delta n_1^p + \cdots + \mu_N^p\delta n_N^p \geqslant 0. \qquad (13.8)$$

The conditions of restraint when written out have the form

$$\delta S = \delta S' + \cdots + \delta S^p = 0, \qquad (13.9)$$

$$\delta V = \delta V' + \cdots + \delta V^p = 0, \qquad (13.10)$$

$$\delta n_1 = \delta n_1' + \cdots + \delta n_1^p + \nu_1^{(1)}\delta\alpha^{(1)} + \cdots + \nu_1^{(r)}\delta\alpha^{(r)} = 0, \qquad (13.11)$$

$$\cdots$$

$$\delta n_N = \delta n_N' + \cdots + \delta n_N^p + \nu_N^{(1)}\delta\alpha^{(1)} + \cdots + \nu_N^{(r)}\delta\alpha^{(r)} = 0. \qquad (13.12)$$

We now use the $(N + 2)$ equations of restraint to algebraically eliminate $(N + 2)$ of the variables in Eq. (13.8), obtaining

$$\delta E = (T'' - T')\delta S'' - (p'' - p')\delta V'' + (\mu_1'' - \mu_1')\delta n_1'' + \cdots + (\mu_N'' - \mu_N')\delta n_N'' +$$

$$\cdots$$

$$+ (T^p - T')\delta S^p - (p^p - p')\delta V^p + (\mu_1^p - \mu_1')\delta n_1^p + \cdots + (\mu_N^p - \mu_N')\delta n_N^p$$

$$- (\nu_1^{(1)}\mu_1' + \cdots + \nu_N^{(1)}\mu_N')\delta\alpha^{(1)} -$$

$$\cdots$$

$$- (\nu_1^{(r)}\mu_1' + \cdots + \nu_N^{(r)}\mu_N')\delta\alpha^{(r)} \geqslant 0. \qquad (13.13)$$

Equation (13.13) is all that remains of our original $(N + 3)$ equations given by Eq. (13.7) or by Eqs. (13.8)–(13.12). Since there are no more conditions or restraints to be satisfied, all the variables in Eq. (13.13) must be independent. These variables are $\delta S''$, $\delta V''$, $\delta n_1''$, $\cdots$, δS^p, δV^p, δn_1^p, $\cdots$, and $\delta\alpha^{(1)}$, $\cdots$, $\delta\alpha^{(r)}$; a total of $[(N + 2)(p - 1) + r]$ independent variables. There appear to be r independent variables more than there were in the case of no chemical reactions. This is as it should be, for we have r additional things that can be varied, namely the degrees of advancement of the r independent chemical reactions.

The rest of the argument now proceeds exactly as before: the only way for Eq. (13.13) to be satisfied for all possible variations is for all the coefficients to be exactly zero. If we write this out explicitly, using a shorthand summation notation for the coefficients of the $\delta\alpha$, we obtain the following set of equations:

$$T'' = T', \qquad p'' = p', \qquad \mu_1'' = \mu_1', \qquad \cdots, \qquad \mu_N'' = \mu_N',$$
$$\begin{array}{ccccc} \cdot & \cdot & \cdot & & \cdot \\ \cdot & \cdot & \cdot & & \cdot \\ \cdot & \cdot & \cdot & & \cdot \end{array}$$
$$T^p = T', \qquad p^p = p', \qquad \mu_1^p = \mu_1', \qquad \cdots, \qquad \mu_N^p = \mu_N', \tag{13.14}$$
$$\sum \nu_i^{(1)} \mu_i = 0, \qquad \cdots, \qquad \sum \nu_i^{(r)} \mu_i = 0.$$

In words: *a heterogeneous system is in equilibrium if and only if the temperature, pressure, and chemical potential of each species is the same in every phase, and* $\sum \nu_i \mu_i = 0$ *for each chemical reaction.*

PHASE RULE WITH CHEMICAL REACTIONS

Now let us count up the number of equations and variables in Eq. (13.14). There are $[(N+2)(p-1) + r]$ equations and $p(n+2)$ variables. The number of degrees of freedom is the excess of variables over equations, less the p uninteresting variables referring to the mass of each phase,

$$F = p(N+2) - [(N+2)(p-1) + r] - p,$$
$$F = (N+2) - r - p, \tag{13.15}$$
$$F = (N-r) + 2 - p.$$

This is the phase rule with chemical reactions allowed. Notice that it can be interpreted to be the same as the phase rule without chemical reactions, by taking $(N-r)$ to be the number of *components* of the system. This is really quite sensible, and on reflection no more than should be expected. For instance, suppose water is one of the components of the system. There is considerable chemical and physical evidence that water is not simply a collection of H_2O molecules, but also contains rather stable larger molecules such as $(H_2O)_2$, $(H_2O)_3$, etc., as well as the ionic species H_3O^+ and OH^-. This appears to be a large number of variables to take into account, but nevertheless the whole complex system can be obtained by taking just one macroscopic substance—water. Every time we include a new species we must also include a new condition consisting of the chemical reaction for the formation of the species, and so the number of independent variables remains one. There may be many *species* in water, but there is only one *component*. This is just a specific illustration of the general result that thermodynamic conclusions must be independent of details of the microscopic structure of matter.

CHEMICAL EQUILIBRIUM—THE LAW OF MASS ACTION

Although the phase rule appears essentially unchanged when chemical reactions are allowed to occur, a new and important additional result has appeared. This is the set of conditions on the reactions

$$\sum \nu_i^{(1)} \mu_i = 0, \cdots, \sum \nu_i^{(r)} \mu_i = 0. \tag{13.16}$$

These equations are the so-called law of mass action, which we formulated in terms of equilibrium constants for ideal gases and solutions in Chapter 9. To see the connection, consider a system containing only ideal gases. According to Eq. (12.40) the chemical potential of each species at equilibrium is

$$\mu_i = RT \ln p_{eq,i} + \mu_i^\circ(T), \tag{13.17}$$

where $\mu_i^\circ(T)$ depends only on temperature. Substituting Eq. (13.17) into any one of the equations in Eq. (13.16), we find

$$RT \sum \nu_i \ln p_{eq,i} + \sum \nu_i \mu_i^\circ(T) = 0, \tag{13.18}$$

or combining all the quantities which are only functions of temperature and calling the combination $K_p(T)$, we obtain

$$\sum \ln (p_{eq,i})^{\nu_i} = \ln K_p(T). \tag{13.19}$$

This is exactly Eq. (9.28). Similar results follow for the other forms of equilibrium constants of Chapter 9, simply by substitution of the proper expression for the chemical potential into $\sum \nu_i \mu_i = 0$.

The condition $\sum \nu_i \mu_i = 0$ is of course a much more general result than we obtained in Chapter 9. If we wish, nevertheless, to retain the algebraic forms for equilibrium constants as given in Chapter 9, we see we need only to use the *fugacity* in place of the pressure for real gases, and the *activity* in place of the concentration (or some measure of the concentration) for non-ideal solutions. The results will then be exact.

The general law of mass action in the form $\Sigma \nu_i \mu_i = 0$ was published in 1876 by Gibbs, but remained virtually unknown to chemists for many years.

MEMBRANE EQUILIBRIUM

An important class of phenomena involving equilibria across semi-permeable membranes can be handled by the same mathematical methods we have just used for chemical equilibria. Three kinds of species are recognized: those that can pass the membrane with no restrictions, those that cannot pass the membrane at all, and those that can pass the membrane only in certain ratios to one another. The first kind of species is usually water and other small uncharged molecules. The second kind is very large molecules, such as proteins. The third kind is usually small charged species (ions) which can only pass the membrane in such ratios that electrical neutrality is maintained. Membrane phenomena are important in many biological phenomena, where the concentrations of large molecules and the distributions of electrolytes are linked together by the conditions for equilibrium that we shall now derive.

Let us denote the two phases separated by the membrane by a prime and double-prime, and let us suppose the membrane is rigidly fixed so that the volumes on each side are constant. To keep the three kinds of species separate, let us use the subscripts a, b, $\cdots$ for those species that can pass freely, the subscripts A, B, $\cdots$ for those that cannot pass at all, and the subscripts 1, 2, $\cdots$ for those that can pass only in a certain ratio. For these last we will have conditions like

$$\frac{\delta n_1'}{\delta n_2'} = \frac{\nu_1}{\nu_2} \text{, etc.,}$$

from which we form a new variable α, defined as

$$\frac{\delta n_1'}{\nu_1} = \frac{\delta n_2'}{\nu_2} = \cdots \equiv \delta\alpha. \tag{13.20}$$

The ν_i are here just the numbers that give the fixed ratios, but we see that the equation looks like that for chemical stoichiometry. We now proceed exactly as before. The criterion for equilibrium is

$$\delta E = T'\delta S' - p'\delta V' + \mu'_a \delta n'_a + \cdots + \mu'_A \delta n'_A + \cdots$$
$$+ \mu'_1 \delta n'_1 + \cdots + T''\delta S'' - p''\delta V'' + \mu''_a \delta n''_a + \cdots$$
$$+ \mu''_A \delta n''_A + \cdots + \mu''_1 \delta n''_1 + \cdots \geqslant 0, \qquad (13.21)$$

and the conditions of restraint are

$$\delta S = \delta S' + \delta S'' = 0; \qquad (13.22)$$
$$\delta V' = 0, \qquad \delta V'' = 0; \qquad (13.23)$$
$$\delta n_a = \delta n'_a + \delta n''_a = 0; \qquad (13.24)$$

$$\cdot$$
$$\cdot$$
$$\cdot$$

$$\delta n'_A = 0, \qquad \delta n''_A = 0; \qquad (13.25)$$

$$\cdot$$
$$\cdot$$
$$\cdot$$

$$\delta n_1 = \delta n'_1 + \delta n''_1 = 0, \qquad \delta n'_1 = \nu_1 \delta \alpha; \qquad (13.26)$$

$$\cdot$$
$$\cdot$$
$$\cdot$$

We now substitute Eqs. (13.22)–(13.26) back into Eq. (13.21). The first thing that happens is that all the terms involving δV disappear because of Eq. (13.23), and that all the terms involving δn_A, δn_B, $\cdots$ disappear because of Eq. (13.25). In other words, the pressures on the phases and the chemical potentials of the species which cannot pass the membrane can be completely arbitrary. The rest of the equation can be written as

$$\delta E = (T'' - T')\delta S'' + (\mu''_a - \mu'_a)\delta n''_a + \cdots$$
$$+ (\nu_1 \mu'_1 - \nu_1 \mu''_1 + \nu_2 \mu'_2 - \nu_2 \mu''_2 + \cdots)\delta \alpha \geqslant 0. \qquad (13.27)$$

Since the coefficients must vanish, we find

$$T' = T'', \quad \mu'_a = \mu''_a, \quad \mu'_b = \mu''_b, \quad \cdots, \qquad (13.28)$$
$$\nu_1 \mu'_1 + \nu_2 \mu'_2 + \cdots = \nu_1 \mu''_1 + \nu_2 \mu''_2 + \cdots. \qquad (13.29)$$

These are our final conditions of equilibrium. The ones given by Eq. (13.28) are just what we might have expected, but the one given by Eq. (13.29) is new. There will be one such relation like Eq. (13.29) for each condition of restraint like Eq. (13.20). Written in terms of activities, Eq. (13.29) takes the form

$$(a'_1)^{\nu_1}(a'_2)^{\nu_2} \cdots = (a''_1)^{\nu_1}(a''_2)^{\nu_2} \cdots. \qquad (13.30)$$

As an illustration of the use of Eqs. (13.28)–(13.30) in treating membrane equilibria, suppose we put a concentration of 10 units of NaP on one side of a membrane and 10 units of NaCl on the other side. Both NaP and NaCl dissociate into ions, $Na^+ + P^-$ and $Na^+ + Cl^-$, but P^- is so large that it cannot pass the membrane. What are the concentrations at equilibrium (assuming concentrations and activities to be the same for purposes of illustration)? From Eq. (13.28) we find that the chemical potential of the solvent is the same on both sides. From Eq. (13.29) we find

$$(a'_{Na^+})(a'_{Cl^-}) = (a''_{Na^+})(a''_{Cl^-}),$$

or calling x the amount of Na^+ and Cl^- which move through the membrane,

$$(10 + x)(x) = (10 - x)(10 - x),$$

$$x = 10/3.$$

So the equilibrium activities are

$$a'_{Na^+} = 40/3 \qquad a''_{Na^+} = 20/3$$
$$a'_{Cl^-} = 10/3 \qquad a''_{Cl^-} = 20/3$$
$$a'_{P^-} = 10$$

Notice how the inability of P^- to pass the membrane and the requirement of charge neutrality have affected the distribution of the NaCl.

This equilibrium was rediscovered (for very dilute ideal solutions) by the English physical chemist F. G. Donnan in 1911, 35 years after its publication by Gibbs, and is often known as the Donnan membrane equilibrium.

PROBLEMS

1. A homogeneous phase is composed of three species s_1, s_2, and s_3 which undergo a chemical reaction,

$$a_1 s_1 + a_2 s_2 = a_3 s_3.$$

(a) Choose s_1 and s_2 as components. From the stoichiometry of the reaction show that the variations of s_1 and s_2 considered as components are

$$\delta n_{c1} = \delta n_1 + \frac{a_1}{a_3} \delta n_3,$$

$$\delta n_{c2} = \delta n_2 + \frac{a_2}{a_3} \delta n_3,$$

where the subscript c denotes the value for a component.

(b) Use the law of mass action and show that the equation,

$$dE = TdS - pdV + \sum_{i=1}^{3} \mu_i dn_i,$$

reduces to

$$dE = TdS - pdV + \sum_{i=1}^{2} \mu_i dn_{ci}.$$

2. The effect of an electrical field on a system can be treated by the addition of the proper work term to the first law equations. This term is $dW_{el} = -\phi_{el} \Sigma dq_i$, where ϕ_{el} is the electrical potential and q_i is the charge on the ith species. It is customary to write dq_i in terms of molar quantities as

$$dq_i = \mathscr{F} z_i dn_i,$$

where z_i is the charge number of the ith species (i.e., $z_i \mathscr{F}$ is the electrical charge on one mole of the species).

(a) Some types of electrochemical cells can be considered to be made up of two regions (phases) with potentials ϕ'_{el} and ϕ''_{el}. If no work is done in crossing the boundary of the two regions with a test charge, then $\mathscr{E} = \phi''_{el} - \phi'_{el}$. (In electrochemical terminology this means that there is no liquid junction potential.) Write the expression for δE for each region and use the criterion $(\delta E)_{S,V} \geqslant 0$ to prove that an electrochemical cell is in equilibrium if and only if $T' = T''$, $p' = p''$, and $\mu'_i + z_i \mathscr{F} \phi'_{el} = \mu''_i + z_i \mathscr{F} \phi''_{el}$.

(b) From the results of part (a) show that

$$\mu''_i - \mu'_i = -z_i \mathscr{F} \mathscr{E}.$$

This gives the emf of a so-called concentration cell. If the solution is ideal, show that

$$\mathscr{E} = \frac{RT}{z_i \mathscr{F}} \ln \frac{x'_i}{x''_i},$$

where x_i is the mole fraction.

3. How many degrees of freedom does each of the following heterogeneous systems have? To which of the systems does the Clapeyron equation rigorously apply?

(a) Liquid sulfur + sulfur vapor.

(b) Solid sulfur + liquid sulfur + sulfur vapor.

(c) $Na_2SO_4 \cdot 10H_2O(s) + Na_2SO_4(s)$ + saturated water solution + water vapor.

(d) $Na_2SO_4 \cdot 10H_2O(s)$ + saturated water solution + water vapor.

(e) Dilute solution of Na_2SO_4 + water vapor.

(f) Dilute solution of Na_2SO_4 + ice + water vapor.

4. Specify the number of components in each of the following systems. Assume chemical equilibrium is established among the various species. Although a large number of conceivable reactions among the species might be

possible, remember that the phase rule applies only to the independent ones.
  (a) $C(s)$, $H_2O(g)$, $H_2(g)$, $CO(g)$, $CO_2(g)$.
  (b) $Fe(s)$, $FeO(s)$, $CO(g)$, $CO_2(g)$.
  (c) $Fe(s)$, $FeO(s)$, $C(s)$, $CO(g)$, $CO_2(g)$.
How many degrees of freedom does each system have?

  5. At high temperatures $CaCO_3$ dissociates according to the reaction,

$$CaCO_3(s) = CaO(s) + CO_2(g).$$

The dissociation pressure at several temperatures is given in the following table.

t, °C	727	748	795	830	898
p, torr	44	70	150	255	760

Discuss in terms of the phase rule what occurs when
  (a) pure $CaCO_3(s)$ is placed in an initially evacuated vessel and heated at constant volume.
  (b) pure $CaCO_3(s)$ is placed in an atmosphere of 150 torr of $CO_2(g)$ and heated at constant pressure.
  (c) pure $CaCO_3(s)$ is placed in an initially evacuated, expandable vessel, and heated at a constant external pressure of 760 torr.

  6. Consider the equilibrium between a solid and its saturated solution in which the solute is ionized, as follows:

$$A_xB_y(s) = xA^{+z_A} + yB^{-z_B},$$

where z_A and z_B are the charges on the ions.
  (a) Use the law of mass action to show that

$$(a_A)^x(a_B)^y = \text{constant},$$

where a_A and a_B are the activities of the ions.
  (b) From the results of part (a) and the condition of overall charge neutrality show that

$$(a_A)^{z_B}(a_B)^{z_A} = \text{constant}.$$

  7. A solution of NaCl is separated from an equal volume of KCl solution by a membrane permeable to all ions except K^+. Derive expressions for the final concentrations of Na^+ and Cl^- on both sides of the membrane in terms of the initial concentrations c_1 and c_2 of NaCl and KCl, respectively. Assume ideal solutions.

  8. A solution of A_2B is separated from an equal volume of a solution of C_2B by a membrane permeable to all ions except C^+. What is the final concentration of B^{--} on each side of the membrane if the initial concentrations of A_2B and C_2B are equal? Assume ideal solutions.

Chapter 14

THE NERNST POSTULATE
(THIRD LAW)

From a purely thermodynamic point of view, the third law is in a different class from the first and second laws. Its purely thermodynamic content is rather limited for one thing, and it is difficult to state the law so that there do not seem to be a number of experimentally observable exceptions. The second law, for instance, is not believed to have any macroscopic exceptions; that is, it is not believed possible to construct a perpetual motion machine. But there are experimental exceptions to many of the common statements of the third law. One of the greatest interests in third law studies lies in the devising of microscopic theories to explain observed exceptions, but this lies outside of thermodynamics from the point of view presented here. Because of these facts, we begin the discussion with some historical background.

Historical Background

We have remarked previously in the discussion of chemical equilibrium in Chapter 9 that a table of standard thermodynamic functions cannot be set up on the basis of *thermal measurements* and the first and second laws alone. The reason for emphasizing the phrase *thermal measurements* is that this is the method an experimentalist would often prefer to use to find the two unknown constants ΔH_0° and ΔS_0°. Thermal measurements are usually easier to make than are direct measurements of equilibrium constants. It may be very difficult to set up a chemical system in thermodynamic equilibrium, and to determine accurately the concentrations of all the different chemical species, some of which may be present in only trace amounts. The constant ΔH_0° can in principle always be determined from thermal measurements; it is the constant ΔS_0° that requires an equilibrium measurement for its determination. The important result of the third law is that if the standard temperature is taken to be $T_0 = 0°\text{K}$, then $\Delta S_0^\circ = 0$ for a large number of cases. It was the systematic effort to accumulate accurate data on thermodynamic functions that led to this postulate.

STATEMENT OF THE THIRD LAW

The statement that $\Delta S_0^\circ = 0$ is not very satisfactory as a statement of the third law, for many exceptions are known. Some care is required to frame the statement so that it is free from exceptions and does not claim anything that is not in principle susceptible of measurement on a macroscopic level. Of many statements which have been given, we believe the following to be the most satisfactory from a purely thermodynamic point of view:

> *The first and second laws of thermodynamics are applicable down to the limit of absolute zero, provided that at this limit entropy changes vanish for any reversible process.*

We emphasize that this statement of the third law defines only entropy *differences* at absolute zero and not absolute values. Just as the absolute value of energy is undefined and only energy differences can be measured, so can only entropy differences be measured. However, if the entropy values for all reversibly connected states are equal at absolute zero, then this entropy value may as well be taken to be zero for convenience.

EXPERIMENTAL EVIDENCE FOR THE THIRD LAW

Some of the experimental evidence which suggested Nernst's postulate is worth noting. Electrochemical cells are particularly appropriate for making very accurate equilibrium measurements over a range of temperatures. In the discussion of these cells in Chapter 10 we obtained the relations

$$\Delta G = -n_{\text{eq}}\mathscr{F}\mathscr{E}, \tag{14.1}$$

$$\Delta H = -T^2 \left[\frac{\partial(\Delta G/T)}{\partial T} \right]_{p,n} = -n_{\text{eq}}\mathscr{F} \left[\frac{\partial(\mathscr{E}/T)}{\partial(1/T)} \right]_{p,n}. \tag{14.2}$$

That is, measurements of $\mathscr{E}$ as a function of temperature are sufficient to determine both ΔG and ΔH. T. W. Richards* measured the electromotive force of a number of cells and found that as the temperature decreased, the value of ΔH increased and that of ΔG decreased. He suggested that they would not only be equal at absolute zero, as

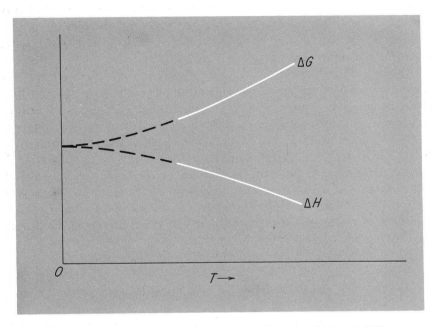

FIG. 14.1. Schematic diagram of the behavior of ΔG and ΔH at low temperatures.

they must be since $\Delta G = \Delta H - T\Delta S$, but that they would approach each other with a horizontal tangent as shown schematically in Fig. 14.1. In other words he suggested that as $T \rightarrow 0$, both

$$\left(\frac{\partial \Delta G}{\partial T}\right)_{p,n} \rightarrow 0, \tag{14.3}$$

and

$$\left(\frac{\partial \Delta H}{\partial T}\right)_{p,n} \rightarrow 0. \tag{14.4}$$

* First American winner of the Nobel Prize in Chemistry. Professor of Chemistry at Harvard during the period 1894–1928.

The first implies that

$$\Delta S \to 0, \tag{14.5}$$

the second that

$$\Delta C_p \to 0. \tag{14.6}$$

The experiments just cited referred to only a few systems and covered a temperature range that did not extend below about 0°C, and Richards did not propose Eqs. (14.3) and (14.4) as general principles of nature. This step was taken later by W. Nernst* on the basis of additional experimental results by a number of workers.

Shortly after the third law was proposed, a number of apparent exceptions to it were found experimentally. Investigation showed that the substances studied were not in true thermodynamic equilibrium. In other words, the processes studied were not reversible. The apparent exceptions have so far all been explainable in such terms in considerable detail; the non-zero values of ΔS have been attributed to the "frozen-in" entropy of mixing of different substances, or to "frozen-in" molecular transitions of various sorts. The discussion of the third law slips very easily into a statistical-mechanical treatment of particular systems. We wish to avoid this, and to limit the discussion here to the purely thermodynamic consequences of the third law.

CONSEQUENCES OF THE THIRD LAW

Going back to our initial statement of the third law, we find that an immediate consequence of $\Delta S = 0$ at $T = 0$ is

$$\Delta G = \Delta H \quad \text{at} \quad T = 0, \tag{14.7}$$

$$\Delta A = \Delta E \quad \text{at} \quad T = 0. \tag{14.8}$$

Further consequences follow from the equations,

$$\Delta S = \frac{\Delta E - \Delta A}{T}, \tag{14.9}$$

$$\Delta S = \frac{\Delta H - \Delta G}{T}, \tag{14.10}$$

* Professor in Berlin from 1905 onward; winner of the Nobel Prize in 1920 "for his thermochemical work."

which are indeterminate in the limit of $T = 0$ as they are written. Using L'Hospital's rule and differentiating the numerators and denominators of the right-hand sides, we obtain

$$\Delta S(T = 0) = \Delta C_V(T = 0) + \Delta S(T = 0), \qquad (14.11)$$

$$\Delta S(T = 0) = \Delta C_p(T = 0) + \Delta S(T = 0). \qquad (14.12)$$

From this follows the result that

$$\Delta C_V = 0, \qquad \Delta C_p = 0 \qquad \text{at} \quad T = 0, \qquad (14.13)$$

in accord with Richards' original suggestion.

Not only are ΔC_V and ΔC_p zero at $T = 0$, but the heat capacities themselves must be zero. Moreover, the heat capacity must fall to zero linearly or faster with T near $T = 0$, or else the entropy would go to infinity. This is easily seen from the relation

$$S - S_0 = \int_0^T \frac{C}{T} dT. \qquad (14.14)$$

Since the left-hand side of this equation must remain finite according to the third law, C must fall to zero at least as fast as $C = aT$ or else the integral on the right-hand side diverges to infinity at its lower limit. This conclusion is confirmed by all known experimental cases.

Since the entropy of a substance at $T = 0$ is the same for all its reversibly connectable states, its entropy value must be a constant at $T = 0$ regardless of the conditions of pressure or volume. Thus the derivatives of entropy with respect to pressure and volume vanish,

$$\left(\frac{\partial S}{\partial p}\right)_T = 0, \qquad \left(\frac{\partial S}{\partial V}\right)_T = 0 \quad \text{at} \quad T = 0. \qquad (14.15)$$

But these derivatives are related to the thermal coefficients of the substances through the Maxwell relations,

$$\left(\frac{\partial V}{\partial T}\right)_p = -\left(\frac{\partial S}{\partial p}\right)_T = 0 \quad \text{at} \quad T = 0, \qquad (14.16)$$

$$\left(\frac{\partial p}{\partial T}\right)_V = \left(\frac{\partial S}{\partial V}\right)_T = 0 \quad \text{at} \quad T = 0. \qquad (14.17)$$

Thus the expansivity α_p and the pressure coefficient α_V (defined in Chapter 7) must approach zero at low temperatures. This result has been confirmed by experiment.

From the Clapeyron equation,

$$\left(\frac{dp}{dT}\right)_{\text{coex.}} = \frac{\Delta S}{\Delta V}, \qquad (14.18)$$

we conclude that $(dp/dT)_{\text{coex.}}$ becomes zero as T goes to zero, provided that ΔV does not also go to zero. For example, the melting curves of solid He^3 and solid He^4 appear to be horizontal at low temperatures in agreement with this conclusion.

TABLES OF THERMODYNAMIC FUNCTIONS

The greatest usefulness of the third law lies in the fact that it provides a means of obtaining the equilibrium constants and thermodynamic functions for a given change in state at any temperature from thermal measurements alone. This is of practical significance since such data are relatively easy to obtain. The entropy, for example, for any system A at temperature T is given by an equation of the form

$$S_A(T) = S_A(0) + \int_0^T C_p \, d \ln T + \sum_{\text{transitions}} (\Delta H/T). \qquad (14.19)$$

A similar equation holds for the entropy of another system B. For the transformation $A \to B$, the entropy change is $\Delta S = S_B(T) - S_A(T)$. Since $S_A(0) = S_B(0)$ by the third law, the entropy change can be obtained just from a knowledge of heat capacities and heats of transition, for any physical or chemical transformation. The enthalpy change ΔH for the transformation $A \to B$ can be obtained by calorimetric means as was discussed in Chapter 9. The Gibbs function is then obtained from $\Delta G = \Delta H - T \Delta S$, and from ΔG the equilibrium constant is found as discussed in Chapter 9. That is, ΔG can be converted to the standard value $\Delta G°$ for reactants and products in their standard states, and then the equilibrium constant follows from $\Delta G° = -RT \ln K$.

The greatest uncertainty in the use of the third law is in the uncertainty in determining whether the systems are in equilibrium states in the sense of the third law at the lowest temperatures of the measurements. Fortunately there is now sufficient experimental and theoretical information about the structure and behavior of matter to obtain a reliable indication as to whether a particular system satisfies the thermodynamic requirements or not.

One remark should be made about heat capacity measurements at low temperatures. These never extend to $T = 0$. Extrapolation is required from some non-zero temperature and such extrapolations are made on the basis of some theory of matter. For example, for non-metals the Debye theory of specific heats predicts $C_V \propto T^3$ at low temperatures, and this form is usually employed for the extrapolation of the heat capacities of such substances. Similarly, the theory of metals predicts $C_V \propto T$ at low temperatures because of the conduction electrons.

Self-consistent values of thermodynamic functions can be obtained in this way, and a short list of such values for some gases is given in Table 14.1. Since only differences in thermodynamic functions can be defined, it is necessary to select some arbitrary zero for each function. The state for which the function is zero is called a standard state. It is sometimes convenient, or just conventional, to choose different standard states for the tabulation of different thermodynamic functions. For instance, it is customary to tabulate the entropy with respect to the entropy at absolute zero; that is, the entropy is chosen to be zero at $T = 0$. However, it is customary to tabulate the enthalpy of formation of a substance at a given temperature with respect to its elements at the same temperature, the elements being in their most stable state of aggregation for that temperature at a pressure of one atmosphere (at unit fugacity if the stable state is gaseous). That is, the enthalpy is

TABLE 14.1—SOME STANDARD MOLAR ENTROPIES OF GASES, AND THEIR ENTHALPIES OF FORMATION, AT 298.15°K.*

Gas	$\tilde{S}^\circ$ cal/mole-°K	$\Delta \tilde{H}^\circ$ kcal/mole	Gas	$\tilde{S}^\circ$ cal/mole-°K	$\Delta \tilde{H}^\circ$ kcal/mole
H_2	31.211	0	CO	47.301	−26.4157
C_2	49.003	0	CO_2	51.061	−94.0518
N_2	45.767	0	CH_4	44.50	−17.889
Cl_2	53.286	0	NO	50.339	21.600
Br_2	58.639	7.34	NO_2	57.47	8.091
I_2	62.280	14.876	N_2O	52.58	19.49
HCl	44.617	−22.063	N_2O_4	72.73	2.309
HBr	47.437	−8.66	NH_3	46.01	−11.04
HI	49.314	6.20	SO_2	59.40	−70.96
H_2O	45.106	−57.7979	SO_3	61.24	−94.45
H_2S	49.15	−4.815			

1 thermochemical calorie = 4.1840 joule, by definition.

* Among the most extensive tables are those of the U.S. National Bureau of Standards, such as: (a) *Selected Values of Chemical Thermodynamic Properties*, NBS Circular 500, February 1952; (b) *Selected Values of Properties of Hydrocarbons*, NBS Circular C461, November 1947. These are widely used and can be found in almost any technical or scientific library.

chosen to be zero for an element in its stable state at one atmosphere, and this choice is made for each temperature so that the standard state in this case depends on the temperature of interest. Although these choices may sound confusing, they have been found to be convenient ones for physico-chemical calculations. The values in Table 14.1 are given on this basis.

It should be emphasized that entropy and enthalpy values can be obtained by other than calorimetric means and the third law. Indeed, because of experimental difficulties in realizing equilibrium states at low temperatures for some systems, other means are often necessary if reliable values are to be obtained. We have already mentioned direct equilibrium measurements at higher temperatures as one such means. Another is the use of statistical mechanics together with spectroscopic data, which for simple diatomic gases gives extremely accurate values of thermodynamic functions. As far as thermodynamics is concerned it makes no difference what the sources of the entropy values are. The power of thermodynamics lies in its ability to calculate other macroscopic properties from a few given macroscopic ones.

Unattainability of Absolute Zero

Because the Kelvin temperature scale has a finite lower limit at $T = 0$, there has tended to be an excessive amount of discussion about the attainment of absolute zero. To a large extent this is an unphysical question, as can be seen from a consideration of the fundamental thermodynamic definition of the absolute temperature scale, which was presented in Chapter 5. The only result which had physical content was

$$-\frac{Q_1}{Q_2} = \frac{\phi(t_1)}{\phi(t_2)}, \tag{14.20}$$

where Q_1 and Q_2 are the heats absorbed at t_1 and t_2 by a reversible engine operating between t_1 and t_2, and $\phi(t_1)$ and $\phi(t_2)$ are functions of t_1 and t_2 alone. What sort of scale we set up on the basis of this thermodynamic result is then a matter of arbitrary choice, subject only to the condition that $\phi(t)$ be monatonic in order to preserve the ordering of temperatures required by the zeroth law. Instead of choosing

$$\frac{\phi(t_1)}{\phi(t_2)} = \frac{T_1}{T_2}, \tag{14.21}$$

we could have chosen the scale

$$\frac{\phi(t_1)}{\phi(t_2)} = -\frac{\beta_2}{\beta_1}, \tag{14.22}$$

which is related to the Kelvin scale by $\beta = -1/kT$, where k is some constant dependent on the choice of reference temperature. The β-scale runs from $-\infty$ to 0, whereas the T-scale runs from 0 to $+\infty$. On the β-scale, "absolute zero" corresponds to $-\infty$, which certainly doesn't seem attainable, or even worth talking about. The β-scale is actually a more logical temperature scale in statistical-mechanical theory.

Another choice might have been

$$\frac{\phi(t_1)}{\phi(t_2)} = \frac{\exp(\tau_1)}{\exp(\tau_2)}, \tag{14.23}$$

which is related to the Kelvin scale by $\tau = \ln k'T$, where k' is a constant. The τ-scale runs from $-\infty$ to $+\infty$, and is related to the scale Kelvin first defined on the basis of the second law alone. The T-scale is actually Kelvin's "second scale," adopted after Joule pointed out the fact that the T-scale would correspond closely to the then-current temperature scale based on the air thermometer.

Furthermore, there is nothing in the laws of thermodynamics (or any other form of experience) to suggest that we cannot get as close as we please to $0°K$. Whether or not we can attain *exactly* $0°K$ therefore seems an academic question. Nevertheless, it is true that the third law implies that $0°K$ cannot be reached by any simple isentropic process. Since this is sometimes given as the fundamental statement of the third law, it is worthwhile to indicate how it is proved from the statement of the third law given in this chapter. We consider the proof only for simple systems which can be described by two thermodynamic variables besides temperature; the proof is more involved for more complicated systems, but the conclusion is the same. We first note that to achieve absolute zero by some process involving such a system, we would start with the system at some temperature $T > 0$ and carry out an isentropic process so that the temperature of the system would decrease. That is, the isentropic curve followed by the system would cross an isotherm of the system corresponding to a temperature less than the initial temperature T. However, we shall easily prove below that at $0°K$ the isotherm and the isentrope coincide. The preceding statement of the third law on the other hand requires that the first and second law equations be valid in the limit of $T \to 0$, and hence the entropy function is a state function in this limit and thus is single-valued. No isentropic curve can meet the 0°K isentrope unless the entropy is the same as that at 0°K. Further, if there did exist one or more such isentropes, these curves would exhibit branch points (see Fig. 14.2). Such a branch point

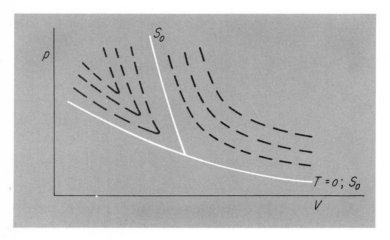

FIG. 14.2. Schematic diagram of isentropes in the vicinity of a zero-degree branched isentrope.

requires that neighboring isentropes have the form shown by the dashed lines in Fig. 14.2. A system having such isentropes would have to have peculiar physical properties since in certain regions

$$\left(\frac{\partial S}{\partial p}\right)_V = \frac{C_V}{T\left(\frac{\partial p}{\partial T}\right)_V} < 0.$$

Thus, either the heat capacity or $(\partial p/\partial T)_V$ would be less than zero. If experiment or theory indicate, as they do, that these are positive quantities, then the 0°K isotherm is unattainable.

The proof that the isotherm and isotrope coincide at 0°K is simple. Consider any isothermal reversible process at 0°K. By the third law $\Delta S = 0$ for the process, and so the system has a constant entropy along the 0°K isotherm. Thus the 0°K isotherm is also an isentrope.

One advantage of the statement of the third law in terms of the unattainability of absolute zero is that such a statement seems to have great generality (like the second law), and does not need any cautious qualification to escape possible experimental exceptions. However, it is necessary to assume that the heat capacity to temperature ratio approaches zero in the limit of absolute zero in order to derive all the results presented in this chapter. Thus, the generality of this statement of the third law is only apparent and not real. Furthermore, as mentioned before, the thermodynamic temperature scale could have been defined so that "absolute zero" was at minus infinity; the unattainability of minus infinity sounds rather absurd as a statement of a physical law.

Problems

1. The specific heat at constant pressure of beryllium is given as follows:

T, °K	1	2	3	4
$\bar{c}_p$, joule/g-°K	2.5×10^{-5}	5.1×10^{-5}	7.9×10^{-5}	1.09×10^{-4}

T	6	8	10	15	20
$\bar{c}_p$	1.80×10^{-4}	2.71×10^{-4}	3.89×10^{-4}	8.42×10^{-4}	1.61×10^{-3}

T	25	30	40	50	60
$\bar{c}_p$	2.79×10^{-3}	4.50×10^{-3}	9.96×10^{-3}	1.92×10^{-2}	3.41×10^{-2}

T	70	80	90	100
$\bar{c}_p$	5.62×10^{-2}	9.06×10^{-2}	1.39×10^{-1}	1.99×10^{-1}

Calculate $\tilde{H}_{100} - \tilde{H}_0$, $\tilde{S}_{100} - \tilde{S}_0$, and $\tilde{G}_{100} - \tilde{G}_0$ per gram-atomic weight for beryllium at 100°K. Draw graphs of $\bar{c}_p$ and of $\bar{c}_p/T$ vs. T and integrate graphically or numerically.

2. The Debye-Sommerfeld equation for metals predicts the following temperature dependence for the specific heat at constant volume at low temperatures:

$$\bar{c}_V = \gamma T + \alpha T^3.$$

(a) This equation is reported to be valid for beryllium from 0° to 20°K. with $\gamma = 25.0 \times 10^{-6}$ joule/g-°K² and $\alpha = 0.138 \times 10^{-6}$ joule/g-°K⁴. Compare the values of $\bar{c}_V$ calculated with this equation with the experimental values of $\bar{c}_p$ given in problem 1 above. Can you draw any conclusions concerning the relative values of $\bar{c}_p$ and $\bar{c}_V$ for this substance at very low temperatures?

(b) Derive expressions for the energy and entropy of a substance that obeys the Debye-Sommerfeld equation.

3. Show that the third law indicates that the values of C_p and C_V for a given substance approach each other at low temperatures.

4. Show that at low temperatures the heat capacity of a saturated liquid approaches C_p; that is, show that $C_{sat} \to C_p$ as $T \to 0$. Refer to Problem 10 of Chapter 8.

5. At very low temperatures the density and the temperature derivative of the vapor pressure of liquid helium are given as follows:

T, °K	0.5	1.0	1.5	2.0
ρ, g/cm³	0.1450	0.1451	0.1453	0.1456
dp/dT, torr/°K	5.503×10^{-4}	1.160	17.41	69.65

Calculate the difference $C_{sat} - C_p$ of liquid helium at the above four temperatures.

6. Use the data in Table 14.1 to show that I_2 will not displace chlorine from HCl at 25°C and 1 atm pressure.

7. Use the data in Table 14.1 to calculate the equilbrium constants for the following reactions at 298.15°K:

$$SO_2(g) + NO_2(g) = SO_3(g) + NO(g)$$
$$H_2(g) + Cl_2(g) = 2 \, HCl(g)$$
$$H_2(g) + Br_2(g) = 2 \, HBr(g)$$
$$H_2(g) + I_2(g) = 2 \, HI(g)$$
$$2 \, CO(g) + O_2(g) = 2 \, CO_2(g)$$

Do the equilibrium constants increase or decrease as the temperature is raised?

8. Assume equilibrium is established among N_2, O_2, NO, NO_2, and N_2O_4 at 298.15°K from air which is initially 80 mole per cent N_2 and 20 mole per cent O_2. If the total pressure is maintained at 1 atm, what are the partial pressures of all these gases at equilibrium? Note that the partial pressures of the nitrogen oxides are extremely small.

9. Heat capacity measurements on H_2 are found to yield different values at low temperatures, depending on whether a small amount of charcoal is present or not, as shown schematically in Fig. P14.9.

(a) Suppose H_2 is cooled to 0°K and then some charcoal is added. If a change in state occurs, will the entropy change be positive, negative, or zero? Is any violation of the third law involved?

(b) Which of the two systems—H_2 alone or H_2 plus charcoal—can be said *not* to be in equilibrium at low temperatures? Why?

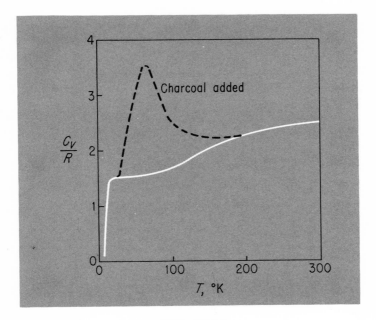

FIG. P14.9

Appendix I

CONSTANTS, CONVERSION FACTORS, AND USEFUL FORMULAS

DEFINITIONS

1 bar $= 10^6$ dyne/cm^2
1 atmosphere (atm) $= 1.01325 \times 10^6$ dyne/cm^2
1 torr (nearly exactly 1 mm mercury) $= (1/760)$ atm
g (standard) $= 980.665$ cm/sec^2
1 liter (lit) $= 1.000028 \times 10^3$ cm^3
1 joule $= 10^7$ erg
1 thermochemical calorie (cal) $= 4.1840$ joule
1 kilocalorie (kcal) $= 10^3$ cal
1 watt $= 1$ joule/sec

PHYSICAL CONSTANTS

$T(°K) = t(°C) + 273.15$
R (gas constant) $= 8.3143$ joule/mole-°K
$\qquad\qquad\qquad = 1.9872$ cal/mole-°K
$\qquad\qquad\qquad = 82.056$ cm^3-atm/mole-°K
$\mathscr{F}$ (Faraday constant) $= 96,487.0$ coulomb/equivalent

USEFUL FORMULAS

$\ln_e x = 2.302585 \cdots \log_{10} x$
$\ln (1 + x) = x - \frac{1}{2}x^2 + \cdots$
$(1 + x)^{-1} = 1 - x - x^2 - \cdots$

Appendix II

PROBLEM ANSWERS

CHAPTER 3

1. (a) $a = 20°C$, $b = -80°C$. (b) $t = 2.6°C$.
2. (a) $t_3 = 25°C_I = 20°C_{II}$. (b) $t_3 = 28°C_I = 19°C_{II}$. (c) $50°C_I$; no.
3. (a) $R_0 = 7.000$ ohm, $a = 3.9239 \times 10^{-2} (°C)^{-1}$, $b = -5.962 \times 10^{-7} (°C)^{-2}$.

   (b) $\Delta t = \dfrac{\Delta R_t}{R_0(a + 2bt)} \approx 0.036 + 1.1 \times 10^{-5}t$.
4. $421.0°C$; $23.6°C$ low.
5. (a) $\Delta p = 0.012$ mm mercury. (b) Yes; $0.89°C$ low.
6. (b) $0.44°C$ low.
7. Thermometer reads $50.1°$ instead of $50.0°$.

CHAPTER 4

1. $W = 10^3 \pi$ joule; positive for clockwise, negative for counter-clockwise.
3. (a) 9.8×10^{-2} joule. (b) -9.8×10^{-2} joule. (c) -9.8×10^{-2} joule.
4. 6.00×10^3 joule.
5. 1.69×10^4 joule. (b) 0.06% neglecting liquid volume; 1.7% assuming ideal vapor. (c) 2.088×10^5 joule.
6. (a) $W_{AB'C} > W_{ABC}$; $Q_{AB'C} - Q_{ABC} = 3 \times 10^3$ joule. (b) $W = 3 \times 10^3$ joule, $Q = 3 \times 10^3$ joule, $\Delta E = 0$.
7. (a) $\Delta E = 1350$ joule. (b) $\Delta E = 1320$ joule. (d) $\Delta E = 30$ joule, $W = -2580$ joule.
9. (a) 83.3 joule/°C. (b) 4.17 joule/g-°C.
10. (a) 2 joule/g-deg. (b) Q (calc.) $= 1200$ joule; Q (actual) $= 1500$ joule.
11. (a) $E_B = 1$ joule, $E_D = 1$ joule, $C_p = 7$ joule/deg, $C_V = 1$ joule/deg.
    (b) 4 deg. (c) $E_C = 4$ joule, $Q_{AC} = 16$ joule, $\bar{C}_{AC} = 4$ joule/deg.

Chapter 5

6. $\epsilon_1 = \epsilon_2 + \epsilon_3 - \epsilon_2\epsilon_3$.
8. (c) $W = 0$ for process (a); $W = C_p[T_1 + T_2 - 2(T_1T_2)^{1/2}]$ for process (b).
9. 0.68 kilowatt.
10. (a) $Q_A = 1514.4$ joule, $Q_B = 10{,}057.2$ joule, $Q_C = -4543.2$ joule, $Q_D = -5028.6$ joule; $Q = 2000$ joule, this is equal to the work. (b) 5.048 ln 2, 8.381 ln 3, -5.048 ln 2, -8.381 ln 3; the sum must be zero since it is the entropy change for a complete cycle.

Chapter 6

2. (a) -60.49 joule/°K. (b) -13.05 joule/°K. (c) -12.19 joule/°K.
3. 16.4 joule/°K.
4. 84 erg/°K.
5. (a) 24.8 joule/mole-°K, 15.1 joule/mole-°K. (b) 3.0×10^{-3} joule/°K, 5.7×10^{-3} joule/°K.
6. 0.72 g solid, 1.6×10^{-4} joule/°K.
7. 0.50 joule/°K.
9. (a) -130 joule/°K, 153 joule/°K, 23 joule/°K. (b) -70.3 joule/°K, 76.5 joule/°K, 6.2 joule/°K. (c) -60 joule/°K.

Chapter 7

11. 9.14 joule/mole-°K.
17. (a) $H_A = 4$ joule. $H_B = 11$ joule, $H_C = 34$ joule, $H_D = 13$ joule. (c) 6.59 joule/deg.

Chapter 8

6. 121°C.
7. 1.0055 atm.
8. 1.47×10^3 torr.
9. 3.13×10^3 atm inert gas.
11. 0.0075°C due to pressure; 0.0013 molal.
12. $\log_{10} p = -\dfrac{3159.8}{T} + 9.2183$.
13. 3.8×10^4 joule/mole.
14. 1.6×10^4 joule/mole.
15. 854 joule/g.

16. 252 g/mole, 8 atoms/molecule.
18. 1.73 kg.
19. 38 meters, $-0.285°C$.
20. 6.48×10^4 g/mole, -2.86×10^{-5} °C.

CHAPTER 9

1. -27.36 kcal.
2. $73.7°C$ rise.
3. -10.57 kcal, $19.3°C$ rise.
4. (a) 1.19 kcal/mole. (b) 4.19 kcal/mole. (c) 1.19 kcal/mole, 4.27 kcal/mole,
5. -18.6 kcal.
6. (a) ±0.10 kcal and ±0.37 kcal for $\Delta t = \mp 10°C$. (b) ±0.46 kcal for $\Delta t = \mp 10°C$.
7. -33 kcal.
8. -24.4 cal/°K.
9. (a) 2.41×10^{-17} (mole/lit)^2. (b) 6.57×10^{-5} mole/lit of H^+ and of HCO_3^-, 5.6×10^{-11} mole/lit of CO_3^{--}.
10. 5.0×10^{-3} atm^3.
11. 1.77 mole per cent, independent of pressure.
12. 0.088% at 1 atm, 0.88% at 0.01 atm, 2.32×10^{-6} atm.
13. 6.9×10^2 lit/mole.
14. 4.97×10^{-2} atm.

CHAPTER 10

1. -0.113 joule.
2. (b) 38 to 68 erg/cm^2; mean $Q_\sigma \approx 53$ erg/cm^2. (c) 47 erg/cm^2 heat absorbed. (d) -72 erg, $+47$ erg, $+0.16$ erg/°K, $+119$ erg.
3. 1.05×10^{-4} cm.
8. 1,000-fold volume increase; 10,000-fold pressure decrease.
13. (a) -17.4 joule/°K. (b) $\Delta T = -1.23°K$.
14. (a) -4.20×10^{-4} joule/°K. (b) $\Delta T = -0.0056°K$.
15. -2.33×10^5 joule.
16. (a) $+0.728$ volt; $K_c = 4.1 \times 10^{24}$ molal. (b) -0.760 volt; $K_c = 2.0 \times 10^{-26}$ molal/atm. (c) -1.581 volt; $K_c = 3.5 \times 10^{-54}$ (molal)^2.
17. -0.772 volt.
18. 1.3910 volt at 0°K; 1.3280 volt at 50°K.
19. 0.54 atm.
20. Fe; 8.2×10^{-7} molal.

CHAPTER 11

6. (b) 0.583 g.

CHAPTER 12

17. (c) ice VI, $F = 2$; ice V, $F = 2$.
18. (a) $F = 1, 1, 1, 0$.

CHAPTER 13

3. (a) $F = 1$. (b) $F = 0$. (c) $F = 0$. (d) $F = 1$. (e) $F = 2$. (f) $F = 1$.
   Clapeyron equation applies to (a), (d), and (f).
4. (a) 3 components, $F = 3$. (b) 3 components, $F = 2$. (c) 3 components, $F = 1$.
8. $0.6034c$ and $1.3966c$, where c is the initial concentration.

CHAPTER 14

1. 40 joule/g-at. wt., 0.53 joule/g-at. wt.-°K, -13 joule/g-at. wt.
5. $2 \times 10^{-3}, 2 \times 10^1, 8 \times 10^2, 6 \times 10^3$ erg/g-°K.
7. 1.4×10^6, decreases; 2.4×10^{33}, decreases; 1.5×10^{19}, decreases; 8.7×10^2, decreases; 1.2×10^{90} atm^{-1}, decreases.
8. $0.80, 0.20, 2.6 \times 10^{-16}, 1.5 \times 10^{-10}, 1.9 \times 10^{-19}$ atm.

INDEX

A

Absolute zero, 218, 224–227
Adiabatic boundaries
  defined, 5
  heat and, 23
Adiabatic demagnetization, 161–163
Adiabatic equation of state, 86–87
Adiabatic work, 19–20
American Petroleum Institute, 128
Analytical methods, 66–91
  adiabatic equation of state, 86–87
  characteristic functions, 71–74
  combined statement of first and second laws, 66–67
  definitions of new state functions, 67–71
  enthalpy, 68–69
  Gibbs function, 70–71
  Helmholtz function, 70, 72–74
  Maxwell relations, 66, 74–85
    calculation of entropy changes, 75–76
    calculation of temperature changes, 77–82
    dependence of heat capacities on p and V, 76–77
    identity of ideal gas and thermodynamic temperature scale, 83–85
    relationship between heat capacities, 82–83
  problems, 88–91
Atomic weight scale, 12 n.

B

Black-body radiation, 146
Boiling point elevation, 110–112, 198–199
Boundaries
  adiabatic, defined, 5
  defined, 3–4
  diathermal, defined, 5–6
  flow of heat across, 23
  impermeable, 4
  permeable, 4

C

Calories, 23
Carnot, Sadi, 29, 30
Carnot cycle, 45, 47
Carnot engine, 103–104
Cavity radiation, 146
Celsius scale, converting to Kelvin degrees, 60
Chemical equilibrium, 126–136
  constants for ideal gas and ideal solution reactions, 128–132
  free energy changes, 127
  problems, 136–139
  properties of constants, 132–135
    combinatorial behavior of, 132–133
    effect of temperature on, 133–134
    from thermal data, 134–135
  standard free energy changes, 128